Telescopes

THE MACMILLAN SKY AND TELESCOPE LIBRARY OF ASTRONOMY

With the advent of space exploration the science of astronomy enters a new phase—that of practical application significant not only to scientists but also to the public at large. The recent critical developments in astronomy that led up to this new phase are presented in this unique library of astronomy made up of articles that first appeared in the prominent journals *Sky and Telescope, The Sky,* and *The Telescope.*

Telescopes

HOW TO MAKE THEM AND USE THEM

EDITED BY THORNTON PAGE & LOU WILLIAMS PAGE

VOLUME 4 *Sky and Telescope* Library of Astronomy

Illustrated with over 120 photographs, drawings, and diagrams

The Macmillan Company, New York
Collier-Macmillan Limited, London

40227

Contents

3. Making a Reflector

4. The Mounting and Drive

5. Visual Observations of the Moon and Planets

6. Observing the Stars

7. Telescope Accessories

8. Special-purpose Telescopes

9. Famous Observatories and Telescopes

Illustrations

Figure

Figure

Tables

Preface

Professional astronomers and astrophysicists are exploring the outside universe with large telescopes, analyzing starlight with spectrographs and photoelectric instruments, detecting faint radio sources, and linking what they find to the laboratory data and mathematical theories of physics. Interest in astronomy and astronomical observations is shared by many other people, without highly technical training or access to a 200-inch telescope, and it is to such nonprofessional astronomers that this book is addressed.

The "amateur astronomers," as they call themselves, are organized in hundreds of clubs and associations all over the United States. Many of them have built their own telescopes or have purchased some of the wide variety of instruments that are available. With relatively small telescopes it is possible to see for one's self the celestial objects that are coming more and more into common knowledge: the craters on the moon, the planets, novae, ageing clusters of stars, and exploding galaxies.

For over thirty years the magazines The Sky, The Telescope, and Sky and Telescope have brought to amateur astronomers suggestions for observing, results of other amateur work, and the principles and techniques involved in telescope making, as well as discussions of many of the professional advances in astronomy. This volume, like the others in the series, is a collection of articles arranged in a logical sequence, with a few explanatory notes and connecting remarks by the editors. We are fortunate to have had the advice and assistance of Robert E. Cox, associate editor of Sky and Telescope, who is exceptionally well informed on amateur telescope making.

Each of the articles in this volume is reproduced essentially as it originally appeared in Sky and Telescope or its predecessors, The Sky and The Telescope, with minor modifications for consistency of style. In order to maintain continuity, some tangential material has been cut. When the deletions are short they are not indicated, but omissions of one or more paragraphs are designated by ellipses. Occasional minor changes have been made in the wording to improve clarity or to eliminate repetition. A few explanatory additions have been made, usually within brackets.

Selections for which there is no author credit were prepared by the staff of the applicable magazine. Footnotes supplied by the editors bear the initials TLP, as do the passages of editors' comments interspersed throughout the volume.

The articles reprinted here are only a small fraction of all that have appeared over the past thirty years. The reader interested in more detail is referred to bound volumes of The Sky, The Telescope, and Sky and Telescope, available in most libraries.

After a brief introduction, which establishes the basic motions in the sky, we turn to principles of telescope design, and go on to methods of construction. Chapters 5 and 6 are concerned with observations, Chapters 7 and 8 with special equipment, and Chapter 9 deals with some of the famous telescopes around the world. The current problems of astronomy are covered in other volumes; this volume is intended to show how a telescope works, how to make one, and how to use one.

THORNTON PAGE

LOU WILLIAMS PAGE

January 1966

About the Editors

Dr. Thornton Page is now Fisk Professor of Astronomy at Wesleyan University, Middletown, Connecticut, and director of the Van Vleck Observatory. After studying at Yale University he went to England as a Rhodes Scholar; he received a Ph.D. from Oxford University in 1938. He then spent two years as a physicist with the U.S. Naval Ordnance Laboratory; during World War II he served for four years as a lieutenant commander with the Navy's Pacific Fleet. In addition to writing articles for scientific journals, and to editing this series, he has been the editor of *Introduction to Physical Science* (3 vols.) and *Stars and Galaxies*.

Mrs. Page, a geologist, is the author of two science books for young readers, *A Dipper Full of Stars* and *The Earth and Its Story*. The Pages have made use of their experience in several scientific disciplines in the preparation of *Telescopes*.

Introduction

The Old Telescope

SIR JOHN HERSCHEL

(*The Telescope*, November–December 1936)

TO BE SUNG ON NEW YEAR'S EVE 1839–40 BY SIR JOHN HERSCHEL,
HIS WIFE, THEIR CHILDREN AND THEIR GOVERNESS
IN HIS FATHER'S OLD TUBE

In the old telescope's tube we sit,
    and the shades of the past around us flit.
His requiem sing we with shout and din
    while the old year goes out, and the new comes in.

Chorus
Merrily, merrily, let us all sing
    and make the old telescope rattle and ring.

Full fifty years did he laugh at the storm,
    and the blast could not shake his majestic form.
Now prone he lies, where he once stood high
    and searched the deep heaven with his broad bright eye.

There are wonders no living sight has seen,
    which within this hollow have pictured been,
Which mortal record can never recall
    and are known to him only, who made them all.

Here watched our father the wintry night,
    and his gaze has been fed with pre-Adamite light;
His labors were lightened by sisterly love,
    and united they strained their visions above.

He has stretched him quietly down at length,
    to bask in the starlight his giant strength,
And time shall here a tough morsel find,
    for his steel-devouring teeth to grind.

He will grind it at last, as grind it he must,
    and its brass, and its iron shall be clay and rust.
But scarceless ages shall roll away,
    and nurture its fame in its form's decay.

A new year dawns and the old year's past;
    God send it a happy one like the last
(A little more sun and a little less rain,
    to save us from cough and rheumatic pain).

God grant that its end this group may find
    in love and in harmony fondly joined
And that some of us fifty years hence once more
    may make the old telescope's echoes roar.

Chorus
Merrily, merrily, let us all sing
    and make the old telescope rattle and ring.

The Stars and William Lyon Phelps[1]

WILLIAM LYON PHELPS

(*The Sky*, April 1939)

Among my extracurriculum activities in school at Hartford was astronomy. I have forgotten how my interest in this subject began, but among the new books sent to my father for review was a copy of Simon Newcomb's *Popular Astronomy*; I read that book over and over again. Thomas Mills Day, son of the former editor of the *Hartford Courant*, was a boy at the West Middle School, and his family had come into the possession of a good telescope. I used to go to his front yard, formed by the intersection of Farmington and Asylum Avenues, and there spent many evenings gazing at the firmament.

I wanted a telescope of my own and had no funds. My schoolmate Arthur Perkins, who had such a talent for scientific pursuits that his subsequently being forced into the practice of the law was a lifelong

[1] Through the courtesy of Oxford University Press, we print in advance of publication a chapter from *Autobiography with Letters* by William Lyon Phelps [1939].

tragedy, offered to make me a telescope if I would provide the materials, the total cost of which was less than three dollars. He made a tube out of cardboard, painted it black, made a tripod, and with an object glass of two and one-half inches at one end, and an eyepiece at the other, I could see the moons of Jupiter, the crescent of Venus, occultations of stars, and such phenomena. I could not afford an achromatic eyepiece, so I had all the colors for nothing. For years I was passionately devoted to astronomy, and my interest in the subject lasted until I was compelled to take a course in astronomy in college which was devoted wholly to mathematical calculations; the stars were neither seen nor mentioned. I was so disgusted that for years afterwards I did not consider the subject. . . .

But the greatest day with my telescope came when I was seventeen—December 6, 1882, when from about nine in the morning till about four in the afternoon I observed the transit of Venus. Hartford was in the best position for this spectacle; two astronomers had been sent over from Germany, and were to cable WOE if the day were cloudy, WONDERFUL if it were wholly clear, and WONDERFUL-WANTING if they missed a contact and yet saw most of the transit.

My schoolmates Day and Peters and I had been talking of nothing else for weeks; I carried my telescope to Peters' yard, where there would be a more unobstructed view of the sun. His interest in astronomy became professional and permanent, and in later years he was one of the astronomers at the United States Naval Observatory in Washington; Day has a very fine telescope in his home in New Jersey.

The transit of Venus is a very rare spectacle, coming one might say in pairs, with long intervals. There had been one in 1874, about which I knew nothing; there was this one in 1882. The next one will be in 2004, followed by one in 2012, when again there will be an interval of more than one hundred years.

Accordingly, on the day before, December 5, I asked my Latin teacher at the high school if he would kindly excuse me for the next day, as I wished to observe the transit of Venus. Like most persons, he had never heard of it, and viewed me with suspicion. He refused. Then I begged him to let me off, telling him I *must* see it. "Oh, wait for the next one," he said. Whereupon I asked him, "Do you know when the next one is coming? It will be in the year 2004." Then he got stuffy, and said, "Well, I won't excuse you." I determined to be a martyr for the sake of science, and stayed away from school all day, expecting to be severely punished and possibly expelled; but I think my teacher must have looked up the matter or consulted the principal, who knew something about astronomy, for when I returned to school no reference was made to my deliberately defiant absence. . . .

That day in 1882 was one of the great days of my life; the spectacle was amazing in itself, and the thought that no one living would ever see it again lent a peculiar air of solemnity to the scene.

When I became a member of the American Philosophical Society, founded by Benjamin Franklin, I immediately associated myself with the astronomers, telling them I was the most enthusiastic nonmathematical astronomer in the world; that I loved the sea and sailing ships, but could not understand navigation; that I loved the stars, but could not comprehend even elementary mathematics. They received me with affection if not with respect; and I am pleased to be the only person not an astronomer making the annual dinner-pilgrimage to the hospitable home of Mr. and Mrs. Gustavus Wynne Cook, where there is probably the finest amateur observatory on the face of the earth.

In 1937 I made a pilgrimage with these astronomers to see the great telescope being made near Philadelphia for the California observatory; and as we were looking at this giant and meditating on the fact that in these days of mass production, here was one individual mechanism that took years to build, I told Harlow Shapley, head of the Harvard University Observatory, that I, as an astronomer, had two advantages over him. This telescope costs about seven million dollars, whereas mine of 1882 cost less than three dollars; second, although his astronomical knowledge compared to mine was in about the same ratio, I had seen a transit of Venus, which he had never seen and never would see, even if he lived to be a hundred. . . .

The great astronomer George Ellery Hale was a very dear friend. He and Mrs. Hale were exceedingly kind when I was lecturing at the Los Angeles branch of the University of California in the summer of 1919. They took us to the summit of Mount Wilson (5900 feet), where we saw and looked through the largest telescope in the world, the 100-inch reflector. That was the only time I saw the moons of Saturn; and the cluster in Hercules was a marvelous spectacle. We had a jolly supper with the staff; and as we descended the mountain late in the night, the lights of Pasadena made almost as gorgeous a display as anything we had seen aloft. Two bonds united Hale and me, apart from his knowledge and my love of astronomy. He worshiped cats, owned a magnificent feline; and he read a good many detective novels every month.

At one of the regular meetings of the American Philosophical Society Professor Miller of Swarthmore College told me a remarkable story of Richard Croker, one of the most famous politicians of America, for many years the inscrutable chief of Tammany Hall and absolute political boss of New York. When Miller was professor of astronomy at the University of Indiana, during the years when Croker was at the height of his fame in metropolitan politics, one night the telephone rang, and

Miller was informed that Richard Croker was speaking. "You don't mean Richard Croker of New York?" "The same." "What can I do for you?" "I am passing through Indiana, and I thought you might be willing to let me look through the telescope." He was cordially invited, and the two men went into the observatory. Croker's remarks showed a fair knowledge of amateur astronomy. After the telescope had been turned on various objects, Croker wished to see the nebula in Orion, and was informed that would not be visible until about two o'clock in the morning. "I shall be glad to wait for it," said the Tammany chief. Accordingly, they stayed, and after seeing it, and expressing his thanks, Croker remarked, "I like the stars; they are dependable."

To turn from the sublime to the ridiculous aspect of astronomy, the late Judge Elbert Hamlin, one of my pupils in the class of 1896, took as an undergraduate the course in astronomy offered by Professor William Beebe. On the final examination one of the questions was "How many moons has Saturn?" Hamlin guessed, wrote down too many, and was flunked. About fifteen years later, he happened to see in the morning paper that some additional satellites had been discovered, making the total number what he had placed on his exam paper. Immediately he sent a long telegram to Professor Beebe, quoting the newspaper cutting. "Fifteen years ago you flunked me, not knowing that my knowledge of Saturn exceeded yours. And your flunking me was a tragedy for Yale. There was the golden opportunity which would have given Yale University immortality in science by announcing a discovery fifteen years ahead of all other institutions of learning. I can forgive you for the personal insult, but it is difficult to forgive you when we remember what my discovery would have meant in adding prestige to Yale."

Professor Beebe was delighted with this telegram; and I wish I could remember his reply.

These reminiscences of unpredictable men and dependable stars serve to remind the reader that astronomy is man made; like any science, it is changing, although it deals with some of the most eternal things we know. The most obvious changes are in astronomical instruments, which have been—and are being—steadily improved.

Our understanding of what can be seen in a telescope, or observed by other means, is also changing; in the last few decades astronomers have come to recognize the ageing of stars and have drastically changed their ideas about the origin of our sun and its planets (see Vol. 3, The Origin of the Solar System). Except for improvements in accuracy, however, the observations of star positions—where they are in the sky—are highly dependable. In fact, they provide our basis for measuring time, as the following article shows. —TLP

■■■

Time and the Sky[1]

(*Sky and Telescope*, December 1958; January, March, May 1959)

Although time is intuitively familiar to all of us, it defies satisfying definition. It is known to us by our sense of duration rather than by what it actually is. When, ages ago, mankind first sought some way of keeping track of time it was natural to turn to recurring astronomical phenomena, such as day and night and the seasons. These are the basis of the units of time we use today.

The sky is a huge clock. The stars and the sun move as hands across the face of the heavens in a steady and unceasing motion. Just as a glance at a man-made clock seems to show its hands stationary, a casual look at the night sky shows the starry dome apparently motionless. A few minutes' watching, however, reveals the westward motion of the stars.

It is the rotation of the earth on its axis that causes this apparent parade of astronomical objects across the heavens. We are not conscious of this rotation. The sun seems to rise, but actually our horizon is shifting downward as we move eastward with the turning earth. Similarly, the sun does not set; each evening our western horizon moves upward, hiding the sun from our view.

To the watcher of the skies at night, there is the distinct impression that he is at the center of an immense, slowly turning heavenly globe to which the stars are fixed. Starting with this useful concept of the *celestial sphere*, time and sky coordinates may be simply explained.

For any observing point on the earth's surface, the *celestial meridian* is an imaginary circle on the sky, passing through the *zenith* or overhead point and the north and south points of the horizon. We measure the flow of time by the steady apparent rotation of the celestial sphere, counting as one day the interval between two successive passages across the celestial meridian of the same celestial object. Because the sun is continually changing its position with reference to the stars, however,

[1] Note [1958]: This series on time is prepared from material originally written by the late Paul W. Stevens and by Carl P. Richards for the Astronomical League observing manual (see p. 219, *Sky and Telescope*, March 1958).

For an excellent 31-page article, with valuable Universal Time and Canadian time-zone charts, see "Standard Time and Time Zones in Canada," by C. C. Smith and M. M. Thomson, in the October 1958 *Journal* of the Royal Astronomical Society of Canada, 252 College Street, Toronto 2B, Canada.

we must distinguish between time as indicated by the sun and that measured from the stars. Time referred to the observer's meridian is *local time*.

Solar Time

Because the sun gives light and heat and in many ways controls our daily life, timekeeping units based on its apparent motions are of greatest importance. Basically, any kind of *solar time* uses the definition that it is 12 o'clock when the sun crosses the meridian, and the day is the time interval between two such meridian transits. . . .

Standard Time

An observer one degree of longitude west of you will see the sun come to his celestial meridian four minutes later than it does for you; therefore, his local time is four minutes behind yours. Until the 1880s, each community in the United States used clocks that showed the *local mean time*. A traveler had to keep changing his watch as he went from one place to another. The inconvenience and confusion spread with the growth of railroads and long-distance telegraph systems over the country.

For practical reasons, therefore, we have adopted a system of *standard time* in the United States, and it is part of a world-wide network based upon the same principles. The country (excluding Alaska) is divided into four zones, and within each the civil time is everywhere the same. The zones of Eastern, Central, Mountain, and Pacific Standard Time use the local times of the meridians 75°, 90°, 105°, and 120° of longitude west from Greenwich. Since 15 degrees of longitude are equivalent to one hour of time, EST, CST, MST, and PST are, respectively, five, six, seven, and eight hours slower than Greenwich time.

Universal Time

Although standard time is convenient for civil use, it does not provide uniformity in astronomical work, such as in the predicting of an eclipse or the recording of a variable star observation. For such purposes, astronomers have agreed to use *Universal Time* (UT). This is the time of the meridian of the old Royal Greenwich Observatory in England, at 0° of longitude, and is counted from 0 to 24 hours, beginning with midnight. Universal Time is, therefore, the same as the standard time at Greenwich. . . .

Sidereal Time

A star that rises at 10 o'clock standard time tonight will rise at about 8 o'clock in the evening one month from now. Similarly, if a star is observed setting at 7 P.M. this evening, it will set about 5 P.M. in a month. Unless they are circumpolar, all stars rise, reach the celestial meridian, and set about four minutes earlier each day, two hours earlier in a month, and one day earlier in a year, according to our clocks that keep mean solar time.

But this would not be the case if our clocks were adjusted to keep time by the stars instead of by the sun. Then the stars would rise, transit, and set at the same time every day, but the sun would not. Suppose a clock running by the stars agreed with the sun on September 21, showing midnight when the sun was on the other side of the world. However, six months later, on March 21, with this clock again indicating midnight, it would be broad daylight outside—midday by the sun.

It is evident from the foregoing that solar time must be used in civil life, but in every professional observatory there is a clock showing *sidereal time*, which is practically that kept by the stars. The sidereal time reference point, which serves the same function as the sun does in solar time, is the March, or vernal, equinox, where the celestial equator is crossed by the sun as it moves northward each year. . . .

It is the motion of the earth in its orbit around the sun that causes the difference between sidereal and solar time. One exact rotation of the earth will suffice to bring the March equinox back to the meridian, completing a sidereal day, but a slight additional turn, requiring nearly four minutes, is needed to bring the sun back to the meridian to complete a solar day. . . .

The great usefulness of sidereal time is in locating stars with an equatorially mounted telescope. But this is a local time, differing from the sidereal time for any other longitude; there is no sidereal time analogous to standard time. Therefore, the observer must either have a clock running on his sidereal time or must compute its value for use in star finding.

Deriving Sidereal Time

The *American Ephemeris* and other almanacs contain for every day of the year the precise value of the sidereal time on the Greenwich meridian at 0^h Universal Time (GST). As this value differs for the same date from year to year, it must be taken from an almanac for the current year. . . .

To find our local sidereal time (LST), we have only to add three numbers to the Greenwich sidereal time at 0^h UT:

$$LST = GST + A + \text{Local Time} + B.$$

A is a small correction, depending on the observer's geographical longitude, and is taken from the accompanying correction table. [Table 1]. For example, if the longitude is 112° 30′ west, or 7 hours 30 minutes in time, the value of the correction is seen to be 1.2 minutes. A is a constant for each station, and is negative for east longitudes.

TABLE 1. CORRECTIONS FOR SIDEREAL TIME*

l	A	l	A	l	A
0:00		8:14		16:45	
	0.0		1.4		2.8
0:19		8:50		17:21	
	0.1		1.5		2.9
0:55		9:27		17:58	
	0.2		1.6		3.0
1:32		10:03		18:34	
	0.3		1.7		3.1
2:08		10:40		19:11	
	0.4		1.8		3.2
2:45		11:16		19:48	
	0.5		1.9		3.3
3.21		11:53		20:24	
	0.6		2.0		3.4
3:58		12:29		21:01	
	0.7		2.1		3.5
4:34		13:06		21.37	
	0.8		2.2		3.6
5:11		13:42		22:14	
	0.9		2.3		3.7
5:47		14:19		22:50	
	1.0		2.4		3.8
6:24		14:55		23:27	
	1.1		2.5		3.9
7:01		15:32		23:59	
	1.2		2.6		
7:37		16:08			
	1.3		2.7		
8:14		16:45			

* If your west longitude is equal to one of the tabulated values, l, use the larger value of A (given in minutes of time).

The next term needed is the local mean time. This is found by adding to the standard time the longitude difference between your station and the central meridian of your time zone. This difference is to be expressed in time, and is negative for places west of the standard meridian. Thus, if the Mountain Standard Time (seven hours slow of UT) is 8:22 P.M. at a station in longitude 7 hours 30 minutes west, the local mean time is 8:22 − 0:30 = 7:52 P.M., or 19:52 in 24-hour reckoning.

The last term in the sum is needed to convert the interval elapsed since 0^h—in our example 19:52—from a mean time interval to a sidereal time interval. Using the correction table again, we find that B is 3.3 minutes.

Therefore the local sidereal time corresponding to 8:22 P.M. MST on January 15, 1959, at longitude 112°30′ west, is
$$7:34.8 + 1.2 + 19:52 + 3.3 = 27:31.3,$$
or 3:31.3 when we discard the excess 24 hours in the answer.

Terrestrial Coordinates

Have you ever seen the planet Uranus? Identifying this slowly moving 6th-magnitude object among the stars is a good example of the usefulness of the sky coordinates, right ascension and declination. The amateur who has some understanding of them will be able to look in the right place for a newly discovered comet or nova, or for a star cluster or nebula.

The coordinate grid of right ascension and declination on a star map is closely analogous to the longitude and latitude grid on a map of the earth's surface. These geographical coordinates therefore make a useful starting point in describing their celestial counterparts.

The definition of geographical latitude and longitude begins with the rotation of the earth on its axis. The axis meets the surface at the North and South Poles, and the great circle midway between them is the terrestrial equator.

The distance of a place north or south of the equator is given by its latitude, in degrees, minutes, and seconds. Places with north (+) latitude are in the Northern Hemisphere, those with south (−) latitude in the Southern Hemisphere. The latitude of the geographical North Pole is +90°, of the South Pole −90°.

To specify one particular spot fully, we need a second coordinate line, a meridian extending from pole to pole at right angles to the circles of latitude. We call the zero meridian that one passing through the original site of the Royal Greenwich Observatory near London, England.

F$_{IG}$. 1. Circumpolar star trails over McDonald Observatory in Texas. Polaris is the short overexposed trail, less than a degree from the true celestial pole.

Then the longitude of the place in question is the distance in degrees, measured along the equator, from where it meets the zero meridian to the intersection of the place's meridian. Longitude is counted east $(-)$ or west $(+)$ from Greenwich, up to 180°. Places with east longitude are in the Eastern Hemisphere; those with west longitude in the Western Hemisphere.

Right Ascension and Declination

Just as the location of a city on the surface of the earth can be specified by its geographical latitude and longitude, so can the position of a star on the celestial sphere be fixed by the two coordinates, declination and right ascension. . . . The north and south celestial poles and the celestial equator are analogous with their terrestrial counterparts.

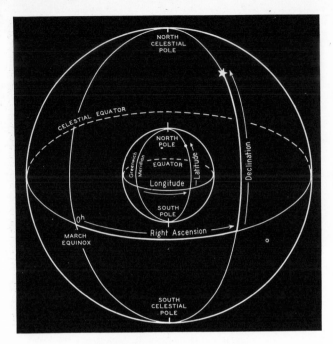

Fɪɢ. 2. The relations between two coordinate systems, latitude and longitude on the earth and declination and right ascension in the sky. The celestial poles, as determined from the daily circles of the stars (see Fig. 1), are the starting points of both systems. The terrestrial poles lie along the same line as the celestial ones. The half circle running from the north celestial pole through the vernal equinox to the south celestial pole is part of the circle in the sky known as the equinoctial colure.

The poles of the sky can be visualized as the centers of the apparent circles described by the stars as the earth rotates, and the celestial equator is midway between these poles.

The declination of a star is its distance in degrees north (+) or south (−) from the celestial equator. . . .

The half circle on the sky that serves the same purpose as the Greenwich meridian on earth is the one joining the celestial poles and passing through the March equinox. . . .

Right ascension differs from its counterpart, geographical longitude, in being counted eastward from the equinox all the way around the sky. Note that it increases eastward, opposite to the direction in which the sky seems to turn.

It is usual to express right ascension not in angular units but in hours (^{h}), minutes (^{m}), and seconds (^{s}) of time. The conversion is easy on the basis that 24 hours of sidereal time represent one full rotation of the sky, or 360 degrees. Thus $1^h = 15°$; $1^m = 15'$; and $1^s = 15''$. Conversely, $1° = 4^m$; $1' = 4^s$; and $1'' = \frac{1}{15}^s$.

The abbreviations R. A. and α (alpha) are in common use for right ascension, as are dec. and δ (delta) for declination. . . .

In the *American Ephemeris* the right ascensions and declinations predicted for the sun, moon, and planets from Mercury to Neptune are *apparent places*. These differ from the positions referred to the coordinate system for the beginning of the year by a slight amount, generally well under a minute of arc.

Equatorial Mounting

Bringing a bright planet or star or a conspicuous star cluster into the field of your telescope is easy. Careful aiming of the instrument in the proper direction is enough to provide a magnificent view of Saturn's rings, Jupiter's moons, or the Pleiades.

Suppose, however, you wish to observe some object not visible to the naked eye. One way is to note its place on a star chart and then slowly sweep over this part of the sky until the object is identified. This method can sometimes be rather laborious, but is the only way with hand-held instruments or a telescope on an altazimuth mounting.

There is a much more convenient procedure possible with equatorially mounted telescopes that are fitted with setting circles, as all professional instruments are, and as all large amateur telescopes should be.

An equatorial mounting has two axes around which the telescope may rotate—the *polar axis*, parallel to the earth's axis of rotation, and the *declination axis*, perpendicular to it. Thus, turning the telescope around the polar axis moves it in right ascension only, and motion around the other axis is solely in declination.

Each of the axes carries a graduated circle. The one on the declination axis is marked in degrees, indicating 0° when the telescope is pointing toward the celestial equator and 90° when toward the celestial pole. The circle on the polar axis is called the hour circle and is marked in time units, its entire circumference amounting to 24 hours. When the circle reading is 0 hours, the telescope is pointing toward the observer's celestial meridian. Ordinarily the hour circle's divisions increase in both directions from this zero point up to 12 hours.

Using setting circles to point a telescope at a desired celestial object should be a fairly simple matter. . . .

The main requirement is that the observer have some timekeeper showing local sidereal time. Professional observatories use a sidereal clock for this. The amateur, however, will find an ordinary watch adequate. Before starting an evening's observing, he should calculate the sidereal time corresponding to, say, 9:00 P.M. standard time, following the instructions given on page 9. Suppose this turns out to be 12:36. Then if the observer sets his watch 3 hours and 36 minutes ahead, it will keep local sidereal time to within a minute or two during the whole night's observing.

Let us follow the observer outdoors to his telescope. The first sky object he selects for viewing is the fine globular cluster M3, in Canes

Venatici. From an observing handbook, its 1950 coordinates are found to be right ascension $13^h39^m.9$ and declination $+28°38'$. . . .

The telescope is now turned around the declination axis until the declination circle reads close to $+28°38'$, and the declination clamp is tightened.

To make the setting in the other coordinate, a simple subtraction is first needed: *Hour angle equals sidereal time minus right ascension.* Thus, if the sidereal time is 13:00, the hour angle of M3 is 13:00 minus 13:40 or -40 minutes, meaning that M3 is east of the meridian, and will not reach it for 40 minutes. (An hour angle of $+3$ hours would mean that the object had crossed the meridian that long ago.)

Therefore, the instrument is turned until the hour circle reads 40 minutes, with the telescope pointing east of the meridian. Looking in the finder, the observer should see M3 as a conspicuous soft glow. A slight shift of the telescope to bring the object into the center of the finder field should then place the cluster in the field of view of the main telescope.

This procedure of locating a sky object with setting circles becomes quite easy and rapid after a little practice. Try it first on a familiar bright star.

The process does require that the equatorial mounting be oriented fairly accurately. The polar axis should make an angle with the horizontal equal to the observer's latitude, and also be in a north-south vertical plane. Instructions for making these adjustments are given, for example, in Chapter 12 of Allyn J. Thompson's book *Making Your Own Telescope.*

Setting circles can also be used differentially for locating sky objects, a simple process that does not depend so critically upon the adjustments of the mounting. In addition, knowledge of the sidereal time is not needed. In this method, the telescope is first pointed at some conspicuous bright star in the same general sky area as the object sought. For instance, if we wish to observe M3, the star Arcturus is a convenient choice. This star's position is $14^h13^m.4$, $+19°26'$ (1950 coordinates), and so the cluster is 33' of right ascension east of it, and 9° north. We point the telescope at Arcturus and read the circles. Shifting the instrument by the differences just given should bring M3 into view.

Finding one's way among the stars is easy with a map. Good ones are found in Norton's Star Atlas (London, Gall and Inglis, 1st ed., 1910, 15th ed., 1964).   —TLP

1

Basic

Principles

Until recently, the only evidence we had of the outside universe came from the stars and planets we could see. True, the sun's heat can be felt, and tides in the sea are raised by sun and moon, but almost all the complex picture of the universe assembled by astronomers came from observations of visible light. Invisible ultraviolet light was observed by photographic techniques about a century ago; then infrared light, and about fifty years ago, cosmic rays were observed. Most recently, radio waves have been discovered coming from sources outside the earth, and large radiotelescopes have been built to observe them.

This book is concerned with optical telescopes, combinations of lenses and mirrors that have been used since 1610, when the Italian scientist Galileo (copying a Dutch invention) first used two lenses to look at the moon and planets. Before that time astronomical observations were all made with the naked eye. (See Vol. 1, Wanderers in the Sky.) In order to understand optical telescopes, one must first understand light, and how it is affected by mirrors and lenses—the subject of optics.   —T L P

What Is Light?

M. J. JULIAN

(*The Sky*, October 1938)

Mankind holds its eminent position in the world because of vision—because of mental vision which is so largely dependent on physical vision.

Sight is the most precious and useful of all our senses. Through our eyes, we see the distant skies, the radiant sunshine. Through our eyes, we know the brightness of light and of objects that reflect it; for vision shows us form, brightness, color, and motion. Vision brings us eighty per cent of our knowledge. It is the very cornerstone of both human and individual progress. The importance of sight is emphasized again and again in nature's struggle to enable us to see like human beings, provided we have light as well as sight. But what is light?

Now that seems like a very simple question. We have either natural or artificial light all the time. Scientists have been studying it for centuries. So one might expect that we should know what light is. But we don't. Some say that light is a form of electrical energy, but this doesn't help us much, because we don't yet know exactly what electricity is. We do know how electricity acts, and we know how light behaves under different conditions. But about the best we can do when it comes to answering the question, What is light? is to say it is energy in the form of vibrations that travel in waves.

There are many other forms of energy which also are vibrations traveling in waves—heat, radio, X rays, electricity, and sound. Vibrations of what? There is another question that is a little too deep for us, yet. Sound seems to be the vibration of some material substance—gas, liquid, or solid, such as the air, water, or a bar of metal; any of these will carry sound. And if an electric bell is put in a vacuum jar and rung, we can't hear it. So, apparently, sound is the vibration of some substance. Vibrations such as light, heat, and radio, on the other hand, go right through a vacuum. And some vibrations, such as X rays, will pass right through substances which light can't get through at all. Why? We don't know. What is it that vibrates? We don't know!

But with all our ignorance, we do already have a great deal of very interesting information about various forms of vibratory energy. We know, for example, that there is a wide variation in rates of vibrations.

Some vibrations are very rapid, and others comparatively slow. There is also a wide variation of wavelengths.

What do scientists mean by waves and wavelengths? If you draw a straight horizontal line with regular curves rising above and dipping below it, you will have a fair picture of the wave in which radio energy travels. And the distance between corresponding points in two adjacent waves—as from the crest of one to the crest of the next—is the wavelength.

Because the various vibratory forms of energy have certain similarities, scientists have grouped them together for study and consideration, arranging them from those with the shortest wavelengths up the scale to those of longest wavelength. And this scale, they tell us, contains sixty octaves. On one end, we have such extremely short waves as the gamma rays of radium emanations. There are more than two billion gamma-ray waves to the inch. On the other end we may have radio waves each of which is several miles in length. In actual practice, we do not use these very long radio waves for broadcasting. What we call short-wave radio uses wavelengths as short as from 16 to 18 inches in experimental work, though most of the foreign stations operate on wavelengths ranging from about 30 to about 650 feet; and the North American broadcast band ranges from about 650 to 1850 feet.

In between the very short waves of the gamma rays and the very long rays of radio are the vibrations of light, about midway in the sixty octaves. . . .

When a ray of sunlight passes through a prism it is broken up into the colors of the solar spectrum—red, orange, yellow, green, blue, and violet. These colors comprise all of the light of the sun that is visible to the human eye; yet the vibrations that create these colors make up only *one* of the fifteen octaves of solar light. There are fourteen times as many light rays that the human eye cannot see. Beyond red, we have nine octaves of infrared light; and beyond violet, we have five octaves of ultraviolet light. Science has developed instruments for discerning and measuring these, even though we cannot see them with our eyes. . . . Another interesting fact about ultraviolet rays is that they will not pass through ordinary window glass. They will, however, pass freely through a glass made of fused quartz. . . .

The fact that radio and sunlight are similar makes it easier to understand one other important point about light.

The sun is like a great broadcasting station sending us waves of light. Our eyes pick up these waves somewhat the way our radios pick up broadcast programs.

When we use our radios we tune them so as to get a single wavelength at a time, because if two wavelengths intermingle and cannot be separated, we hear only a squeal or jumble of sound. But with sight, it is quite different. We prefer to receive the wavelengths of all the different colors of the solar spectrum at once, because when these come to the eye, combined as they are sent out by the sun, we see what we call white light; that is, light without the appearance of any color. That is the kind of light under which we are used to seeing—the light under which we see most easily and clearly. . . .

....

Notes on Basic Optics

EARLE B. BROWN

(*Sky and Telescope*, May 1953; January, March, and May 1954;

January, March, and May 1955)

Basic optics will aid the amateur who seeks to have sufficient understanding of optical principles to be able to put a few lenses together to form a collimator, telescope, periscope, and the like, but who is not interested, for instance, in designing a photographic lens. We shall be presenting what John Strong has called "burning-glass optics." . . .

Simple Lenses

Everyone knows what a lens is—it is a piece of glass with curved surfaces that is used for optical purposes. The borderline cases of strange materials and queerly shaped surfaces we leave for possible discussion elsewhere. Here we are going to talk about the simple properties of lenses, and therefore we shall keep our lenses simple; they will be made of glass, and their surfaces will be spherical or flat. Furthermore, we shall assume that the lenses have no thickness. This procedure immediately does away with a host of questions that would only confuse the issue at this stage. . . .

We [also] assume that a lens will converge a bundle of light to, or diverge it from, a perfect image point. Lenses do not do this in practice. But there is a very neat way of getting around this practical difficulty. . . . It is this: Any failure of a lens to do what we assume is called an aberration, and complex mathematical processes have been developed for discussing these effects by themselves.

Actually, lenses come very close to doing what we describe here as long as the conditions of the problem are kept simple; therefore, we are perfectly justified in developing the present discussion around an ideal lens and leaving aberrations as a separate topic. . . .

The reader, who is probably interested principally in mirrors, may ask why we talk about lenses first. The answer is that mirrors are considered as special cases of lenses; and it is in many ways better to use lenses to discuss basic principles.

If the lens has no thickness, we can represent it by a straight line, as in Figures 3A and 3B. The lens has a property we call its focal length. This may be positive or negative. A positive lens converges the light rays that pass through it, as in Figure 3C, and a negative lens diverges the light rays that pass through it, as in Figure 3D. Thus, the lens has a positive or negative number assigned to it, which is called its focal length. Later, we shall discuss how the construction of a lens and its material affect its properties.

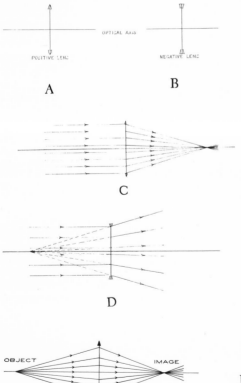

FIG. 3. A,B,C,D. Positive and negative lenses. E,F. The formation of images.

We may think of any object as a collection of points; from each point a bundle of light rays emerges, spreading out in all directions. If a lens intercepts a portion of one of these bundles of light rays, its converging or diverging action will cause the bundle, after it has passed through the lens, to converge at or diverge from a *different* point. This is called the image point.

If the light actually passes through the point, we might have the condition shown in Figure 3E. This is called a "real" image. Sometimes, as in a negative lens (Fig. 3D), the light rays after passing through the lens may merely appear to come from an image point without actually passing through it, in which case the image is called "virtual." This condition can occur in positive lenses as well as in negative ones.

Objects, however, are not usually points, but areas, and the image of an object area will be an area also (Fig. 3F).

There is a very simple mathematical relation that tells us where the image will be located. It is

$$\frac{1}{d'} - \frac{1}{d} = \frac{1}{f}, \tag{1}$$

where d and d' are the distances of image and object from the lens, and f is the focal length we talked about above. Some caution is necessary in using this equation. Distances to the left of the lens are negative, for the light is presumed to be traveling from left to right; distances to the right of the lens are positive. The focal length, f, must be given the proper sign for the lens concerned.

If we are careful about the arithmetic sign convention, we will always come up with the right answer. For example, in Figure 3F, we would write $\frac{1}{+6} - \frac{1}{-9} = 1/f$, whence $f = +3.6$ (inches). Were f known originally, the equation would have been solved for d', which would have come out $d' = +6$. Because this value is positive, it indicates that the image is to the right of the lens. This problem of the significance of algebraic signs may bother a student all through optics, so we point out its importance at the very beginning. . . .

Pupils

The subject of pupils is seldom adequately covered in optical texts, yet its importance cannot be overestimated in understanding the function and design of optical systems.

The general situation is this. Every optical instrument consists of two distinct optical systems. The more familiar *image-forming* system defines essentially what the instrument does, and determines its magnification and image quality. The second is the *pupil-forming* system, which determines how well the instrument works, its illumination, eye relief, and the like. To give a workable instrument, the optical components must be chosen to satisfy the requirements of both systems simultaneously.

By considering a simple telescope, shown in Figure 4A, we can explain the function of the *exit pupil*. The telescope has an objective of focal length f' and an eyepiece of focal length f'', separated by the distance $f' + f''$. From previous discussions, we know that a parallel beam incident on the objective from a point object on the optical axis at infinity will focus to a point F and then be transformed by the eyepiece into a parallel emergent beam, shown by the thin solid lines in Figure 4A.

Now consider a parallel beam incident from an off-axis point, entering the same system at an angle θ. As shown by the dashed lines, this bundle will also emerge from the eyepiece as a parallel beam, at an angle $\theta' = m\theta$, m being the magnification.

The two emergent beams intersect at P', at a distance S from the eyepiece. If bundles of rays at other angles are constructed, they will all intersect the axial bundle at this same point. The exit pupil is the constricted area through which all these bundles of light pass, and is named for its analogy to the pupil of the eye.

Evidently, in using the telescope, the observer must place his eye at the exit pupil to see all the image. If his eye is displaced from the exit pupil, some of the light bundles will be lost. The exit pupil is the knothole through which one must look to see the image, and as any small boy knows, to see effectively through a knothole, one must put his eye as close to it as possible.

The exit pupil is readily located. In Figure 4A, note the central ray of the bundle, pr, which passes through the center of the objective and through the off-axis image point, and then emerges as the central ray of the emergent beam. This is commonly called the *principal ray* of the oblique bundle; it crosses the optical axis at the center of the pupil.

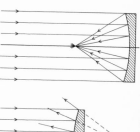

Fig. 4. A. The formation of the exit pupil. B. How convex and concave mirrors focus a beam of light.

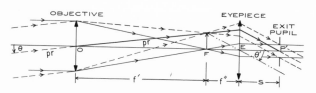

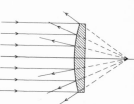

On drawing this ray as the heavy line in Figure 4A, we see that P' is the image of the point O formed by the eyepiece. Hence, its location is found by Equation 1, $1/d' - 1/d = 1/f$, where d' is S, d is $-(f' + f'')$, and $f = f''$. Therefore,

$$S = \frac{f'' \, (f' + f'')}{f'}. \tag{2}$$

Clearly, the whole exit pupil is nothing but the image, formed by the eyepiece, of the objective lens. The diameter of this image is given by

$$\frac{\text{Exit pupil}}{\text{Objective}} = \frac{S}{f' + f''}, \tag{3}$$

as the diameter of the objective lens is the object in this case. Substituting into this the value for S found in Equation 2 gives:

$$\frac{\text{Exit pupil}}{\text{Objective}} = \frac{f''}{f'} = \frac{1}{m}. \tag{4}$$

Image Formation by Mirrors

The properties of lenses and lens systems described above can be applied quite directly to mirrors. Mirrors as well as lenses can be used to form images. A concave mirror acts upon a beam of light in the same way as a positive lens; a convex mirror is equivalent to a negative lens (Fig. 4B).

The basic equation for mirrors is the same as for lenses, that is, Equation 1:

$$\frac{1}{d'} - \frac{1}{d} = \frac{1}{f},$$

where d' and d are the distances of object and image from the mirror, and f is the focal length. There is one important difference in the way this equation is to be applied, as a result of the change in direction of light when it is reflected from a mirror. While there are several ways this could be allowed for, the preferable method is described here.

When this equation is applied to lenses, the distances are considered positive to the right and negative to the left, as explained on p. 20. We now change this convention, so that distances measured in the direction of the light are positive, and those measured opposite to the direction of the light are negative. We will also follow the rule that all measurements are *from* the lens or mirror *to* the point in question.

In using the basic equation to lay out an optical system, we have to remember that the direction of the light is changed at each mirror surface. A concave mirror has a positive focal length f, and a convex mirror a negative f.

With the convention of signs just described, the basic equation applies to lenses as well as to mirrors. We frequently have to deal with optical systems which contain both lenses and mirrors, and it is useful to have a single equation which is valid for both.

All the rules for image formation by lenses, for magnification and inversion, and for a pair of thin lenses in series apply equally to optical systems comprised of, or including, mirrors if we adopt the convention on algebraic signs given above.

A pair of concave mirrors, in view of what has just been said, is evidently equivalent to a pair of positive thin lenses. While such an arrangement is theoretically feasible, it does not represent any standard optical system—even if the separation of the two mirrors were to equal the sum of their focal lengths, which arrangement would constitute a telescope. If, however, we use one mirror and one positive lens, separated by the sum of their focal lengths, we have a Newtonian telescope, as in Figure 5A. The plane diagonal mirror is added, of course, merely to avoid the observer's head getting in front of the mirror.

A pair of positive lenses whose separation, t, is greater than the sum of the foci, $f_1 + f_2$, constitutes a compound microscope. The counterpart of this formed by two mirrors is not used, but there are microscopes with positive reflecting-type objectives of complex form, and lens eyepieces, working with ultraviolet and infrared light.

There is one mirror system which does not have a lens analogue in practice. This is the case where t is slightly greater than $f_1 + f_2$, namely, the Gregorian reflecting telescope, shown in Figure 5B.

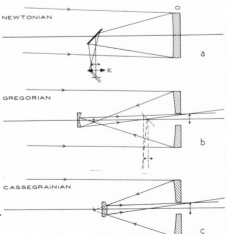

FIG. 5. Three telescope systems.

It is customary in Gregorians to cut a central hole in the primary mirror to make the focal plane accessible to an eyepiece. An alternative arrangement, using a diagonal, is indicated in the figure by dotted lines. At present the Gregorian form is seldom used astronomically. It gives an erect image, which is an advantage for terrestrial use, but its excessive field curvature allows only a very small useful field of view.

In the case of systems with a positive and negative element, two mirrors form a Cassegrainian telescope if their spacing, t, is less than the focal length, f_1, of the positive element. This is illustrated in Figure 5C.

The properties of the Cassegrainian form are exactly the same as those of the telephoto lens. . . . The Cassegrainian is, of course, a reflecting system with a positive focal length, and this type of system is used frequently as the positive element in the reflecting microscope referred to earlier.

Lastly, the case of two convex mirrors may be dismissed as not used in any representative optical instrument. . . .

Refraction

Every transparent substance transmits light at a velocity characteristic of the material. This velocity is conveniently measured by the refractive index of the material, which is inversely proportional to the velocity. The index of refraction of a vacuum is unity and that of air is 1.0003 (unity for most practical purposes). For glass, the index of refraction varies from 1.5 for crown to as great as 1.9 for very dense flint. This means that in crown glass light travels only about $\frac{1}{1.5}$, or two thirds, as fast as in a vacuum.

Strictly speaking, the speed of light in a transparent medium changes with wavelength. This variation causes chromatic aberration in a lens system, but consideration of this effect will be postponed to page 27.

When a ray of light strikes obliquely the surface separating two materials of different refractive indexes, the ray is bent. This is seen when a pencil is thrust part way into a glass of water; the pencil appears bent at the surface. (The apparent bending of the pencil is opposite to that of the rays of light.) The rule that states how much the light is bent is the *law of refraction*, or Snell's law—one of the most important principles in optics:

$$n \sin I = n' \sin I'. \qquad (5)$$

What it means is this. The ray passes from a medium with refractive index n into another medium with index n'. I and I' are the angles of incidence and refraction, respectively, measured from the perpendicular

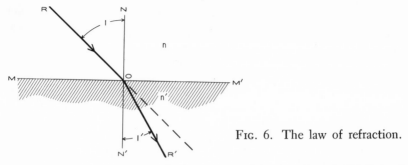

FIG. 6. The law of refraction.

to the surface. In Figure 6, illustrating this situation, MOM' is the surface that separates the media, and NON' is its perpendicular or normal; RO is the entering ray and OR' the refracted ray.

Since we are dealing with a single ray which meets the surface at only one point, the surface need not be flat, or even regular, for the law to hold. Further, the same diagram could be drawn with the arrows pointed in the reverse direction, and the primed letters interchanged with the unprimed. This is a case of the *principle of reversibility*, which states that any light ray, passing across any number of refracting surfaces, would retrace the same path if it were reversed in direction. This is often a useful rule in optics.

Note that the bending occurs only at the interface between the two media. The light path within any one medium is a straight line, provided the medium is homogeneous, that is, has the same refractive index throughout. This is usually the case in optical materials. On the other hand, the atmosphere is a medium whose index gradually decreases with height, due to change in density—with important astronomical consequences.

Looking at Figure 6 in terms of Equation 5, we see that the ray is bent toward the normal when light enters a medium with higher refractive index, that is, a denser medium. Similarly, it will be bent away from the normal when it enters a lighter medium. In general, the physical density and index of refraction increase together, although this is by no means a universal rule. . . .

Aberrations of Lenses

This discussion of lenses can be extended to take up the finer properties of lenses, and to show why optical design is difficult and laborious. Equation (6), on next page, gives the focal length of a lens in terms of the radii of its surfaces and the refractive index of the glass. This formula works very nicely if the conditions we stipulated are met—all the light rays lie very close to the optical axis and are nearly parallel to it. This amounts to a pinhole-sized aperture, with object and image points on the axis. If lenses behaved according to this equation for large apertures and for points off the axis, lens design would be absurdly simple. Using the law of refraction, Equation 5, it is possible to show that the focal length of a thin lens can be calculated approximately from the curvature of the two faces.

$$\frac{l}{f} = (n - 1)\left\{\frac{l}{r_1} - \frac{l}{r_2}\right\}. \tag{6}$$

More precise equations can be derived from the law of refraction that tell us . . . what a ray of light really does. As the aperture and field of view of an optical system approach zero, the precise equations become more and more like the simpler approximations, such as Equation 6. The difference . . . between the results of the two sets of equations is the *aberration* of the system. . . .

Spherical Aberration.   First consider an object point and image point on the optical axis. There are two aberrations that affect axial image points: spherical aberration and chromatic aberration.

The only difference between the actual and the simplified ray-tracing equations is that the latter assume the sine of an angle to be equal to the angle itself (measured in radians). This is very nearly true for small angles, and the difference is only 1 per cent at 15°. However, as the angle gets larger, the disparity between angle and sine increases, and the actual ray departs more and more from the ideal ray. This is shown in Figure 7A for a positive refracting surface. The farther an incident ray is from the axis, the closer to the lens is the intersection of the refracted ray and axis.

We draw the paraxial image plane through the point P, where the simplified Equation 6 tells us that rays very close to the axis are focused. Now, the amount by which each ray falls short of the paraxial image plane is called the *spherical aberration* of that ray (strictly, the longitudinal spherical aberration). If the ray falls to the left of the paraxial image plane, the spherical aberration is positive in sign, and the surface is *undercorrected;* if the ray falls to the right, the spherical aberration is negative, and the surface is *overcorrected.*

FIG. 7. A. Spherical aberration. B. Chromatic aberration.

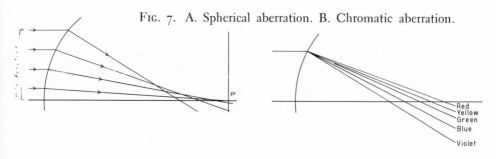

We could compute the shape of a single refracting surface that would have no spherical aberration for a given object point, but the aberration would not be zero for other object points. For off-axis object points such a surface would be particularly objectionable. In modern lens design, however, nonspherical lens surfaces are often used to correct spherical and other aberrations. Parabolic surfaces, in particular, are frequently used.

The spherical aberration given by an optical element can be either positive or negative, depending on the positions of the object and image points. Obviously, a lens system can be corrected for this aberration by combining surfaces of positive and negative curvature so that their separate contributions to the spherical aberration add to zero. In general, we cannot bring all the rays to an exact focus; the best that can be done is to minimize the departure from perfection.

Equation 6 gave the focal length of a thin lens in terms of its refractive index and the radii of curvature of the lens surfaces. We can rewrite this as:

$$\frac{1}{f} = (n - 1)\ (c_1 - c_2), \tag{7}$$

where $c = 1/r$, and is called the *curvature* of the surface. Clearly, we can redistribute the curvature between the two surfaces without changing the focal length. This procedure, called "bending" a lens, is the most powerful means for correcting spherical aberration.

Chromatic Aberration.   The second type of aberration which affects axial images is chromatic aberration. This arises from the fact that the index of refraction is not the same at all wavelengths. Therefore, the focal lengths for different colors of light are different. As a result, a simple lens will give images for each color distributed along the optical axis, the violet image nearest the lens, the red image farthest away. When we look at an image of a star made by a lens which is uncorrected for chromatic aberration we see a central core formed of the color that happens to be in focus, surrounded by a halo of the other colors, which are out of focus.

Since chromatic aberration comes from a property of the glass itself, it cannot be corrected by varying curvatures or thicknesses. The only way is by combining two or more kinds of glass. The difference between the refractive indexes for two different colors of light is called the *dispersion* of a particular kind of glass. By combining a positive lens of low dispersion and a negative lens of high dispersion, an *achromatic lens* results. In general, glasses with high refractive indexes have high dispersions, and low indexes go with low dispersions. Were the dispersions of all glasses exactly proportional to their indexes, any attempt to correct chromatic aberration would result in a lens of zero power. Fortunately, a difference in index of 10 per cent is usually combined with a difference in dispersion of the order of 30 per cent. Hence a weak negative lens and a strong positive lens can be combined to give an achromatic lens with net positive power.

Figure 7B illustrates the chromatic aberration of a positive lens. If the violet focus is to the left of the red focus, the chromatic aberration is positive; if the reverse is true, the aberration is negative. The terms under-correction and overcorrection, with reference to chromatic aberration, mean positive and negative aberrations, respectively.

A combination of positive and negative lenses of different kinds of glass will, in general, bring only two specific wavelengths to the same focus; the rest of the spectrum is still spread out along the axis. However, this spread is much less than if the chromatic aberration were uncor-rected, and for most purposes this degree of correction will suffice. The spread of the colors along the axis which remains after two specified colors have been brought to a common focus is the *secondary spectrum*. As a general rule, three kinds of glass are needed to bring three colors to the same focus. A lens of this construction is known as an *apochro-matic lens*; it is a type widely used in photography and in microscopy.

Off-axis Image Points

The aberration of an optical system is the difference between the actual path of a light ray and the prediction of the simplified Equation 6. We have seen that if object point and image point are on the optical axis, spherical and chromatic aberration arise. If these points are not on the optical axis, several other types of aberration have to be considered.

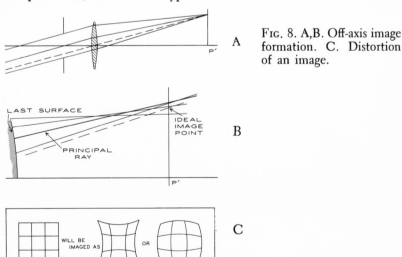

Fɪɢ. 8. A,B. Off-axis image formation. C. Distortion of an image.

1. *Distortion and Coma.* Figure 8A shows ideal image formation for an off-axis point. Usually the aperature stop is separated from the lens. All the rays will meet in the paraxial image plane at the point where the ray through the optical center and parallel to the principal ray meets this plane. (The *principal ray* is defined as the ray through the center of the entrance pupil.)

Ordinarily, the actual rays will not conform to the ideal imagery, and the case will resemble Figure 8B. Here there is no perfectly defined image point anywhere; the various rays are unsymmetrically distributed around the principal ray; and the principal ray does not intersect the paraxial image plane at the point required for ideal imagery.

From this situation we can define two other aberrations. *Distortion* is the departure of the principal ray from the ideal image point; *coma* is the unsymmetrical deformation of the image patch.

Distortion is positive if the principal ray meets the image plane closer to the axis than it should; negative, if it is farther away. This aberration leads to distorted images, whence its name. A square grid pattern will be imaged as barrel-shaped; if the corners are pulled in toward the center, we have positive distortion; if the corners are farther from the center than they should be, giving a pincushion shape to the image, the distortion is negative. The terms barrel distortion and pincushion distortion are often used. (See Fig. 8C.)

Coma causes the image of a point to appear like a small comet. If the tail points away from the axis, the coma is positive. This aberration is the worst offender in parabolic mirrors.

2. *Astigmatism.* So far we have considered only rays in a single plane—the plane of the paper in the diagrams. To define the other two important aberrations, we must now visualize a three-dimensional picture. The plane that contains the optical axis and the object and image points is known as the *meridional*, or *tangential*, plane. This is the plane in which all of our diagrams have been drawn so far. The plane perpendicular to it is called the *sagittal* plane. Rays that lie in these two planes behave differently for off-axis points. For a point on the axis, the two planes are of course indistinguishable; for off-axis points, the distribution of angles of incidence for a bundle of rays is unsymmetrical about the principal ray for the tangential plane, while it is symmetrical for the sagittal plane.

The rays in the sagittal plane come to a precise focus on the principal ray (neglecting the effect of spherical aberration). If there were no coma, the rays in the tangential plane would also come to a point focus, but at a different distance from the lens. In an actual case there will be spherical aberration and coma, and hence no actual point images at all if more than one pair of rays is considered.

The separation between the sagittal and tangential focal points is known as *astigmatism* (strictly, the astigmatic difference of focus). For a simple positive lens, the tangential focus will be closer to the lens than the sagittal focus. . . .

<hr />

Refractor versus Reflector

EARLE B. BROWN

(*Sky and Telescope*, July 1942)

A refractor is a telescope which has a lens for its *objective*, while a reflector has a mirror, often called the *primary*, as there are usually one or more secondary mirrors. The lens in the refractor bends the light rays to form an image, whereas in the reflector they are reflected from the curved surface of the mirror for the same purpose. Our intention here is not to explain how the images are formed, since this has no bearing on the relative merits, but to consider the advantages and disadvantages of the two types.

Some of the features of a good astronomical telescope are:

1. Definition
2. Achromatism
3. Magnifying power
4. Light-gathering power
5. Resolving power
6. Size of image (usable field)
7. Flatness of field
8. Versatility
9. Economy and ease of construction
10. Convenience of handling and upkeep

FIG. 9. The three principal types of reflecting telescopes. F′ is the Cassegrainian focus.

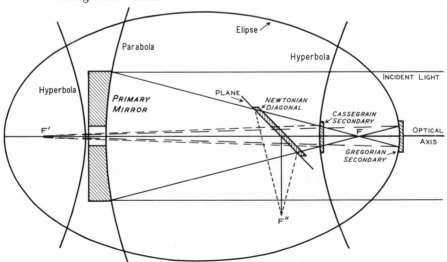

This list is not complete, nor does it apply in every case, since for some particular purpose, many of these features may not be important. However, let us compare the average reflector and refractor according to these requirements.

1. *Definition.* The refractor is definitely superior in definition. A lens can be corrected to almost any desired degree (theoretically) for all of the six primary[1] and many of the higher aberrations. The usual astronomical refractor contains a lens of two components, comprising four surfaces, which the designer can balance against each other to overcome aberrations; for finer corrections, more components may be added. In the reflector, however, the designer is restricted to certain specifically required geometrical surfaces, and he must accept the aberrations as they come. Each of the reflector types, Newtonian, Cassegrainian, and so forth, has its own degree of correction for the various aberrations, beyond which no further corrections can be made. In certain cases, correcting lenses are placed in the optical system to correct for some aberrations, particularly coma, with which the reflector is especially afflicted.

Generally, refractors are more thoroughly corrected for aberrations than reflectors, with two exceptions: First, the reflector is completely free of chromatic aberration, because the law of reflection is independent of the wavelength of the light (but the law of refraction is not). Second, the parabolic mirror is completely free of all aberrations *on the optical axis.* But this second condition can be theoretically true for only a single geometric point, that is, for one star.

Obviously, any aberration reduces the quality of the image. Further, the reflector is subject to a loss in definition because of the blocking out of light by the secondary and because of diffraction from the legs of the secondary support.

Hence, if excellent definition is the essential quality of a telescope, the choice of a refractor is indicated.

2. *Achromatism* is freedom from chromatic aberration, and here, as stated above, the reflector is superior, being completely achromatic by reason of its operating principle. For spectroscopy, and any work involving the quantitative or qualitative analysis of light, the reflector is definitely superior.

3-4-5. *Magnifying power* depends upon the focal length; *light-gathering power,* upon the area of the objective; and *resolving power,* upon the diameter of the objective. Theoretically, there is no choice between the two types for any of these factors. But in practice certain restrictions are present. Lenses can be made only so big (40 inches is

---

[1] Chromatic and spherical aberration, coma, distortion, astigmatism, and flatness of field.

considered the largest practicable) because too large disks cannot be supported around the edges and still retain their shape. Hence, telescopes of large size must be reflectors—the 100-inch, the 200-inch. Thus, for the great light-gathering power needed to study the Milky Way star clouds and the distant nebulae, as well as for the great resolving power for resolving globular clusters and spiral nebulae, large reflectors are necessary. They are also invaluable in spectroscopy, where high-dispersion spectra require great light-gathering power. . . .

Magnifying power is the ratio of the focal lengths of objective and eyepiece. But the highest practicable magnifying power for a given telescope is dependent, of course, upon the resolving power of the telescope and the quality of the image (definition). The quality of the refractor image is slightly better, hence it is usually possible to use a slightly greater magnifying power than in a reflector of similar optical dimensions.

6. *Size of image.* Except for certain special types of work, it is usually desirable to have a large field of good definition. This is especially true in mapping the sky and star counting. Here the refractor is immeasurably superior. The usable field of a reflector is limited both by the oblique aberrations and by the necessarily small size of the secondary mirror. The diameter of a reflector image is never as great as one half the diameter of the primary mirror, while it is not unusual to cover a 20-by-24-inch photographic plate with a 5-inch or 6-inch lens, and to obtain reasonably good definition all over the plate.

7. *Flatness of field.* Since nearly all modern astronomical work is photographic, flatness of field (that is, of image surface) is advantageous. Only the refractor can have a flat field over any reasonably large area.

8. *Versatility.* Here the reflector comes into its own. Nearly all large reflectors are so made that they may be converted, in a few moments' time, from Newtonian to Cassegrainian, and even to several different applications of the Cassegrainian. If provided for in the original design, any reflector may be made convertible into as many different focal lengths as desired by merely substituting one secondary mirror for another. This cannot be done with a refractor.

9. *Economy and ease of construction.* Cost is not usually a problem for an observatory instrument, but it may be so in the amateur's case. Although the tube and mounting for a small refractor would probably be less costly than for a reflector, the refractor, diameter for diameter, is a much larger (that is, longer) instrument, as refractors are usually made with a focal ratio of about f/15, whereas reflectors are f/8 or shorter. And the cost of the optical glass alone would make the refractor far more expensive.

A professional telescope maker would probably consider the refractor easier to construct, but the reverse is true for the amateur. In the first place, most telescope makers want to build their telescopes according to their own individual designs. Unless an amateur is thoroughly familiar with theoretical optics, the computation of a good objective lens is a problem he cannot possibly handle. And further, even if he adopts a standard design, he has four surfaces to grind, polish, and figure, instead of the single surface of the reflector. Refractor construction is a project for an experienced and conscientious hand; nevertheless, let no one believe that an amateur cannot make a good objective lens. Many amateurs have, and many more should try.

10. *Convenience of handling and upkeep.* Because of its shorter focal length, and because, in such forms as the Cassegrainian, the tube may be made much shorter than the focal length, the reflector is much more conveniently handled than the refractor of the same aperture. A 12-inch reflector may be carried in an automobile, but a 12-inch refractor is a tremendous instrument requiring a 20-foot dome to house it.

A mirror, being unprotected, requires much more upkeep than a lens. It must be resurfaced from time to time, and frequently cleaned, when constant care must be taken to see that it is not scratched or damaged.

Certain types of telescopes, which are neither refractors nor reflectors, but a combination of the two, have been developed, notably the Schmidt camera . . . which has a wide angular field of good definition, but the limitation on size of plate permitted in the reflector still holds for the Schmidt.

Evidently, there is no answer to the question, Which is better, refractor or reflector? unless it be, Well, that depends on whether. . . .

Principles of the Cassegrainian

EARLE B. BROWN

(*Sky and Telescope*, August 1946)

The Cassegrainian is an adaptation of the reflecting telescope which provides two improvements over the Newtonian design. It permits a tube length which is only a fraction of the focal length, thus providing a telescope of f/10 to f/15 of considerable diameter in a very short and easily mounted tube; and it provides for an eyepiece position along the main optical axis, as is the case in the refractor. The latter position is not always convenient, as when observing objects in the zenith.

The principle of the Cassegrainian is that of a hyperboloidal secondary mirror operating in conjunction with the usual paraboloidal primary. The secondary is convex, and is placed inside the principal focus of the primary, so as to form a new principal focus for the instrument at a selected distance behind the primary mirror, which is pierced with a central hole.

The principal focus of the primary mirror and the final focus of the telescope are the two foci of the hyperbolic figure of which the secondary mirror is a part.

Computations. The equivalent focal length of the combination is defined as the focal length of a thin lens or single mirror which would give the same magnification as the combination. This is represented in Figure 10A by the mirror shown in dotted lines at the extreme right, produced by extending the rays backward from the final focus to their intersection with the entering rays. The equivalent focal length (e.f.l.) is given by

$$F' = \frac{F_1\,F_2}{F_2 + F_1 - d},$$

where F_2 is to be taken negative; F_2 is the focal length of the secondary mirror (one half the vertex radius of curvature). The ratio F'/F_1 is known as the amplification.

Usually, the aperture A, the equivalent focal length F', and the distance, p, of the final focus behind the primary mirror, are known, and the rest of the data must be computed. [The useable field is designated by b in Figure 10.] The greater the amplification the steeper will be the curves on primary and secondary (disadvantageous) and the smaller will be the diameter of the secondary and the length of the tube (advantageous). A compromise must be struck between these two factors. . . .

Mounting. One of the undesirable features of the Cassegrainian is

FIG. 10. A. Equivalent focal length. B. Shielding the perforation.

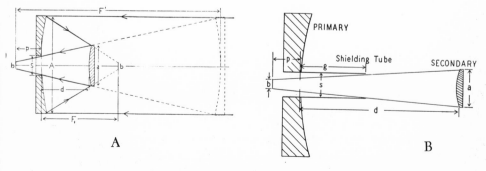

that the eyepiece is pointed directly at the sky, and the field of view is therefore especially subject to stray light. To avoid this, it is desirable to shield the tube (if it is a lattice construction) for a considerable distance above the primary mirror. It may also be desirable to introduce a short length of tube, as shown in Figure 10B, to prevent direct sky light from entering the hole in the primary. As an added precaution here, the secondary mirror should always be somewhat larger than the hole in the primary. The length of the shielding tube, g, is given by the equation

$$g = \frac{(d+p)\ (s-b)}{a-b} - p.$$

The Cassegrainian, because of its stubby tube, is well adapted to the fork type of mounting, although this may lead to difficulties in observation of the polar regions.

Because the eyepiece frequently gets into inconvenient observing positions, it is usually fitted with a diagonal, such as is commonly used with eyepieces on refracting telescopes, and often referred to as a zenith eyepiece or star diagonal.

For the reasons given in the last article, the Cassegrain-type reflector is a popular general-purpose telescope. Many of the large professional telescopes can be quickly converted from Cassegrain to Newtonian form by substituting a flat diagonal mirror for the hyperboloid secondary shown in Figure 10. Alternatively, the largest reflectors are equipped with a structure in the middle of the tube at the upper end so observations can be made at the prime focus without any secondary mirror. This is practical only when the aperture is very much larger than the photographic plateholder or other equipment.

A third type of mirror arrangement is called coudé. With three or more secondary mirrors the light beam is carried down to a fixed focus along the polar axis (see p. 13), where it can be fed into heavy equipment on a firm foundation. With Cassegrainian and Newtonian forms, or at the prime focus, all analyzing equipment is mounted on the movable telescope tube, and added weight must be carried on the mounting.

— T L P

Early
Telescopes

Before the design and construction of modern telescopes is discussed, it is interesting to look briefly into past designs, including sighting devices used before the invention of the lens and paraboloid mirror. This historical digression serves to illustrate the principles covered in Chapter 1 and to gain proper appreciation for the instruments available today. It also establishes the long period over which astronomical observations have been made. For practical reasons (keeping track of the seasons), political reasons, and religious reasons, men have been recording celestial motions and eclipses since 2000 B.C. and earlier.   —TLP

A Visit to Peiping's Ancient Observatory

RICHARD H. COOKE

(*The Sky*, November 1938)

While following the sun around this terrestrial globe we call ours, we eventually arrived in that "Rome of the Far East," the city of Peiping (Peking) in northern China. Having spent some days enjoying the many wonders of this interesting and historical city, we were advised not to omit a trip through the Chinese section of the city and to be sure to visit the ancient Chinese Imperial Astronomical Observatory, located on top of one of the old watchtowers of the great wall which completely encloses the city.

As we finally approached our destination, strange looking objects met our gaze set out in orderly array atop one corner of the wall, about forty feet above the city. From below, the collection appeared to be a meaningless array of iron bars and circles. . . .

Alighting at the foot of the wall, we entered a large courtyard, and there we were treated to our first surprise. Before us stood a massive instrument known as the Abridged Armilla. This instrument consisted of a series of horizontal and vertical bronze circles, each of which was divided into degrees, minutes, and seconds by small bronze pins. It was supported by round cast-bronze beams embellished with the Chinese cloud motif, and these beams in turn were supported on cloud-covered beams around which great dragons wound themselves. The dragon is used throughout in the ornamentation of the various pieces rather than

FIG. 11. The ancient observatory at Peiping, China (from Le Conte's *Voyage to China*, 1698).

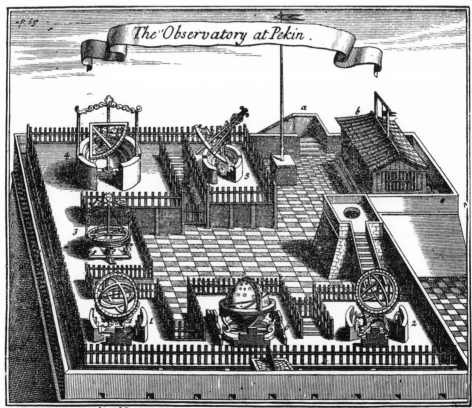

a. Steps going up to the Observatory |1: a *Zodical Sphere* | 3 an *Azimuthall Horizon*| 5 *A Sextant*
b. A Retiring Room for those that make Observations| 2 an *Equinoctial Sphere*| 4 a *Quadrant* | 6 a *Celestiall Globe*

Fig. 12. Instruments on the elevated platform of the observatory at Peiping; here the ancient astronomers made their observations.

some other creature because it appears upon the imperial coat of arms of the emperor of China. . . .

In this same courtyard is located another large piece, known as the Ancient Armilla. This is as beautiful as its companion piece. The dragons themselves support this instrument in their mouths, while four separate bronze pillars of clouds flank the base. . . .

On a raised platform beside the court are several old instruments and other objects (shown in Figures 11 and 12). One of the most interesting is a large, 6-foot-diameter, bronze celestial globe, upon which are set, in their true locations, well-made many-pointed raised stars, which differ in size in accordance with their celestial magnitudes. This globe has the lines of longitude and latitude engraved upon its surface, and it is so well balanced that a touch of the finger makes it revolve on its north-south axis. . . .

One of the most artistic pieces in the collection is the quadrant. This instrument has a radius of about 6 feet. Its limb is divided into markings of 10 seconds, and the index arm, secured at the angle end, moves easily along the limb. The sides and arc of the quadrant are held together by means of a gracefully twisting bronze dragon, wrapped up in clouds. The dragon seems to be ready to take a bite out of the sun which appears in the upper corner.

The whole of the quadrant is supported on a central axis, around which it swings to point to that part of the heavens the astronomer wishes to observe. The base shows dragons supporting round columns. These in turn support a crossbeam of clouds to which is secured the upper end of the axis.

The sextant, a large, heavy, and rather clumsy instrument, has a radius of about 8 feet and represents the sixth part of a circle. In general appearance it reminds one of a large bow and arrow. Its base is circular and embellished with dragons and clouds, supporting a bronze post at the upper end of which is located a mechanism which serves to facilitate the movement of the instrument. The sextant itself rests upon a crossbeam secured to the upright post. To one end of this post is secured the index arm, while the other end extends beyond the limb about 2 feet. This extension was used to raise and lower the machine to its required position by means of pulley and rope. The limb and crossbeam are held together by a series of heavy scrolls, representing clouds. . . .

The observatory has been in disuse for many years and is now nothing more than a museum, but when one looks back over the many centuries and thinks of the astronomical knowledge the ancient Chinese gathered in the study of the universe by means of these instruments, and much cruder ones which preceded these, one marvels at their ingenuity. . . .

The Chinese were the first to observe spots upon the sun's face.

Records of comets have been found dating as far back as 2296 B.C., but their records were not dependable until 611 B.C., and thereafter.

About the year 1100 B.C. they determined the obliquity of the ecliptic.

Chinese records show that the gnomon was used as early as 2300 B.C. in measuring the height of the sun. A gnomon was part of the equipment of the Peiping observatory.

They were among the first to take serious notice of eclipses of the sun and moon. In ancient times it was thought that an eclipse was caused by a great dragon who was an enemy of both the sun and moon and ready at all times to appease his appetite by devouring them. In the year 2136 B.C. the official astronomers Hsi and Ho were put to death for incorrectly forecasting an eclipse of the sun.

It is said that five astronomers watched from the Imperial Observatory. One watched overhead, one to the north, one to the east, one to the south, and one west, so that nothing could escape their observations. In this way they kept track of all unusual phenomena, such as comets, meteors, planet movements, eclipses, and conjunctions, no matter where they appeared. . . .

In India, Egypt, and Greece similar observations were made in early times. By 1600, when the Danish nobleman Tycho Brahe had made accurate measurements of the positions of planets, the art of sighting on a star or planet was highly developed, and most of the instruments described above were well known in Europe and the Middle East as well as in China. Then, in 1610, Galileo used the first telescope to examine the moon and the planets. Other scientists followed his example, but more than fifty years passed before telescopes were used in accurate observations of position. It is clear that the principles of optics (Chapter 1) were not recognized at first.   —T L P

. . . .

Story of the Telescope

ROBERT FLEISCHER

(*The Sky*, September 1937)

A petition was presented to the States-General of Holland on October 2, 1608, asking a patent on an instrument for seeing at a distance. Jan Lippershey, the petitioner, thus recorded himself as the first man to make a telescope and tell the world about it. Once the invention became known, other men claimed the discovery credit, but there is no documentary evidence to disprove Lippershey's priority.

The primary usefulness of the device was expected to be military, but time and circumstance conspired so that it changed the course of science. Before 1608 the universe was extremely limited; Tycho Brahe, who died just seven years before, had had his life's work limited to measuring more accurately objects which had been known and observed for thousands of years. But once the astronomical value of the telescope was realized, the physical limits of the universe began to recede, as they are still doing today.

Jan Lippershey was a spectacle maker, which would easily explain how he might have happened to invent the telescope. But just how he chanced upon the right combination of concave and convex lenses and noticed that they would make an object seem nearer will always remain a mystery. One legend has it that his children, playing with some lenses from their father's shop, made the discovery and told their father; another, that one of Lippershey's assistants was the first to notice telescopic vision.

In any event, once it was rumored that a combination of lenses would make things seem nearer, spectacle makers all over Europe began experimenting, and within a year "Dutch trunks" (as they were known in

England) were being sold in several of the principal cities of Europe. In May 1609, Galileo Galilei, already a famous scientist, heard about the new instrument while visiting in Venice.

Shortly afterward, receiving a letter from a friend in Paris who had seen the telescope, he decided to make one. The day after he returned to Padua, he obtained the proper lenses, put them in a lead tube, and produced an instrument which magnified 3 diameters. Encouraged with his success, he made two more, reaching a magnification of 32 diameters —just about the limit of that type of telescope.

With this last telescope began modern observational astronomy. Galileo looked first at the moon and immediately upset the age-old theory that it was a flawless sphere. He noticed the phases of Mercury and Venus, that the planets seem to have disks while stars do not; saw for the first time some of the myriads of stars invisible to the naked eye; solved the problem of the Milky Way's composition; and perhaps most important of all, discovered the four brightest moons of Jupiter.

The telescope responsible for these epochal discoveries, with its original lenses and tubing, is still preserved in the Galileo Museum in Florence, Italy, and a replica of it is in the Hayden Planetarium in New York. The objective and ocular, or eyepiece, in this telescope and others of its type were separated by a distance equal to the difference of their focal lengths, and the power of the instrument was determined by dividing the focal length of the objective by the focal length of the eyepiece. Prominent among the instrument's defects was its small field, which showed barely one quarter of the moon's surface at one time.

Johannes Kepler, author of the famous three laws of planetary motion, remedied this fault in 1611. He did not himself make a new telescope, but presented plans for it based on a study of optics. The Galilean instrument had a concave (curved inward) lens for the eyepiece, but Kepler's had a convex (curved outward) lens, and it gave an inverted instead of an erect image. The lenses were spaced at the sum of their focal lengths, and the power was determined the same way as in the other instrument. This arrangement permitted a larger field and greater power, and is essentially the type of telescope used today.

With this improvement, however, came difficulties, which led men to build telescopes over 200 feet long and to invent an entirely new type of telescope, the perfection of which taxed some of the greatest minds of two centuries. The difficulties were brought about for this reason:

Our eyes see because an image of what we are looking at is formed on the retina by the lens of the eye. The more distant the object the smaller it appears, and since the image is smaller, less detail is visible. Things very faint and far away become invisible altogether because not enough light enters the eye to make an impression on the retina.

The amount of light which enters the eye is directly dependent on the diameter of the lens, and the purpose of a telescope objective is to collect more light than can the unaided eye. The size of the image formed by the glass need not be greater. That depends on the focal length of the lens, but the image will contain much more light. We can enlarge it, spreading the light from each point over a larger area, by using an ordinary magnifying glass (eyepiece). The enlarged image will have more detail, of course, because two points inseparable in the original will have acquired individual identities.

But, also, the amount of light per unit area in the second image will be less than in the first image and will become even smaller as magnification increases. If it becomes small enough, there will not be enough light from each unit area of the second image to make any impression on the eye, and the image will be so thin as to be invisible. There is, then, a limit to the magnification possible with any given lens diameter, and since seeing fainter stars and more detail is the object of astronomers, bigger lens diameters are obviously wanted.

But when we consider lenses of a fixed focal length we find that as we increase the diameter we increase also the aberration—the circles and colored fringes which form around star images and other bright objects. When this happens, measuring of true shape and size are impossible.

The cause of aberration, that the lens surfaces were spherical, was discovered in 1637 by Descartes, who suggested two remedies. One, to make lenses with elliptical or hyperbolic surfaces, which would theoretically be free from aberration, was not within the reach of craftsmen of the day. The other and more practical solution was to lengthen the focus of the lens while keeping the same diameter—which did not remove but lessened the aberration. The day of really lengthy instruments was yet to come though, and in 1650 most of them were only in the neighborhood of 6 feet.

Shortly after 1650 the Huygens brothers acquired an interest in astronomy and developed and improved a new method for more accurate grinding of lenses. They favored longer focus as a means of reducing aberration and in 1655 made a glass of 12-foot focus. With it they studied the planet Saturn and discovered its largest satellite, Titan. They also found the two occasionally appearing "planets" at the side of Saturn to be a flat ring surrounding the planet. The next telescope they made was 23 feet long and had a $2\frac{1}{3}$-inch objective.

From that time until 1722 objectives of longer and longer focal length were used, and telescopes between 150 and 200 feet long were not at all uncommon. Mounting them was a feat of engineering. The lenses were placed at the ends of two long planks arranged so that their cross section was a "T", and a complicated system of block and tackle, dangling from a vertical mast, was used to support the planking. Hard to mount, clumsy to use, these telescopes gave little practical results except in plotting positions.

It was during this period that early experiments on reflectors were made, as men despaired of ever obtaining a practical refractor. James Gregory drew plans for such an instrument in 1663, but opticians of the day were incapable of grinding a spherical mirror to suit, and his suggestions fell by the wayside. Gregory's plan called for a light-gathering mirror with a hole at the center, and a concave mirror outside the focus which reflected light back through the hole to the eyepiece.

Men were really searching for a way to make an "achromatic" lens, a lens which would refract all colors equally without aberration. Sir Isaac Newton reasoned correctly that if two substances could be found which would refract light at different angles, they would be combined into an achromatic double lens in which the aberration would have canceled out.

He therefore took a hollow prism and a glass prism, filled the hollow one with sugar-of-lead solution, and then compared the angles of a refracted beam of light. Unfortunately, he happened to mix the sugar-of-lead solution to a density that just equaled that of glass in refractive power. Thus he came to the conclusion that all transparent substances refracted equally and that it would be impossible to make an achromatic lens. For the next sixty years no one thought of contradicting this conclusion.

What Newton did after this was to design a reflector, and he, like Gregory, used a spherical mirror. Newton's design differed from Gregory's in that it featured a small plane mirror (within the focus of the main mirror) which reflected the rays to an eyepiece at the side of the tube. This arrangement, conceived in 1672, is in frequent use today. But the spherical mirror was Newton's stumbling block—just as it also proved an unconquerable obstacle to Sieur Cassegrain, a telescope-making French sculptor.

In the early part of 1723, however, John Hadley presented a slightly changed Newtonian reflector to the Royal Astronomical Society. It had a 6-inch *paraboloid* mirror, a focal length of $62\frac{5}{8}$ inches, and worked better than the 123-foot refractor owned by the society. Hadley was very helpful in spreading knowledge of how to make and test the new parabolized mirrors, and reflectors were soon replacing refractors everywhere.

So ended the age of ridiculously long telescopes, and so nearly ended the age of refracting telescopes. The latter were saved through the steady faith of a few people in the belief that an achromatic lens could be constructed. In 1733 Chester Hall made such an achromatic lens, using crown and flint glass, but the flint glass of his time was so poor that it was impractical.

Twenty-five years later, aided by a superior flint glass and a better design, John Dolland was able to patent an achromatic lens, and with his son, Peter, he manufactured many of them. A 3-inch lens was considered large, but at least it was good, and telescope work was largely done at the end of the eighteenth century with refractors such as this and Gregorian-type reflectors.

Sir William Herschel, a musician who acquired an interest in astronomy with the gift of a telescope in 1772, began to grind very good large mirrors. He mounted them at an angle in the tube so the image was sent to the top edge of the tube and could be examined without any light-consuming reflection.

Speculum metal was impractical for large mirrors because it bent easily under its own weight and had to be refigured every few months. Improvement of refractors was sought again, and work on good glass for use in achromatic objects, the next step, was taken by a Swiss named Guinand, who started work in 1784 and was producing 6-inch disks of good optical glass in 1799. He moved to Munich and began working with Fraunhofer, a scientist with many discoveries to his credit. Fraunhofer was able to grind lenses excellently, and since he used Guinand's fine glass, the pair produced efficient lenses. This put reflectors in the background again, and modern achromatic telescopes of considerable size (12 inches) began to appear.

But then, around 1850, Liebig and Steinheil in Germany and Foucault in France made silvered mirrors of glass. Foucault, although his work came a little after Steinheil's, made more noise spreading the news, and his mirror received some notice, while Steinheil was forgotten. At any rate, that was the beginning of the modern reflector.

Since that time we have had both good reflectors and good refractors, each suited to certain types of work. Equatorial mountings and clockwork drives were designed by Fraunhofer, and there has been little improvement in telescopic principle since then. Glass is now coated with aluminum instead of silver, with the advantage that aluminum does not tarnish; and slight improvements in mounting—variations of the equatorial—have been made. With electricity, driving of the telescope to follow the motion of the stars has become simpler. But recent advantages in telescopes have been matters of size, and the time is ripe for some new time-, space-, and efficiency-saving idea to be evolved, to carry the story of telescopes into another chapter.

....

Herschel as a Telescope Maker[1]

EDWIN F. BAILEY

(*The Sky*, August 1939)

Sir William Herschel's interest in the stars first turned him toward telescope making in the year 1772, when he resolved to take nothing on trust but to see with his own eyes all that other men had seen.

In May of 1773 he obtained a few lenses which he placed in pasteboard tubes and fashioned several very poor refractors. These tubes were so unstable that he found it very difficult to observe with them and practically impossible to show anyone else anything through them. He then had several tin tubes constructed. These were quite an improvement, but he soon became discouraged because of their great length and awkwardness (one of them was 30 feet long) and complained because of the great amount of time wasted in arranging for observations. He had so little time to spare that he was compelled to look for a better, more compact instrument.

Fortune now began to beam on Herschel, for he was able to rent a Gregorian telescope which was very much to his liking. Then he tried to buy a mirror for a 5-foot tube but found the price too high.

Like most amateur astronomers, Herschel was not overburdened with money, but this only made his desire that much keener, and he decided to make the mirror himself. A friend who was having difficulty with a mirror was glad to sell his material to Herschel, and he also instructed him in the art of grinding.

In nine months he finished the first mirror, which gave him 40 power, and on March 1, 1774, he began his journal by entering the observation of Saturn and the Orion nebula.

It is interesting to note that about five years previous to this, David Rittenhouse had constructed a transit instrument which was the first telescope built in America.

---

[1] Address given before Rittenhouse Astronomical Society.

By 1776 Herschel had completed the 7-foot telescope with the 6¼-inch mirror, and this he used until after his discovery of Uranus in 1781. This famous instrument was a typical amateur job for he describes the planet as a diffuse cometlike body, which sounds like a good case of spherical aberration.

The blanks necessary for mirror making were not as easily acquired in Herschel's time as they are today, for now it is possible to buy disks at any glass-house. In the good old days a telescope maker cast his own metal blanks. Herschel was unfortunate in that he never mastered the founding art to the extent of making the best metal alloy but was content to use a softer mixture that worked up easier but was far from permanent and tarnished very readily. Because of this fault, he made several mirrors for most of his telescopes, so that he could use one while he repolished and refigured the others. . . .

In 1781 Herschel cast his first mirror, but the mold broke and let out a good deal of the metal. When the casting cooled it broke into many pieces. This casting contained 29 per cent tin. When the second casting was to be made the tin was reduced to 26 per cent because it was felt that the high tin percentage made the material brittle.

During the second melting the furnace split, and the hot metal ran out, cracking the flagstone floor, so they were forced to leave the heated area rather hurriedly. . . .

The natural emery or sand used for grinding was very poor compared with the quick-cutting abrasives available today. The working time must have been enormous because speculum metal is so hard. From my experience in working this metal I would say that it took Herschel at least 100 hours to make a 6-inch mirror, and from the number he claimed to have made he must have worked about 24 hours a day! According to his record he made 200 7-foot, 150 10-foot, and 80 20-foot telescopes. These sizes have reference to the focal length. The 7-foot had an aperture of 6 inches, the 10-foot from 10 to 12 inches, and the 20-foot about 18 to 20 inches. However, there is no record of this number in his notes. The grinding time was reduced by short cuts, for often the blanks were cast with the curve on them. Grindstones were shaped with the proper curvature and used for tools; sometimes small stones were cemented to backing tools to form a sort of built-up stone. Herschel apparently kept most of his methods of working to himself, at least as far as the mirrors were concerned, but he does mention the books which he used for reference. Probably the most exhaustive work is that of Robert Smith, A *Compleat System of Opticks*. . . .

In 1787 Herschel first used his telescope as a front-view instrument, and the following year he made an 18-inch which was designed as a

Herschelian. This method of tilting the mirror to eliminate the usual diagonal gave him an increase of about 40 per cent in light transmission, but the heat from his body played havoc with the definition, and it was of little value except in observing faint objects. . . .

Herschel really used the high powers attributed to him, and he also knew the actual power of a given eyepiece. Apparently there was some controversy while he was still alive, and he wrote a paper on his method of testing the power of a lens. He arrived at a standard by first measuring the solar focus of the lens (this was the average of five measurements); then he used the lens as a simple magnifier, and by measuring the diameter of a wire and also the enlargement through the glass, he was able very accurately to tell the power. It was then a very simple matter to find the power in the telescope.

The highest power he had was 7676, which was given by a lens $\frac{1}{45}$ inch in diameter. This is smaller than the front element of an oil immersion microscopic objective and gave a field of 20 seconds—which is something to try to use on a moving star with a driveless telescope! . . .

Herschel made and sold many mirrors, and his telescopes were scattered all over Europe. The prices he received for these mirrors were very high, if we convert the English money of that day into dollars.

His own listing of parts sold amounts to about $75,000, which was quite a sum to make in the twenty-five years that he worked on telescopes, and we can class him as a successful optician.

Most of the mirrors were sold unmounted, only the diagonal and mirror being furnished. A 7-foot telescope completely mounted sold for $1000. . . .

A 25-foot telescope was made for the Madrid Observatory, and it cost $15,000; later a large 7-foot and 10-foot were sold to them for $11,500. . . .

The Adler Planetarium in Chicago has a Herschel telescope, formerly at the Royal Observatory at Greenwich. . . .

In 1785 Herschel asked the Royal Society to obtain a grant from the King so he could make a very large telescope. They were successful in obtaining 2000 pounds. Herschel intended to make a 30-inch mirror, but the King decided that he should make a 4-foot mirror. In two years the money was used up, and the King gave him another 2000 pounds, along with 200 pounds which was to be an annual grant for the upkeep of the great telescope.

The construction of the eighth wonder of the world took four years and required the assistance of a great army of workmen. The mirror alone required two crews of twelve men each for the polishing. These workmen were difficult to manage because each of them had his own idea as to how the work should be done. Herschel became disgusted and built a machine to do the work. This proved so successful that thereafter all his work was done on the machine. Probably all of the best mirrors were made with it.

Herschel made two 4-foot mirrors for the 40-foot telescope. The first, which has since been lost, was a very poor blank because it was so thin. He used it, however, to gain experience. The second mirror was slightly better, due to an additional inch in thickness. It can still be seen resting in its cell, hanging on the wall at Observatory House [Herschel's residence, in Slough, England]. It weighs 2118 pounds. . . .

The great telescope was not the expected success. Although it confirmed several of his previous discoveries, it was unmanageable, and the polish was far from permanent. Apparently it was necessary to repolish the mirror every two years.

Fig. 13. In 1789 the 40-foot telescope, then the largest in the world, was installed on the lawn of Observatory House, the residence of Sir William Herschel, in Slough, England.

It is well known that Herschel did very little work with the 40-foot telescope, preferring the 20-foot and smaller. This was due to greater ease in handling. It was necessary to have two assistants to move the large telescope while he was observing, and perhaps their efficiency had something to do with the disuse of the telescope. The mounting of this telescope was so large that it was necessary to have speaking tubes in order to communicate. The tube was made of 20-gauge sheet iron and weighed almost a ton. The mirror was mounted on a giant hinge, and perhaps the tube was unnecessary, as the mirror end of the telescope was well supported by the base of the mounting. The bearings for the azimuth motion were flagstones laid in a nearly flat circle, and the telescope rolled over them on casters. I fear that the motion was far from vibrationless.

The iron tools that remain at Slough show that . . . there is apparently no modern practice which was not used in those days. No one has ever rivaled Herschel as a telescope maker. The number, the size, the efficiency of his instruments, when considered in the light of materials, methods, time, still place him in the lead. . . .

Some of the difficulties of making a high-quality reflector are now clear. It was thought in the late nineteenth century that refractors (lenses) could be made more accurate than reflectors, and most of the telescopes of that vintage, many of which are still in use today, are refractors. Some of the highest quality lenses were made by Alvan Clark.

— T L P

....

Alvan Clark and Sons

RALPH S. BATES

(The Telescope, July–August 1940)

Alvan Clark, maker of many of America's largest telescopes, began constructing his first telescope as the result of a very unusual accident. In 1843, George Bassett Clark, the eldest son of Alvan Clark, a well-known portrait painter in Boston, was studying civil engineering at Phillips Academy at Andover. He had developed an interest in astronomy and was considering how he might possess a telescope, when an unexpected thing happened. Another student, while summoning his fellows to lunch one day, swung the old-fashioned dinner bell of the academy

FIG. 14. Alvan Clark.

so vigorously that it suddenly burst into pieces. Clark, remembering that Newton had made his telescope of bell metal, collected the fragments and took them to the kitchen of his father's home in Cambridge, Massachusetts. There, he melted the metal in the fire and cast it into a 5-inch disk. When he began the laborious task of grinding and polishing it into a mirror, Clark, Sr., became interested in the work of his seventeen-year-old son; together they finished the mirror and made a telescope with which they saw the satellites of Jupiter and the rings of Saturn. Alas, the enthusiasts presently encountered the problem of tarnishing, necessitating frequent refiguring of the mirror, as Sir William Herschel and other predecessors of the Clarks had found to their sorrow. It was this difficulty that led Alvan Clark to give up making reflecting telescopes and to turn to refractors, and thereby to launch upon his career as the first great telescope maker that America produced.

Alvan Clark was born on March 8, 1804, at Ashfield, Massachusetts. . . . He worked in Providence, New York, and Fall River at his trade as an engraver. Studying painting in his spare time led him to resolve to try his fortune as a painter of portraits and miniatures in Boston. Accordingly, he set up a studio in that city in 1836 and took up residence in the nearby suburb of Cambridge, or Cambridgeport, as the eastern part of Cambridge was then called. For about a decade and a half he painted portraits at his studio on Tremont Row. . . .

The "Great Refractor," as the 15-inch telescope at Harvard College was called, went into operation in 1847, and at that time shared the honor of being the world's largest telescope with its 15-inch twin at the Pulkovo Observatory in Russia. Eagerly, Alvan Clark asked to look through the Harvard instrument, but Professor W. C. Bond informed him that he would have to get written permission from President Everett, a permission which was speedily granted. Clark tells us in his "Autobiography"[1] that he immediately perceived the errors of figure in the costly $12,000 lens, a fact that led him to take heart and try his own hand at manufacturing refracting telescopes. He began by working some old object glasses, and when he thought he had gained enough proficiency to warrant it, he imported a pair of $5\frac{1}{4}$-inch disks and also bought larger glasses of good quality in New York.

Although he manufactured and sold some few instruments, his business was rather slow in growing. Then it so happened that he was rewarded for his excellent figure work by discovering in 1852 with a telescope of his own making that the star 8 Sextantis was double. The following year he finished a telescope of $7\frac{1}{2}$-inch aperture, with which the companion of the star 95 Ceti was found. Clark reported his discoveries to a correspondent, the Reverend W. R. Dawes, a famous double-star observer in England. Dawes purchased the latter telescope and some others which Clark made for him. One of these, an 8-inch, soon passed into the hands of William Huggins, a pioneer in astronomical spectroscopy, who used it to photograph his first stellar spectrum. In 1859 Clark went to England, visited Dawes, and was introduced to the circle of Britain's astronomical elite, including Sir John Herschel and the Earl of Rosse. Reports of discoveries made with Clark instruments were printed from time to time in the *Monthly Notices* of the Royal Astronomical Society. At last Alvan Clark had secured the publicity that he needed; the success of his telescope-making business was assured, and orders began to pour in upon him.

In 1860, F. A. P. Barnard, at the time head of the University of Mississippi, and later to become president of Columbia, ordered from Clark a refractor larger than any then in existence. To fill this order Clark sold his house for the purpose of raising money, borrowed besides, and bought an acre of ground on Henry Street, Cambridge, where, together with his sons George Bassett Clark and Alvan G. Clark, henceforth to be his business associates, he erected the first telescope factory in America. . . . Clark also set up an observatory, housing one of his telescopes equipped with an equatorial mounting, a driving clock, and

[1] The "Autobiography of Alvan Clark" [a letter written by him in 1887 to the Hon. William L. Richardson, Washington, D.C.] was published in the *Sidereal Messenger*, 1889, 8, 109.

a micrometer. The huge revolving dome of his observatory, resting on cannon balls, long remained a familiar sight in Cambridge, and the great pier telescope mounting has been demolished only within the last decade.

An 18½-inch glass for the University of Mississippi telescope was imported from Messrs. Chance Brothers and Company, of Birmingham, England, and was worked into shape. On January 31, 1862, Alvan G. Clark began to test the lens, and soon exclaimed, "Why look, Father, Sirius is a double star." A few nights later G. P. Bond verified the discovery at Harvard. Two decades earlier Bessel had suspected the existence of the relatively faint companion star as a result of his detection of the irregularity of the proper motion of Sirius. For the production of the lens coupled with the discovery, the Académie des Sciences at Paris awarded the Lalande Prize for 1862, consisting of a gold medal and $120 in gold to Alvan G. Clark. Clark later discovered a number of other doubles.[2]

The Civil War intervened, and the 18½-inch telescope never reached Mississippi. The Chicago Astronomical Society had been formed in 1862 by an enthusiastic group of amateurs who desired to purchase a large telescope, and in the following year they secured the Clark instrument. It was later used by S. W. Burnham, noted for his large catalogues of double stars published by the Carnegie Institution.

The firm of Alvan Clark and Sons went on from triumph to triumph. Six times since 1860 it has been called upon to build the largest telescope in the world. A telescope of 26-inch aperture was delivered to the Naval Observatory in 1872, for which the national government paid $46,000. It was with this telescope that Asaph Hall discovered the two small satellites of Mars in 1877. About the same time, the Clarks were filling an order for Leander J. McCormick of Chicago, son of the inventor of the reaper, who secured a similar 26-inch telescope, which he placed in the Leander McCormick Observatory of the University of Virginia, where it has been used extensively for measuring stellar parallaxes and proper motions. The year 1879 found the Clarks at work on a 30-inch telescope for the Pulkovo Observatory. Otto Struve came to America to examine the finished lens and was a guest of the Clarks. Czar Alexander III presented Alvan Clark with the Golden Medal of the Empire for producing this telescope.

In 1880 the Clarks began work on the 36-inch telescope of the Lick Observatory. James Lick had provided in his will for "a powerful telescope, superior to and more powerful than any telescope ever yet

[2] Burnham, S. W., "Double Stars Discovered by Mr. Alvan G. Clark," *American Journal of Science*, 1879, 17, 283, 289.

made."[3] It took seven years to complete the instrument, which was shipped to California in 1886 in a special car. Alvan G. Clark headed a party of sixteen persons who accompanied it to its destination on Mt. Hamilton. Clark felt greatly relieved when at last the lens rested safely in its cell on the mountain top. On September 9, 1892, E. E. Barnard, while using the Lick telescope, discovered the fifth satellite of Jupiter.

Less than a year after the delivery of the Lick lens Alvan Clark died, in 1887 at the age of eighty-three. . . .

FIG. 15. Alvan G. Clark and Carl Lundin with the crown lens of the Yerkes 40-inch objective (Yerkes Observatory photograph).

Alvan G. Clark, who lived on until 1897, was responsible for the 40-inch lens completed in 1895 for the Yerkes Observatory at Williams Bay, Wisconsin, which went into operation a few months after his death. This lens, originally ordered for the University of Southern California, had been secured by G. E. Hale, who met Alvan G. Clark by chance at a scientific gathering in Rochester, New York, shortly after financial difficulties had prevented the glass from going to its original destination. Clark, who had purchased the glass from Mantois in Paris, was thus facing a $20,000 loss. The trolley car magnate of Chicago,

---

[3] "An Extract from the Will of James Lick (Recorded in the Office of the Recorder of County of San Francisco, State of California, in Liber 810 of Deeds, pp. 26, *et seq.*; Nov. 10, 1876)." Reproduced in Shapley, Harlow, and Howarth, H. E., *A Source Book in Astronomy*, New York, McGraw-Hill, 1929, p. 316.

Charles T. Yerkes, gave Hale a check for this amount to buy the lens and ultimately expended $349,000 for making and housing what has ever since been the world's largest refracting telescope. . . . Actual construction of the Yerkes lens was in the hands of Carl Axel Robert Lundin, a Swede who had become associated with the firm in 1873. The mechanical parts for the Yerkes telescope, made by the firm of Warner and Swasey, were completed in 1893 and set up at the Columbian Exposition in Chicago. On the first night of observation with this telescope, May 21, 1897, E. E. Barnard discovered the companion of Vega.

After the death of Alvan G. Clark, Lundin carried on the business until his own death in 1915. Lundin and Alvan G. Clark made the 24-inch refractor for the Lowell Observatory, the instrument with which Percival Lowell carried on his major observations of Mars. At the same observatory, the planet Pluto was spotted photographically on March 13, 1930, with a Clark 13-inch telescope.

The Clarks are gone. However, the legacy of their telescopes still enables an inquiring human race to plumb the outer depths of space.

3

Making

a

Reflector

Although Herschel had his difficulties, and the modern techniques of lens and mirror figuring may seem complex and expensive, it is a fact that thousands of amateurs have made excellent telescopes on their own without great expense. These amateur telescope makers form a well-knit group, sharing the many bits of "know-how" so necessary in their effort, and the unmatched satisfaction of observing with an instrument of one's own making.

Experience and tricks of the trade have been shared for the past twenty years or more in the magazine Sky and Telescope in "Gleanings for Amateur Telescope Makers," a column edited successively by Earle B. Brown and Robert E. Cox. The articles reproduced here give a broad view of what is required in amateur telescope making. (For more details see Making Your Own Telescope, by Allyn J. Thompson, Cambridge, Massachusetts, Sky Publishing Corp., 1947.) — TLP

••

Practical Advice and Aid
in Telescope Making

HENRY L. YEAGLEY

(*The Sky*, December 1937; January, March, April, June 1938)

. . . One of the first problems to be solved when starting to make a telescope is to choose the size of the aperture. The factors to consider are the cost, the size and type with their accompanying difficulties, and the observing conditions prevalent in the locality involved. The latter consideration dictates, for most places, a maximum aperture of 20 inches. The ill effects of air motion on telescopic observations are greatly increased by comparatively small increases of the mirror diameter.

As for the cost, a small instrument is preferable. Whereas the materials for a suitable 6-inch reflecting telescope may range from ten to fifty dollars, the cost to produce a 10-inch of equal quality would be well over five times as much. On the other hand, one smaller than 6 inches . . . requires quite as much time and care to make the proper curvature, polish, and figure . . . as the larger sizes. . . . A 6-inch telescope is, from many viewpoints, the optimum size. Its ability to receive light and produce an image of a celestial or terrestrial object (a property known as its light-gathering power) is over two thousand times as great as the eye and about thirty-six times as great as for a 1-inch telescope. . . .

Another important property of a telescope is its ability to separate features of a single object, or if two bodies are close together, to form separate images for the eye to see. This depends on the diameter of the aperture and is known as its resolving power. With a properly made 6-inch telescope and a $\frac{1}{2}$-inch eyepiece, the dark bands of Jupiter, the ice caps on Mars, and the dark space between the rings of Saturn and the planet itself may be readily observed.

Choosing the proper kind of glass for the mirror is also not difficult, since it is now generally recognized by authorities that the carefully annealed Pyrex disks made at the Corning Glass Works are by all odds the best. Their combined low coefficient of expansion and price give them a unique position among other possible materials. Although quartz has a much lower coefficient of expansion, its cost is from fifty to one hundred times as great. A Pyrex disk, 6 inches in diameter, costs less than five dollars. . . .

The diagram on page 60 (Fig. 17A) illustrates the optical system for a Newtonian-type telescope, the type generally constructed by the beginner.

The light from the celestial object arrives in rays which are almost parallel because of the great distance from the source. The parabolic mirror has the property of reflecting this light in such a manner as to bring it to a focus in one plane, the focal plane, which is at a distance f (the focal length) from the mirror. Since the observer's head would stop the incoming light if the eyepiece were in front of this plane, viewing it from the natural position, a small flat mirror, called the diagonal, is placed on the axis at an angle of 45° with the direction of the axis of the reflected cone of light, which sends it off to the side where the image may be viewed without interference.

Assuming that the reader has decided to make a 6-inch Newtonian telescope (although with proper changes in the dimensions, the methods apply to other sizes equally well), directions will now be given for grinding and polishing the mirror.

The equipment and materials needed for this initial work are as shown in Figure 16.

1. A well-weighted barrel (A) or solid table with waterproofed top, into which screws may be driven.

FIG. 16. A,B,C. An oil barrel makes an ideal stand upon which to fasten the grinding tool. D,E. Construction of a handle for the mirror. F,G. Grinding strokes.

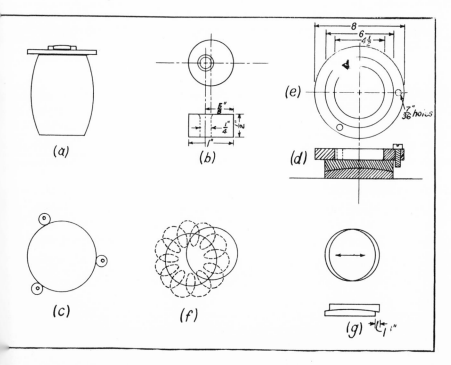

2. Two glass disks, 6 inches in diameter. The mirror disk (which will be designated from now on as "the mirror") should be not less than $\frac{3}{4}$-inch thick and of carefully annealed glass. . . .

The "tool" may be of any kind of glass and preferably at least $\frac{3}{4}$-inch thick. A second piece of Pyrex is as economical as any.

3. Anchor blocks (B). Cut out three hardwood anchor disks $\frac{1}{2}$-inch thick and about 1 inch in diameter. Slices sawed from an old broom-handle serve well for this purpose. Drill $\frac{1}{4}$-inch holes through each, but offset them about $\frac{1}{8}$ inch from the axis. Lay the tool, trademarked side up if Pyrex, on the table, and space the blocks equally around it (C). Orient the blocks in such a manner that when screwed in place and rotated, the offset or cam effect will wedge the glass tool in position.

Care should be taken to have a $\frac{1}{8}$-inch clearance between the tops of the anchor blocks and screws and the top of the tool.

4. In order to protect the mirror from the heat of the hands in the more refined stages and facilitate its handling during the initial grinding, a handle is required. A most efficient and convenient one (D) can be made from a piece of hardwood 1 inch thick and 8 inches square, as follows: On the block (E) inscribe three concentric circles $4\frac{1}{2}$ inches, 6 inches, and 8 inches in diameter around its center. With a jig or keyhole saw, saw out the $4\frac{1}{2}$-inch disk and saw around the 8-inch circle to eliminate corners. After painting or shellacking, drill three equally spaced holes, $\frac{7}{32}$ inch in diameter so that their inner edges are tangent to the outer edge of the 6-inch circle. Insert in these holes three one-quarter-inch-twenty round-head machine screws, one and a half inches long. A few turns of adhesive or tire tape wound onto the protruding ends should serve to make this device hold the mirror snugly, as shown in Figure 16D.

5. Total amounts of grinding and polishing materials required and the approximate quantities needed for each renewal of charge are shown in Table 2.

It will be comforting to note that, contrary to common belief, it is no longer necessary or desirable to work in a dark and damp cellar, but rather to have a place where the light and temperature are suitable for the worker's comfort. During the latter stages of polishing and figuring it is well for the workroom to be free from dust, and the temperature should not fluctuate greatly.

The first job is to "rough out" the mirror to the approximate desired curvature; but before proceeding, the mirror maker should have some understanding of the factors involved in choosing and obtaining the correct curvature.

The distance between a telescope mirror and the image of a star

TABLE 2. GRINDING AND POLISHING MATERIALS NEEDED FOR A 6-INCH NEWTONIAN TELESCOPE

Abrasive	Total needed (in ounces)	Approximate quantity for each application (in teaspoonfuls)
No. 60 carborundum	16	$\frac{2}{3}$
" 100 "	8	$\frac{1}{3}$
" 150 "	4	$\frac{1}{4}$
" 220 "	4	$\frac{1}{4}$
" 280 "	4	$\frac{1}{4}$
" 400 "	4	$\frac{1}{4}$
No. M302 emery	2	$\frac{1}{4}$
" M302½ "	2	$\frac{1}{4}$
" M303 "	2	$\frac{1}{4}$
" M303½ "	2	$\frac{1}{4}$
" M304 "	2	$\frac{1}{4}$
" M305 "	2	$\frac{1}{4}$
Barnsite or cerium oxide	1	..
Pitch mixture*	16	..

* 49 per cent pitch, 49 per cent rosin, 2 per cent beeswax, or other prepared compound.

formed by it (f in Fig. 17A) is known as its focal length. It so happens that its value is equal to half the mirror's radius of curvature. Choice of the focal length and the radius of curvature ($R = 2f$) turns out to be a matter of following a simple rule: the focal length of a telescope mirror divided by the diameter of the disk, f/D, known as the focal ratio of the mirror, should be about 8. . . . Here we will use f/D equal to 8.5. For a 6-inch mirror, we have:

$$f = 8.5 \times D = 8.5 \times 6 = 51.0,$$

and since the radius of curvature is equal to $2f$ the value of R will be 102 inches. With this knowledge, a simple calculation will give the required depth of the mirror at its center (see Fig. 17B). This depth is called the sagitta, s, given by the formula

$$s = \frac{r^2}{2R},$$

where $r = D/2$ is the radius of the mirror. In this case, $s = 0.044$ inch, very nearly equal to the diameter of No. 17 B-and-S-gauge wire.

Figure 17C illustrates how a short piece of wire (B) of the correct diameter may be laid on the mirror center with a straightedge (A) above, to check the depth of the mirror.

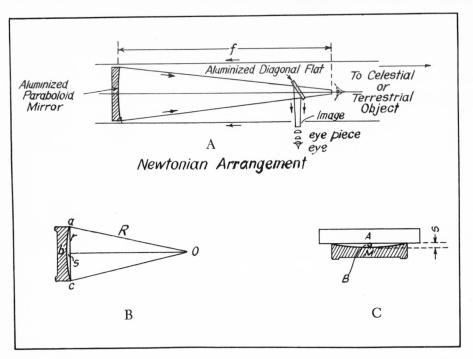

FIG. 17. A. Optical system for Newtonian-type telescope. B. The sagitta (*s*) of a reflecting telescope mirror. C. Finding the sagitta with a straight-edge and a wire.

Procedure

Clamp the tool in place on the workbench with the ridged or smaller face upward. Place on its surface two thirds of a teaspoonful of No. 60 carborundum, moisten with water, and lay the chamfered-edged surface of the mirror over it. Start grinding by moving the mirror center in a "rose-petal" path around the edge of the tool as shown in Figure 16F. At the same time, to avoid lack of symmetry of both surfaces, rotate the mirror around its own center by hand and walk around the barrel to obtain the equivalent of rotating the tool. This combination of motions will subsequently be referred to as stroke A. It can be seen that the overhanging edge of the upper disk will cause excess pressure on its own center and on the edge of the lower. The result is to make the latter convex and the former concave, which is just what we have set out to do.

After a minute or two of manipulation, the carborundum will have crushed down and should be renewed. It is poor economy to continue work after the harsh grinding noise of the larger particles has ceased. At this stage the entire purpose is to gouge out material and not to smooth the glass surfaces. . . .

Particles of glass broken from the mirror's edge detract from the finished mirror as an object of beauty when exhibited to friends, but actually in no way lessen its usefulness in the telescope.

After the grinding has been continued for some time, the depth of the mirror should be tested at regular intervals. If the test shown in Figure 17C indicates that the sagitta is too great, the positions of mirror and tool should be reversed, after which further grinding with the same stroke (now moving the tool) will serve to reduce s. A little thought will make it clear that under these conditions the edge of the mirror will be cut away more rapidly than the center. Continue the grinding, interchanging mirror and tool positions when necessary, until both surfaces are ground uniformly from center to edge.

The fact that depth s is correct, does not imply that the ground surfaces are uniform spheres. However, nature steps in here in a most obliging way to help take care of the situation; only two types—flats and spheres—can be paired off in such a manner that all points of the paired surfaces are in contact at the same time. This principle, applied to our problem, indicates that if we want our mirror surface spherical, it must be ground against the tool in a way that brings the surfaces into complete, intimate contact. Fortunately, this is easily accomplished by discarding stroke A and substituting one (to be referred to as stroke B) in which the center of the mirror moves back and forth over the center of the tool. (See Fig. 16G.) The turning of the mirror in the hands while walking around the barrel is the same as in stroke A. Only ten or fifteen minutes of this is required to gain the desired result. If now the depth s is still correct, the first stage is complete.

You are now ready to proceed with fine grinding. This consists of continuing stroke B, using successively the finer abrasive sizes carborundum No. 100, 150, 220, 280, 400; then emery No. M302, M302$\frac{1}{2}$, M303, M303$\frac{1}{2}$, M304, M305. Each grade of abrasive should be renewed about four times, or until the cleaned and dried surface appears absolutely uniform when examined with and without a magnifying glass.

The abrasives are handled most efficiently by placing the required quantities (as indicated in Table 2) on the center of the tool, moistening them with sufficient water to spread evenly over the tool, and then carefully placing the mirror on the mixture. The mirror should be pressed downward with a slight rotatory motion in order to spread the abrasive grains and then should be moved slowly back and forth with a gradually increasing length of stroke. The longest should not be more than 1 inch past center in any direction. Gradually lessen this 1-inch overhanging stroke to a $\frac{1}{4}$-inch maximum as the abrasive sizes are successively reduced from No. 100 carborundum to No. M305 emery. Where the finer grades are being used it will be found that smaller quantities are desirable. Beginning with emery grade M302 the wetted material on the middle of the tool should be pressed and spread evenly over the surface with the tip of the index or middle finger. Any noticeable particles should be crushed down or pushed over the edge. No pressure should be applied to the mirror while using emery. The weight of the worker's hands upon the handle is sufficient. Special attention should be paid during the use of the finest grades to insure that the edges of tool and mirror do not tend to become dry in the intervals during which they are exposed to the air. This is easily avoided by adding water frequently to the protruding surface of the tool. Small bottles with nozzles inserted in the stopper can be bought at the five-and-ten-cent stores and are ideal for this purpose.

Although three or more "wets" of ten minutes' duration are desirable for the coarser grades, only one each is needed for the M304 and M305 sizes. Grinding with the latter two, however, should be continued for longer periods. The M304 wet should last about twenty minutes, whereas the M305 session continues for about one half hour. Frequent applications of water to the exposed edges are of paramount importance at this stage, and the mirror must be kept in motion every second. Even the shortest lapse may permit the two disks to "freeze" together. Should that occur, separate by placing in a pan of cold water, which is then heated to the boiling point. This method will prevent scratching, and after cooling, work can proceed normally.

When the final stage of grinding has been completed, wash and dry the surface and place the mirror, concave side up, over fine newspaper print. If the letters stand out clearly and appear to be covered by a layer of slightly turbid water, the surface is ready for polishing. If, however, the print is not easily read, or if it is more opaque toward the edge than in the center, repeat the last stage of the process.

All through the fine-grinding stages the "worn" abrasive materials should be carefully wiped from tool and mirror with cloth or paper towels. Quarter sections of newspaper sheets are very satisfactory for this purpose. It is also desirable to keep the table space around the mirror wet by means of a water-saturated blotter of cloth. During the grinding this precaution serves to keep dust from getting on the glass surfaces, but while polishing, it is essential in order to prevent rapid evaporation of moisture from the protruding mirror edges, which would be detrimental to the formation of the parabolic figure in this region.

The polishing process differs in nature from grinding. When one glass surface is moved across another, with carborundum or other hard granules between, there occurs a rolling-sliding motion which breaks out glass particles from both surfaces as the abrasive material is reduced to finer and finer pieces. Polishing, on the other hand, is accomplished by rubbing the finely ground glass surface over a prepared pitch surface which has hard rouge or Barnsite particles partially embedded in it. Each particle is held like a cutter bit, and as the glass moves against the pitch surface, fine particles are shaved off to give the glass a "polished" or highly reflective surface.

The "pitch" mixture used in the polishing process is, when cold, capable of flowing slightly under pressure yet hard enough so the thumbnail barely marks it when pressed against it for a few seconds. A material having these properties may be prepared by melting in a broad-bottomed pan 1 ounce of beeswax and 25 ounces of pitch, and then adding to this 25 ounces of melted rosin. [Recently there is a preference for 80 per cent blocking pitch, 15 per cent asphalt, and 5 per cent Burgundy pitch.] The final mixture should be thoroughly stirred and strained through two thicknesses of cheesecloth. If a prepared pitch-rosin mixture is bought from some optical company, there remains only to add the proper percentage (2 per cent) of beeswax.

Next, prepare a rouge bag from a double piece of closely woven outing flannel about 4 inches square. Lay it on a clean dust-free surface and place on its center two heaping teaspoonsful of Barnsite or rouge. Gather the edges of the cloth together and bind securely with tire or adhesive tape. Place this gourd-shaped bag in a cup of clean water and keep covered with a dust-free inverted tin can.

Before proceeding with the polishing it is necessary to make a specially perforated rubber mat (Fig. 18A) to act as a mold in forming the polishing surface. On account of the intimate contact between the latter and the mirror, the two would tend to "grab" and make polishing extremely difficult. For this reason the pitch surface must be formed with grooves or alleyways to maintain atmospheric pressure and to retain the polishing material.

Making the Pitch Lap

First, prepare a large electric soldering iron "pitch groover" as illustrated in Figure 18. To do this, saw off the nose of the soldering tip with a hack saw. Cut a rectangle of hard, thin ($\frac{1}{2}$ mm) brass plate about $5\frac{1}{2}$ cm long and 3 cm wide, bend this into a lengthwise "V" of angle 60° to 70°, and file the leading edge to a knife edge. Make this trough fit on the copper end of the soldering iron and silver-solder it on, as shown in Figure 18, making sure that the cut-off nose leaves a drain space through which molten pitch can pass.

With a rim of Scotch tape around the edge of the glass tool, cover its surface with about 4 mm of hot pitch mixture. As soon as this cools and starts to thicken, so that it will not flow readily, quickly remove the Scotch tape, leaving the tool face up with the soft pitch on top.

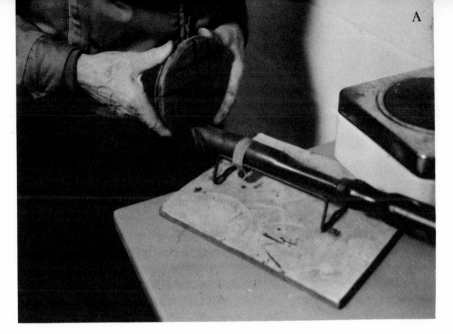

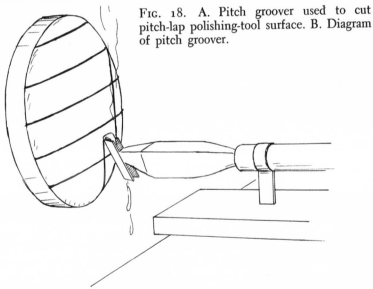

Fig. 18. A. Pitch groover used to cut pitch-lap polishing-tool surface. B. Diagram of pitch groover.

B.

Having covered the unpolished mirror surface with an even coating of a thick, watery mixture of Barnsite or rough polishing compound, lay the mirror face downward on the soft pitch. Eliminate air bubbles by first making contact between glass and pitch on one edge. Then slowly but firmly press the other edge of the mirror down to complete the contact. Slide the mirror back and forth with slight pressure for a few minutes to insure complete contact over the whole pitch surface, then slide it off and allow the pitch to cool.

Draw a groove pattern (a grid of straight lines) on the pitch with pencil and ruler. Any size squares between 1.5 cm and 4 cm will work well. It is preferable to use 4-cm squares on tools 10 inches or larger.

Next, clamp the pitch groover on the edge of a table as shown in Figure 18 and bring it to a temperature that will cause pitch in contact to melt rapidly. Hold the pitch-lap surface as shown in Figure 18A. You can readily guide the pitch-covered surface by hand so that the V-cuts are straight, or curved grooves can be cut if other patterns are desired.

After all the grooves are cut, slightly soften the pitch by immersing the polishing tool in hot water for a few seconds and pressing the mirror surface against it for several minutes. The tool is now ready for use.

Wet the new lap thoroughly with the rouge (Barnsite) bag and place the mirror on it. After a few minutes' pressing, it is time to start the polishing stroke. This is the over-center stroke B which was previously used for the fine-grinding stages. The charge of Barnsite (or rouge) and water will last from thirty minutes to an hour. Whenever it is renewed, the old should not be washed or wiped away. Also the worker should keep in mind that a high pitched, barely audible sound (rather than the low grinding noise) indicates progress in polishing. The desired condition is obtained by adding a very watery mixture of rouge or Barnsite.

To prevent possible scratching, press the mirror on the pitch lap for thirty seconds each time a new charge is applied. In addition keep the surrounding table wet at all times, especially while working on the mirror. Use not more than sixty strokes per minute. A good way to time the strokes is to support a pipe fitting or other heavy object from the ceiling by a string 4 feet long. If this is given a side push and allowed to act as a pendulum, its backward and forward motion will set the pace for the polishing speed.

As a rule the polishing stroke should be about 3 inches long. In this way the mirror edge will not protrude more than $1\frac{1}{2}$ inches (see Fig. 16G) during each stroke. No testing of the polish is necessary until about fifteen minutes' total work has been done. It is then desirable to clean and dry the mirror with a newspaper towel and note whether or not the embryo polish is uniform from center to edge. If not, examine closely the pitch-glass contact. If all the pitch squares do not have the same dull appearance, additional pressing should be resorted to. If the latter does not remedy the situation after fifteen minutes more of rubbing, the pitch lap should be removed from the tool and the M303$\frac{1}{2}$, M304, and M305 stages repeated. The pitch is most easily broken up by "ploughing" through its central portions with the point of an icepick, after which a broad wood chisel will finish the job. Short, quick strokes are most effective, but care should be used to prevent getting glass from the tool edge into the pitch. There is little or no likelihood that any trouble will be experienced at this point by the mirror maker, and if polishing proceeds normally, it may be continued for three hours without further testing.

Although the polishing periods may be regulated to suit the whims of the worker, the mirror should always be pressed hard onto the tool at the start of each session. When not being worked the mirror should be centered on the tool, after renewing the charge and rewatering the table. An inverted aluminum pan placed over the glass disks, edges in contact with the table, will prevent sticking for several days of "rest." If no work is to be done for longer periods, it is best to submerge them in a pan of water with a cover.

For the benefit of those who have made mirrors before and have used older techniques for forming and patterning the pitch lap, a list of the new lap's advantages is given:

1. The mixture of water and rouge (or Barnsite) is retained almost indefinitely. Polishing may continue easily for an hour or more without interruption.

2. The larger amount of water-rouge mixture present acts as an effective heat distributor and levels off temperature differences over the surfaces.

3. The danger of scratching the mirror edge or other zones is negligible.

4. Turned-back edges occur only in their mildest form.

5. Mirrors polish out more quickly.

6. The glass-pitch contact is quickly obtained and maintained.

7. Amount of pitch which is desirable is half that required for other laps.

8. Air bubbles do not occur on the polishing surface.

9. If zoning occurs at all, it is in its mildest form, and correction is easily made without altering the lap.

10. Used laps can be readily adapted for other mirrors of the same approximate radius of curvature as the original.

11. A great variety of patterns can be tried.

12. When a pitch lap has been prepared, it may be used by any number of individuals, who can then pool their findings, and in time an optimum pattern may be evolved for the benefit of all interested. . . .

It is essential that the finished surface be highly reflective. One way to determine when the polishing is complete is to glance across the mirror at a low angle toward a bright light. Then lower or rotate the mirror until the image of the light bulb just passes over its edge. A critical examination of the edge surface in this position will reveal a whitish cast or individual irregularities if the polishing is not good. A second method, which is very reliable, consists of focusing the image of a bright light, with a hand lens or eyepiece, directly on the mirror surface. Any considerable lack of polish will be evidenced by the intensity of the reflected-diffused light. . . . Try this test on the polished surface of plate glass to get a minimum standard of comparison.

A third method is to look through the mirror surface toward a lighted incandescent lamp bulb. If the surface is highly polished, it is difficult for the eye to discern it. If, however, there are pits or the polishing is incomplete, irregularities of the surface will be clearly seen with the unaided eye. Examination of the surface directly with an eye lens or microscope is also a simple and useful method. Particular attention should be given to the condition of the edge zone. When it appears to be highly polished it is a pretty safe bet that other zones are also.

Although it is sufficiently good practice to let testing of the mirror wait until the polishing is complete, a wiser plan is to start testing it qualitatively after the first half hour of polishing. By so doing, the telescope maker may learn more quickly about the great sensitivity of the Ronchi (grating) and the Foucault (knife-edge) tests [see p. 68]. In this manner he may experiment with deepening the mirror to a parabola. . . . Older technique depended on bringing the mirror to a polished oblate spheroid and then altering the lap to produce the paraboloid. If by chance a hyperboloid was produced, it then became necessary to re-alter the existing lap and probably pour one or two additional laps in order to finish the job. By the use of the special flattening-parabolizing lap described in this article, only one not-to-be-altered lap, with the use of a few simple special strokes, serves for all required alterations of the mirror's figure. . . .

Cautions for the Telescope Maker

1. Leave the mirror resting on the pitch lap when not being polished. Sticking is easily prevented by placing a wet cloth on top of the mirror and covering with an inverted pan.

2. Work under a clean, smooth ceiling to prevent stray pieces of grit or dirt from falling on the tool.

3. If the mirror is deepened too much, giving a hyperboloid, flatten it by a return to stroke B.

4. Take extreme precautions not to jar or accidentally change the position of either the tester or the mirror during the quantitative tests. Check all results as an added precaution.

5. Remember that when the knife edge is moved into the light cone from the left, inside the focal plane of any zone, it appears to arrive from that direction. When it is moved from the left but is outside the apex of light, it appears to come from the right side.

6. In working for the paraboloid, test the mirror after every thirty strokes. Keep a complete record of the number and type of strokes used and the results obtained.

7. If scratches or deep pits occur at any state of polishing or grinding, go back at least two sizes of abrasives and continue as before.

8. Should the mirror maker desire to avoid the parabolizing process, he can make a 6-inch mirror with a radius of curvature of 120 inches and 60 inches focal length, in which case a spherical surface is satisfactory. The corresponding mirror depth, or sagitta, would then be

$$S = \frac{r^2}{2R} = \frac{3 \times 3}{2 \times 120} = 0.0375 \text{ inches.}$$

A piece of No. 19 B-and-S wire has a diameter of 0.036 inches and would serve, along with a straightedge, to gauge the proper depth for the rough grinding previously described. . . .

9. After the mirror has been polished and parabolized it is necessary to place a metallic coating on the surface in order to step up its reflectivity from that of about 5 per cent for polished glass to that of about 90 per cent for a silver or aluminum coating.

Although a first-class silver deposit will reflect a slightly greater percentage of visible light than aluminum, the former deteriorates rapidly in air and must be renewed frequently. The chemical deposition of silver on glass is rather precarious, but it has the advantage that the process can be studied (the Brashear method described in chemical handbooks is the standard method) and carried out with very little expense except the cost of a few chemicals.

The case for aluminum is a stronger one, since, once it is successfully applied to the glass surface, it will last indefinitely if properly cared for. Aluminum films reflect almost as great a percentage of visible light from their surfaces but are far more efficient in reflecting ultraviolet light, a great advantage when the telescope is being used for photography.

There is more to come on the aluminizing process (p. 83), and a great deal more should be said about optical testing. Two standard optical tests that show what parts of a mirror surface are incorrectly shaped are the Foucault "knife-edge" test and the Ronchi "grating" test.

In 1858 the French scientist Leon Foucault invented a simple laboratory test of the surface quality and figure of a telescope mirror. The operator places an "artificial star," a pinhole a few thousandths of an inch in diameter, near the center of curvature ($R = 2f$ from the center of the concave surface) and examines its image formed by the mirror close to the pinhole. A perfectly spherical mirror will form a perfect image of such a point source, but if there are aberrations in the mirror surface, such as zones of different curvature, then the image will not be a point of light. Foucault looked at the mirror with his eye just outside the center of curvature. From this viewpoint the mirror appears completely covered with light from the point source. A straight knife-edge is pushed across the light beam from one side until the pinhole image is cut in half. If the mirror is perfectly spherical, and if the knife edge is exactly at the center of curvature, the surface will be seen to darken evenly all over, or "null," to a flat gray surface. But if there are zones of different curvature, the light rays reflected from them will get past the knife edge in the region outside the perfect point image, thus giving an appearance of bright areas on the mirror. A paraboloid mirror, viewed in this way, gives a characteristic "doughnut" shadow pattern (see p. 71).

It is also possible to test a paraboloid surface by placing ring-shaped masks over it and measuring the distance of the knife edge from the mirror that makes each zone black out suddenly. Such measurement is delicate work; the ideal test is one in which the desired paraboloid shape gives a "null," as the sphere does, with no zones to measure or interpret (see p. 76). However, the sensitivity of the Foucault test is very high; it can be said to "magnify" surface irregularities about 100,000 times!

In the Ronchi test, a more recent development (1922), a grating replaces the knife edge between the eye and the mirror, illuminated by a slit source near the center of curvature. The grating is a set of parallel opaque lines, about one hundred to the inch, and may be made from a piece of engraver's halftone grating or from a piece of silk bolting cloth. With the eye just outside the center of curvature (as in the Foucault test), and with the slit parallel to the grating grid, the grating is adjusted, toward and away from the mirror, until three to five bands are seen silhouetted against the mirror surface. If the mirror is spherical, the bands are perfectly straight and parallel; if zones are present, the bands are irregular. A perfect paraboloid will show bands with smooth curved arcs (p. 77), and these can be matched to a wire grid or drawing of the shape expected for a perfect paraboloid.

The Ronchi test is easier for the amateur; it can even be carried out with a single vertical wire (instead of the grating) by moving the wire across the light beam and examining the shape of the band as it sweeps across the mirror surface. However, the sensitivity is not as high as that of the Foucault test. Many workers use the Ronchi test for approximate figuring and the Foucault test for final finishing.

Allyn Thompson recommended the Foucault test in figuring mirrors, and his description of the action of the shadow pattern and how to check for figure accuracy is presented now to help make the principles clear.   —T L P

....

The Paraboloid

ALLYN J. THOMPSON

(*Sky and Telescope*, March 1945)

In a telescope the parallel rays from a star are made to converge to a point image. A spherical mirror will not do this [as is shown in Chapter 1, p. 27]; we must convert it into a paraboloid. In this process the mirror is deepened at the center so that the radius of curvature there is shorter than it is at the edge.

The difference in radii is called the *correction*. Ellipsoidal and spherical mirrors are referred to as *undercorrected*. Hyperboloids are *overcorrected* mirrors. The paraboloid is a fully corrected mirror. Theory and practice have shown that equally good performance is obtained from 6-inch f/8 ellipsoids and hyperboloids if the difference in radii of edge and center zones is within 40 per cent of the exact value of r^2/R. . . . Larger mirrors and those of lesser focal ratio must be far more exactly figured. . . .

We must have a means of accurately locating the zonal shadows on the mirror. For this purpose we make a mask, or diaphragm, of a 6-inch disk of cardboard, with a central aperture not more than 2 inches in diameter, and edge openings $\frac{1}{2}$ inch in width. We also make a measuring stick, with pins stuck into it, which may be suspended across the horizontal diameter of the mirror.

Testing the Paraboloid.[1] Place the mirror on a rack with the mask in front of it. Set up the testing apparatus, bringing the knife-edge block against the guide cleat so that the indicator is over the scale, and shift the whole device around until the knife edge is at the center of curvature of the edge zone. This will be when the first faint shadows appear simultaneously in each edge opening and are of an equal depth of gray-

---

[1] A. W. Everest of Pittsfield, Massachusetts, is the originator of this method of testing the paraboloidal mirror. A discussion of this method, by Everest, first appeared in *Amateur Telescope Making* and again, more completely, in *Amateur Telescope Making—Advanced*. [These books are Vols. 1 and 2 in the series *Amateur Telescope Making*, A. G. Ingalls, ed., New York, Scientific American Publishing Co.; latest edition 1953.]

ness. Do not wait for the shadows to get dark before comparing them. This will call for some nice judgment of shadow tone, particularly as the eye must be shifted from one opening to the other to be sure the shadows appear at the same moment. Now let us study how the shadows look on the overall mirror. Remove the mask and hang up the measuring stick. When the knife edge is cut in, the first shadow to appear will be found at Pin 1. As the knife edge is moved farther across, this shadow quickly expands, spreading to the right and to the left. Its boundaries should reach the right edge and the center (Pin 3) together. At the same moment a thin wisp of shadow appears on the left edge (Fig. 19A). These edge shadows are the ones that were seen with the mask. Continuing the knife-edge movement, the left edge and center shadows approach and meet at Pin 5. Unless the shadows behave as described, the mirror does not have the paraboloidal shape. Now note carefully the indicator reading on the scale.

Without disturbing anything, remove the measuring stick and replace the mask. Slide the knife edge toward the mirror until the central area is seen to darken evenly all over, just as though that exposed part were a small spherical mirror. We are now at the center of curvature of the center zone. Remove the diaphragm and replace the measuring stick. As the knife edge is again cut in, a shadow appears on the left edge and advances, slowly at first, then more rapidly, until it reaches Pin 4, when it seems to leap across to Pin 2. The mirror has the appearance of an inverted bowl (Fig. 19B). The flat gray central area is bounded by Pins 2 and 4. Again note the reading on the scale. The difference in these radii, or between the knife-edge settings, for these two cases, should be 0.09 inch, although we can tolerate corrections between 0.06 inch and 0.13 inch. . . .

How to Obtain the Paraboloid. Figuring. In altering the sphere any stroke or combination of strokes that will progressively deepen the mirror may be used. These may include long diametric strokes, half- or three-quarter-diameter, mixed up with straight or elliptical overhang strokes. Or any strokes that we may invent which are calculated to deepen the mirror may be experimented with. . . . It is imperative that the lap be kept in contact with the deepening mirror, so about one minute of work and five minutes of pressing should be the rule. As the correction approaches r^2/R, the mirror should be allowed to stand about fifteen minutes before testing, so don't try to do the whole thing in one evening. Contact must always be restored after testing, or the whole of the previous efforts may be spoiled.

In general, a narrow zigzagging W stroke of two-thirds length gives best results. This stroke should carry the 6-inch mirror from a centered position to about $1\frac{3}{4}$-inch overhang on one side, back across the center

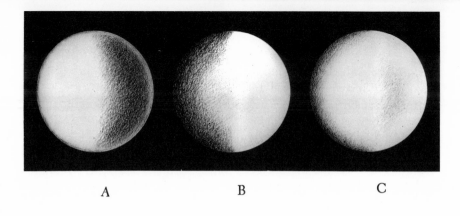

A   B   C

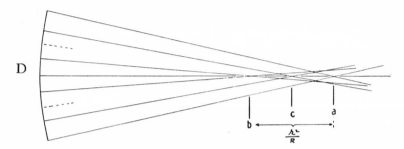

Fig. 19. Knife-edge shadows on the paraboloid. A. At center of curvature of the edge zone. B. At center of curvature of center zone. C. At center of curvature of the 50-per-cent zone. D. The reason for the shadow behavior at the various knife-edge settings is made apparent by a study of how the rays proceeding from the mirror are intercepted by the knife edge.

to an overhang of 1 inch on the other side, and thence back to center, where it is given a slight rotation, and the sequence repeated from a new position. Then allow the work to press for five minutes. After two such spells, test for location of the shadow crests. If these are too far out, the stroke should be lengthened; if they are too far in, shorten the stroke.

The amount of correction obtained at this stage will tell us how fast the lap is cutting and will be an indication of the probable amount of work remaining to be done. The Foucault test is our guide, and we must proceed with great caution, as the correction increases at an accelerated rate in proportion to the polishing.

Despite the tyro's best efforts, he will seldom be able to measure the full amount of correction on his mirror, so if the shadow locations are good, it is advisable to call the job finished when the measured correction is about 0.08 inch, as there is an excellent chance that the full correction is there anyway.

If the edge has suffered slightly through use of the long stroke, it can be improved or restored by grinding the mirror face down, with light pressure, on a large piece of plate glass, using No. M304 emery for about fifteen or twenty seconds. This will grind flat an edge area about $\frac{1}{40}$ inch wide, and will result in a light loss of less than 2 per cent from the mirror's area of 28 square inches, but there is a resultant gain in darkness of field. . . .

It is seldom that a paraboloid will be achieved on the first attempt. Anyway, in the event of failure, you are finding out what not to do. And your skill in judgment and figuring is improving, and after the second or third trial, the figure obtained will be far superior to what might have been accepted on the first venture.

Testing at Focus. A more delicate test than the one just described is made at focus, using parallel light from a star such as Polaris, which is stationary enough for the purpose. Get the star centered in the field, remove the eyepiece, and see if the mirror "blacks out" as a knife edge is cut slowly across the focal plane. When the knife edge is cut in, the paraboloidal mirror darkens all over, evenly and instantly, just as our sphere did when tested at center of curvature. This is understandable when it is realized that all of the reflected rays intersect in a single point. . . .

∎∎

The Diagonal

ALLYN J. THOMPSON

(*Sky and Telescope*, April 1945)

How Large? The diagonal is a very vital part of the telescope, and in order to perform its function well, it must be of the proper size, and it must be flat enough. The size can be arrived at by formula, but there is the related question of illumination of the field which enters into the discussion, and which should be understood, so we had better take out the drawing board and expose the workings of the telescope graphically. Here the amateur should make his own drawing, to half scale at least, based on his exact focal length. Figure 20 is a diagrammatic solution of the problem for a 6-inch f/8 telescope.

Draw MA to represent the axis of the mirror, and M'M'' the mirror's surface. At the scale distance of 48 inches from M, draw PP' to represent the focal plane. If a strip of ground glass were laid across this plane, an evenly illuminated image of the distant landscape would be seen on it, extending clear across. The same width of image might be produced at pp' (if the opening at the side of the tube were wide enough) by the introduction of the diagonal, but the same brightness would be found only near the center of this new image, which would become fainter toward the edges. The area of greatest brilliance will depend on the size of the diagonal, and it is only necessary to illuminate as much of the field as can be received into the eyepiece. Good Ramsden oculars of low power, $1\frac{1}{4}$-inches to $1\frac{1}{2}$-inches focal length, have a field lens of 1-inch clear aperture, and that is the linear width of the field (vv') taken in by that ocular. Now draw MV and MV'. Angle VMV' is the angular size of the *real* field of view which, based on a radius equal to the focal length, is equal to $1\frac{1}{6}°$ of arc. Two moons side by side would fit easily into this field. (The image of the moon at the focus of a 6-inch f/8 is about $\frac{2}{5}$ inch in diameter.) Or two stars, separated by $1°10'$ of arc, would just fit into the field, and would be seen at V and V' or v and v'.

Draw $M'V$ and $M''V'$, forming the figure of a truncated cone, in which are confined all of the rays from about one square degree of sky which makes up the image VV'. Wherever we place our diagonal, it is apparent that it ought to take in the full width of the trapezoid, and the nearer it is to the focal plane the smaller it can be, so let us see how near we can place it. From a constructional standpoint it will be found most convenient to have the deflected focal plane lie about 3 inches outside the tube, and this plus the radius of the tube is the distance inside of focus that we place the diagonal.

We should like to have the tube no larger than the mirror if possible, but as can be seen from the angle VMV', the field of view is an expanding one, and at the focal plane it is $\frac{1}{2}$ inch larger all around than the mirror. So the tube may not be less than 7 inches in diameter. This places the diagonal $6\frac{1}{2}$ inches inside of focus, and there we draw it, at an angle of $45°$ to the mirror's axis, and measure its inner and major dimensions, D_1 and D_2. Its shape is an ellipse, with the minor axis $1\frac{7}{10}$ inches, and the major axis $2\frac{4}{10}$ inches (a ratio of 1 to 1.4). It will obstruct a little more than 8 per cent of the light coming to the mirror. A rectangular shape of the same dimensions (by far the easiest to make) will obstruct a trifle more than 10 per cent of the light.

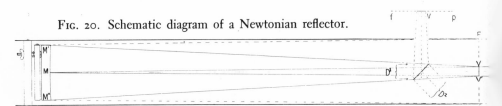

Fig. 20. Schematic diagram of a Newtonian reflector.

The formulas for the dimensions of the flat diagonal mirror are

$$D_1 = f + \frac{c(M - f)}{F} \text{ and } D_2 = 1.4\ D_1,$$

where f is the width of field VV', c is the distance of the diagonal inside the focal plane, F is the focal length, and M the diameter of the mirror.

What is the effect of using a smaller diagonal? Briefly, the result is a loss of illumination in the outer edges of the field of the low-power eyepiece. Take, for example, the off-axis star whose image is formed at V. It is apparent that if the diagonal fails to take in the ray M'V, there will not be full illumination in that image, and the star will appear fainter than one of equal magnitude lying nearer to the center of the field. In other words, the outlying stars would not get the benefit of the full aperture of the mirror when using the low-power eyepiece. The field lens of a $\frac{1}{2}$-inch ocular is about $\frac{3}{8}$ inch in diameter and takes in a correspondingly smaller field, so unless the diagonal were tiny, high-power oculars would not be affected. . . .

How Flat? We have taken great pains to produce a curve of remarkable precision on our mirror. We should be equally concerned that nothing shall happen to alter the course of the rays from the mirror and interfere with the formation of a perfect image. While annealed plate glass appears perfectly flat, we shall seldom find one among several pieces, say 2 inches square, that is flat to better than one 10,000th of an inch. Placed an inch or so inside of focus, a diagonal of that quality could do no harm, but at our distance of $6\frac{1}{2}$ inches it must be optically plane to within one wavelength of light, about one 50,000th of an inch.

A prism is sometimes used instead of the aluminized plane mirror, but it has three surfaces, each of which must be flat to a quarter of a wavelength, and the cost of such a prism is considerable. In reflective ability, prism and diagonal are about equal. The aluminized flat reflects about 90 per cent of the incident light; the prism is totally reflecting; but in the prism about 4 per cent is lost in reflection from each of the square faces, and a negligible amount is lost in absorption.

Plane surfaces are tested for flatness by placing two polished surfaces together and studying the interference bands that appear between them under monochromatic light. The surfaces must be cleaned of all grease and dust, or the bands may not be seen. The explanation of these bands, or fringes, is fully covered in textbooks on physics, and will not be discussed here. Suffice it to say that they should be interpreted just as are the contour lines on a map, where the terrain along any given line is all of the same elevation. . . .

■■■

An Experience with the
Dall Null Test

S. J. WARKOCZEWSKI

(*Sky and Telescope*, October 1955)

For testing parabolic telescope mirrors, a null method has been devised by H. E. Dall which differs from the familiar Foucault knife-edge test by the insertion of a planoconvex simple lens between the mirror and the slit (or pinhole) that illuminates it. When the reflected beam is cut at the center of curvature by the knife edge, the whole mirror surface darkens uniformly if the mirror is properly corrected.

The spherical aberration of the lens closely neutralizes that of the mirror. Interpretation of the knife-edge shadow is much easier than in the original Foucault test, particularly for mirrors of short focal ratio. Using Dall's test, the amateur can produce surfaces with aberrations reduced to whatever minimum his patience and skill will allow.

There is a complete description of the test in *Amateur Telescope Making* Vol. 3 [A. G. Ingalls, ed.], p. 149–53. . . .

The following tells of my experiences in figuring a 16⅜-inch Pyrex disk of f/6 to a quality that probably would not have been possible without the Dall test. . . .

My Foucault test equipment comprises a ¾-inch tube housing a No. 46 GE bulb, condensing system, adjustable slit, and a knife-edge holder with micrometer movement horizontally and along the axis of measurement—all mounted on an adjustable and movable stand. To adapt this rig to the Dall test, I cut threads on the tube containing the light source and screwed onto it a larger tube holding the compensator lens. The axial position of this lens was adjustable within the tube. . . .

For the compensator lens, I used at first a 1-inch war-surplus planoconvex lens with a focal length of 10 inches, carefully spaced from the slit to the recommended distance for this mirror and lens. . . .

After all difficulties had apparently been squared away, the spherical mirror, which had looked quite "flat" under the Foucault test, now exhibited the shadows of an oblate spheroid of very long radius. The problem was now to make the mirror appear flat as viewed with the Dall test. . . .

As the proper corrective measures were applied, the mirror gradually

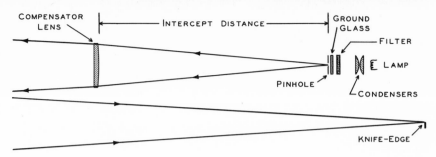

FIG. 21. The arrangement for testing a mirror by Dall's method. The planoconvex compensator lens should have a focal length between ⅕ and ½₀ of the mirror under test; the actual ratio determines what the distance between lens and slit should be.

took on a flat appearance, but I was puzzled by the appearance of a dark area at the left edge which jumped into prominence long before any other portion of the mirror darkened. Since no corresponding lighter area could be discerned at the right edge, the possibility of a turned-down edge was discounted at first. However, I found that the shadow appeared when the separation of the slit image and the knife edge was about three slit widths. Reducing the radius of the edge zone eliminated the condition completely.

As the mirror finally assumed the proper appearance, marked only by faint zones, trouble occurred in the form of astigmatic effects that had not been discernible when the mirror's figure was irregular. However, the Foucault test did not show this, and the Ronchi test gave the straight lines indicative of a spherical surface. . . . [This] was properly assigned to the war-surplus lens. A new lens of crown glass was made for me by a local firm, and when this was installed the test showed the same figure and degree of overcorrection that the Foucault method did. If you use the Dall test, know your lens! . . .

The mirror was finished after almost three months of spare time had been spent in changing the surface from a completely polished spheroid to its present form. Zonal measurements of the completed mirror, inspection of the smooth-flowing Ronchi lines illustrated here, and the degree of flatness under the null test all seem to substantiate the conclusion that the figure of the mirror is good.

The preceding articles serve to illustrate the problems of accurate optical polishing—and several practical methods of approaching them. The same optical tests can be applied to finished telescopes or other optical systems, and it is generally advisable to ask about the results of optical tests when purchasing a telescope.

In addition to being of good optical quality, the components must be properly aligned. Alignment poses further problems. —TLP

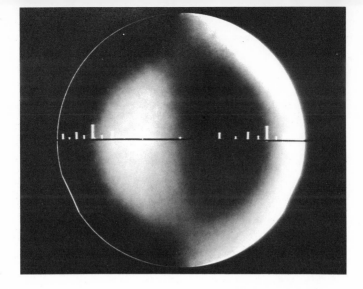

A

FIG. 22. A. The Foucault knife-edge test gives these shadows on the finished 16-inch mirror. The Everest pin stick seen in front of the mirror has bright pins on a dark crosspiece to mark the positions of shadows in the Foucault test. B. The Ronchi test gives this pattern on the 16-inch mirror. In this modification of the classical Foucault test, a grating replaces the knife edge. When the bands are straight the mirror is spherical; a paraboloidal mirror gives bands that are portions of parabolas. (Photographs courtesy of S. J. Warkoczewski.)

Some Aids to Collimating a Newtonian

ALLYN J. THOMPSON

(*Sky and Telescope*, May 1955)

Telescope collimation consists of bringing into line the axes of the objective lens (or mirror) and the eyepiece. In the Newtonian reflector, the eyepiece adapter tube is first mounted so that its axis intersects the axis of the telescope tube at a 90° angle. Then the mirror is installed, and its axis made to coincide with that of the tube.

The final step consists of inserting a diagonal so that the mirror's axis will be reflected to coincide with that of the adapter tube. This, the first of two conditions for perfect collimation, is effected by inclining the secondary reflecting surface 45° to both axes. Also, the secondary should be placed so that the evenly illuminated portion of the deflected focal plane will symmetrically surround the adapter-tube axis. To meet this second condition, the diagonal should be centered on neither the mirror axis nor the adapter axis. Instead, it should be slightly offset, both away from the eyepiece and toward the mirror. The amount of offset, equal in both directions, depends mainly on the focal ratio of the mirror. At $f/8$ it is roughly 2.7 per cent of the diagonal's minor axis, and at $f/4$ roughly 5.4 per cent. A diagonal so placed is said to be *optically centered*.

A rectangular diagonal, apparently square when viewed through the adapter tube, should be given the same offset as an ellipse. The mirror should appear imaged in it as a circle inscribed in a square. A prism, however, must be exactly centered, so that its square faces symmetrically surround the optical axis.

Even the most careful workmanship in building the telescope cannot automatically assure optical centering; means for adjustments should be incorporated into the secondary support. Their use is much simplified if the eye is in the proper position [centered behind VV′ in Fig. 20 (see p. 74)], where the bounding field rays cut the optical axis. From this point the diagonal (assumed to be elliptical) and the mirror imaged within it are of the same apparent size, so their outlines can be made to coincide. The distance of this point from the axis of the telescope tube is about equal to $FD_1 (M - D_1)$, where F is the focal length of the mirror, M its aperture, and D_1 is the width, or minor axis, of the diagonal. You will need an extra adapter tube of about double the usual length, capped with a $\frac{1}{16}$-inch peephole.

Seen through this peephole, the mirror reflection must appear concentric with the inner open end of the adapter tube. Within the imaged mirror are seen, via two reflections, the spider vanes and the round outline of the elliptical diagonal. (Except in a low-ratio telescope, the radial offset of the latter may not be noticeable.) Finally, within the secondary's image there is seen, via three reflections, the interior of the adapter tube capped by its peephole. The tube-wall interior must appear as a symmetrical ring, as if the tube were pointing squarely away from you. It and the peephole reflection must be exactly centered in the mirror image, as in Figure 23. When these requirements have been met, the adjustments are complete, and the collimation is quite perfect.

Much depends upon personal judgment, but a positive check is possible with the *double eyepiece test*. In principle, one eyepiece is inserted in the adapter tube, and another of lesser power is used to examine the exit pupil. It is more convenient to replace the two eyepieces by their equivalent—a small low-power telescope that will fit in the adapter tube. For this purpose I designed the two-power telescope and easily made reticle illustrated in Figure 24.

War-surplus lenses were used. A is a 1-inch Ramsden eyepiece, and B is a separate part containing the reticle. The latter is $\frac{1}{16}$-inch-thick Lucite, on which were inscribed two concentric circles—the smaller for $f/8$ mirrors, the larger for $f/4$ mirrors. C is a 2-inch length of $1\frac{1}{4}$-inch outside-diameter tubing containing an objective lens of 2-inch focus. This lens acts as the first of the dual eyepieces, and its focal length was chosen as giving a satisfactorily large exit pupil.

The size for the reticle circle can be determined from the formula for exit pupil-diameter: mirror diameter divided by magnification. The latter is the focal length of the mirror divided by the focal length of the lens in C. It is better, however, to make the circle a little larger than the exit pupil, to distinguish between them.

In use, first insert C a convenient distance into the eyepiece adapter tube. The eyepiece A is pushed into B until the reticle circle is in focus, and the two as a unit are then inserted into C until the mirror image is seen in sharp focus on the reticle.

The mirror image must now be centered on the reticle circle. The re-

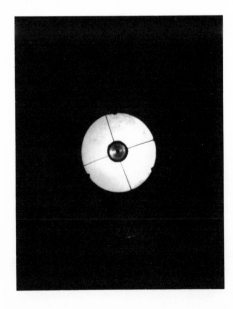

FIG. 23. The exit pupil of a perfectly collimated Newtonian, with the camera lens replacing the eyepiece. The adapter tube was capped with a perforated aluminum plug, and the camera lens placed close to this peephole, focused for the distance to the mirror. (Photograph courtesy Allyn J. Thompson.)

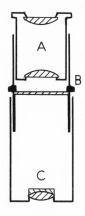

FIG. 24. The double eyepiece, or two-power telescope.

flection of the spider vanes, secondary, and adapter tube will not be seen in sharp focus because they are, via the extra reflections, considerably farther from C than is the mirror. Accordingly, A must be pushed a trifle farther into B to focus on the images. Under magnification, the offset of the diagonal may now be noticeable. But the adapter-tube interior and the lower end of C, now seen in the secondary's image, must be exactly centered with respect to the mirror image.

Adjustments can now be made in comfort, ending by having the mirror image concentric with the reticle circle. With this device, the diagonal's inclination can be corrected to within a few minutes of arc.

Telescope Making at the Adler Planetarium

LOUISE RYAN

(Sky and Telescope, May 1962)

The secrets of the telescope maker's art are now in plain view for everyone to see at the Adler Planetarium and Astronomical Museum in Chicago, Illinois. In November 1960, its old one-room optical shop was supplanted by a modern, professionally equipped work area. Three of its six rooms are furnished with ten barrels each, for grinding, polishing, and figuring, respectively.

As illustrated here, the shop is a "living" exhibit because one wall is mostly glass, permitting visitors to watch the progress of telescope making. Small exhibits in the windows explain what is being done. With an active weekly enrollment of two hundred students in the shop, there are always plenty of "exhibitors." They range in age from ten to seventy-eight, with about half of them juniors.

The equipment includes an 8-inch diamond saw, a drill press, sets of diamond and brass-core drills, a double-wheel grinder, two centering and edging machines, a four-spindle production polishing machine, and a heavy-duty polisher. There are two Foucault testers and a complete set of test mirrors. Most optical testing is carried out on a 16-foot steel I-beam optical bench. It has polished faces and rests on massive supports. A vacuum chamber for aluminizing mirrors up to sixteen inches in diameter is being constructed.

Up till now, only Newtonian, Cassegrain, Gregorian, and Schmidt optics have been made, as well as optical flats, but equipment and test facilities for lens making will soon be completed. Besides the regularly used shop, part of the museum basement houses a Zeiss grinding machine and is also used for calibrating long-focus optical systems.

There is a large waiting list for places in the shop classes. Approximately one hundred pupils work on their telescopes at home, coming to the museum for consultation and instruction. During the past year some hundred students completed their instruments, and many are working on their third and fourth mirrors. A few of the more advanced workers assist supervisors Ronald Zussman and Richard Monnier in the teaching program. At public star parties on the museum's observation deck, many amateurs bring and operate their own telescopes. These special events attract an average of two thousand persons.

So great has interest in the shop been in the Chicago area that the staff decided to hold a telescope fair from March 10 to 31 this year. About forty amateurs exhibited instruments they had made in whole or in part at the museum. . . .

FIG. 25. Visitors to Adler Planetarium wat tivities in the work polishing room.

■■■

A Grinding Machine

EARLE B. BROWN

(*Sky and Telescope*, February 1956)

The grinding machine pictured here (Fig. 26) was made by A. M. Donnelly of Montreal, Canada, an amateur telescope maker since 1934.

Donnelly's machine follows the general design described by John H. Hindle (*Amateur Telescope Making*, Vol. 1, A. G. Ingalls, ed., 1952, p. 235–36). The polishing tool is anchored to a rotating table, and the mirror floats freely, face down, upon the tool. The rotation of the mirror is automatic, for over it and the spindles of the machine is placed the framework that is here shown detached at the left, leaning against the wall behind the machine. The mirror is held loosely between the sponge-rubber buffers of the framework; as the driving crank moves the latter, the mirror is rotated at the end of each stroke.

Once the mirror for a reflector is polished and tested it must be "silvered"—coated with a reflecting metal. Until thirty years ago this was done by a chemical solution that deposited silver on the glass surface. This method is still the simplest; but the silver surface tarnishes, and the chemicals are messy. The best modern coatings are of aluminum, which must be evaporated onto the glass surface in a vacuum tank. Because of the elaborate equipment necessary, this is generally done by a professional at a university or industrial firm. —T L P

■■■

Aluminizing Telescope Mirrors

JOHN STRONG

(*The Telescope*, August 1934)

The coating of mirrors by the evaporation of various substances grew out of an attempt to deposit a protecting surface on the faces of deliquescent prisms, such as rock salt. Among the films which were deposited during this investigation, films of quartz on the prism surfaces and also on silver mirrors were tried. . . . Silvered mirrors having a quartz film

Fig. 26. A. M. Donnelly's grinding machine is made from an old battery table, a used washing-machine motor, an old sewing machine, and a very old flywheel. The length of stroke and the overhang are changeable without stopping the machine.

coating are able to withstand exposure to weathering and continue to maintain their high reflectivity for a period of about a year, whereas the silvered mirrors which are unprotected by a quartz film become very dark with tarnish in a few weeks.

Further experiments were performed to improve the reflecting surface of astronomical mirrors, using metals other than silver. Among the metals which were studied as reflectors, aluminum appeared promising because of its strong reflectivity for ultraviolet light. There were, however, technical difficulties involved in evaporating aluminum coats on mirror surfaces, and it was not until the summer of 1932 that these difficulties were surmounted and the aluminization of telescope mirrors was made possible. At that time a telescope mirror of 12-inch diameter was coated with aluminum, and this aluminized mirror has been in constant use ever since. . . .

In at least four ways, aluminum coats are more desirable than silver coats for telescope mirrors.

1. Aluminum coats deposited by evaporation are free from "bloom" and therefore need not be burnished with rouge after deposition. Thus scratches such as may appear during the burnishing of a silver coat are eliminated.

2. An aluminum coat is brilliant. It reflects 89 per cent of the visible

Fig. 27. John Strong and the apparatus used by him to coat the 36-inch mirror of the Crossley reflector of the Lick Observatory with aluminum. (Photograph from Los Angeles Bureau, Wide World Photos.)

light, and its reflectivity drops only gradually to 85 per cent for invisible ultraviolet light. . . . Tests at Lick Observatory show that, for stellar photography, aluminum reflects 50 per cent more light than does silver.

3. An aluminum coat is permanent. . . .

4. Aluminized mirror surfaces are rugged. This quality arises from the fact than an oxide coat (sapphire) is formed on exposure to the air. The hardness of this coat makes it possible to remove dust and dirt with soap and water and dry the surface with a soft towel without affecting the optical properties of the coat, a procedure hardly applicable to the thin silver coats which are soft and easily damaged.

Figures 27 and 28 show the equipment which is used for the preparation of aluminum films on telescope mirrors. Aluminum is heated in tungsten coils to such a temperature that the metal evaporates. This occurs in a large bell jar which is evacuated, so that an aluminum molecule, evaporating from the tungsten coil, travels in a straight line without interruption by collision with other molecules until it strikes some object, either the walls of the container or the mirror face to be coated. In order to obtain this collision-free path it is necessary that the container be evacuated to a pressure of about one ten-millionth normal atmospheric pressure. In order to maintain this vacuum in the container, very fast pumps are required, that is, pumps which have a speed of the order of 200 liters per second (50 gallons per second). The vacuum thus obtained is so high that an electrical discharge will not pass in this space because there are too few molecules to provide carriers for the electrical current. The pumps used are of the oil-diffusion type.

In the process of coating an astronomical mirror the films are formed by evaporation from twelve coils arranged in a circle above the mirror. This arrangement of coils forms a film, on mirrors as large as 40 inches in diameter, one 1000th of a millimeter (one 25,000th of an inch) in thickness, and uniform to 4 or 5 per cent. Such an aluminum film is approximately 1000 atom layers thick, the same order of thickness as the allowable deviation from a true parabolic curve in the figure of the mirror. A fluctuation of 5 per cent, or $\frac{1}{20}$ this thickness, is far too small to cause a noticeable change in the figure of the mirror or to affect the quality of the star images obtained with the telescope.

The aluminizing of optical mirrors was rapidly developed so that it could be applied to large professional telescope mirrors, and to a wide variety of industrial products. Thin coatings of other materials can be

FIG. 28. Diagram of the apparatus used in aluminizing the Crossley mirror. A, mirror to be aluminized (36 inches in diameter); B, bell jar (39½ inches inside diameter); C, base plate; D, groove for lead fuse-wire gasket; E, bolts to fasten bell jar to base plate; F, filaments of tungsten wire from which aluminum is evaporated; G, conductors to supply current to filaments; H, switch; I, baffle; J, packing gland for switch control; K, electrode for cleaning the mirror face; L, observation window; M, pump connection; N, plate to carry filaments and switch; O, removable brass cylinder to carry N.

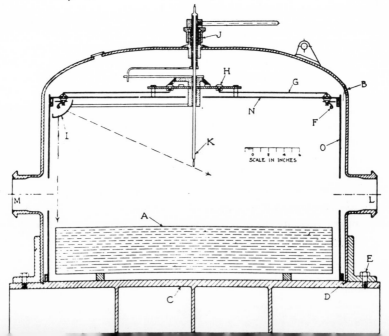

applied by the same technique; some of them prevent reflection and are used on lenses to cut down light losses.

It is appropriate to end this chapter with an account of the new technique applied to one of the world's large reflectors. — T L P

•••

Aluminizing the 72-inch Mirror at Victoria

ANDREW MCKELLAR

(*Sky and Telescope,* June 1943)

One might well ask why silver has been largely replaced by aluminum as a reflecting coat on telescope mirrors. The reason is twofold. First, for light in the ordinary photographic wavelengths (blue and violet light) and particularly for the astronomical ultraviolet, the reflecting power of aluminum is definitely superior to that of silver. Second, aluminum effectively maintains its high reflectivity for months and even years, whereas the reflectivity of silver exposed to the atmosphere falls off very markedly within a period of days; an exposed silver surface deteriorates so rapidly that it must be replaced every few months. These points are illustrated in Figure 29, which shows the respective reflecting powers for different wavelengths or colors of light.

The combination of high reflectivity and durability accounts for the superiority of aluminum surfaces over those of other available metals.

The technique of depositing thin coats of aluminum on optical surfaces (those actually deposited, which are just opaque to sunlight, are approximately one 20,000th of an inch thick) was developed largely by John Strong at the California Institute of Technology during the years 1930 to 1933. From 1931, R. C. Williams, [then] at Cornell University, made independent contributions to this development. The method used is called the *evaporation process,* since it involves the evaporation of the aluminum from heated tungsten coils, the whole process taking place in a high vacuum. Briefly, the process is as follows.

A chamber is constructed of size suitable to enclose the optical part to be coated. This customarily consists of two parts, a base plate and a bell jar. For small mirrors, up to about one foot in diameter, glass bell jars are often used, but for larger sizes the chamber is usually made of steel. Vacuum pumps enabling the pressure in the chamber to be reduced to about one ten-millionth to one hundred-millionth of an atmosphere are attached to the bell jar or base plate. Within the chamber and connected electrically with the outside, a suitable array of tungsten coils is arranged and on each coil short lengths of pure aluminum wire are clamped.

The very carefully cleaned optical surface is placed in the tank, the pumps are started, and the necessary vacuum attained. Then an electrical current is passed through the tungsten coils, heating the aluminum, first to beyond its melting point (660°C), upon which it forms a liquid globule held to the tungsten by its surface tension, and then to its boiling point (1800°C). The melting point of tungsten, it should be remembered, is 3370°C. Now the aluminum begins to evaporate, the aluminum atoms fly off (because of the high vacuum they are unhindered by collisions with air molecules) and coat everything inside the chamber, including the optical surface or surfaces exposed there. The resulting coat of aluminum is then ready for use as a reflector. It does not require burnishing with rouge as do most chemically deposited coats of silver. . . .

In 1933 and 1934, Strong aluminized a considerable number of the Newtonian, Cassegrainian, and coudé secondary mirrors at Mount Wilson Observatory, as well as the 36-inch Crossley mirror at Lick and the 24-inch Yerkes reflector. Then, in 1935, using a large steel chamber of 108 inches diameter, he successfully aluminized the great 60-inch and 100-inch mirrors of the Mount Wilson reflecting telescopes. Subsequently, the principal mirrors of many of the world's other large reflecting telescopes have been aluminized, including the 82-inch of the McDonald Observatory, by Williams in 1938; the 61-inch of the Harvard College Observatory, by Focke, Goldberg, and Scott in 1939; the 74-inch at the David Dunlap Observatory, by Young in 1941; and finally, early this year, the 72-inch reflector of the Dominion Astrophysical Observatory.

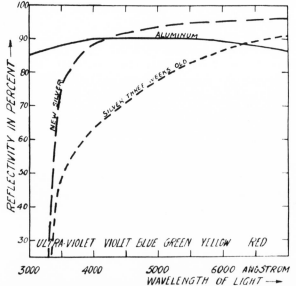

FIG. 29. These curves reflecting power plott against wavelength indic: the superiority of aluminu especially for violet and ult violet light. The two cur for silver show how the flectivity of this metal creases when silver is expos to air. The reflectivity aluminum does not decre appreciably in months even years.

The aluminizing project at our observatory was started in 1937. It seemed advisable first to construct a chamber large enough to coat the 20-inch Cassegrainian and Newtonian secondary mirrors. It was, of course, as important to coat the secondary mirror as the primary one, since the light is reflected once from each before reaching the spectrograph. Also, we realized that the experience gained in designing, assembling, and operating a small chamber would be of great value in setting up a large one for the primary mirror.

A steel chamber of 24 inches inside diameter was therefore designed. It was constructed by the shipbuilding firm Yarrows Ltd., at Victoria. The chamber was made of steel plate $\frac{1}{4}$-inch thick, while the base plate, also of steel, was 1-inch thick. Two concentric rubber gaskets with a space some 2 inches wide between, which could be evacuated, made an excellent seal between base and chamber. The pumps were attached so as to evacuate the apparatus through a tube connected to the center of the base plate, and the electrical leads to the 6 tungsten filaments were also introduced through the base plate. . . .

The chamber and base plate were obtained during the last month of 1937 and the apparatus was made ready for use by February 1938. It could be successfully evacuated using a Cenco Hyvac pump and a 2-inch metal Apiezon oil-diffusion pump. In February 1938, both our Newtonian and Cassegrainian secondary mirrors were successfully aluminized and a resulting definite improvement in the performance of the telescope was noted.

Therefore, in 1938, plans for acquiring an aluminizing chamber large enough to coat the 72-inch mirror were started. A combination of circumstances, including the considerable cost of such a large piece of apparatus and the advent of war the following year, caused progress on the project to be very slow. . . . The tank was of steel, $\frac{3}{8}$-inch thick, 84 inches in diameter, and 58 inches high. The base plate was of 1-inch steel plate, suitably reinforced and mounted on casterlike wheels. The apparatus was to be in general appearance a larger edition of the 24-inch tank. . . .

The general scheme was to assemble and test the aluminizing chamber in the workshop on the ground floor of the dome and then to hoist the apparatus to the observing floor, where the actual aluminizing of the 72-inch mirror would take place. The first step was to heat the tank, area by area, and to coat its inside surface and also the top of the base plate with Apiezon hard wax, and thereafter to apply several coats of glyptal lacquer to the outer surfaces.

After the pumping system was assembled and attached to the tank, . . . the supports for the 66 tungsten filaments were made and installed, as were the filaments themselves. All the electrical connections had to be covered by baffles to prevent short circuits when the evaporated aluminum film was deposited. Finally it was possible to carry out a trial aluminizing, and late in December 1942, the whole apparatus was hoisted to the observing floor of the dome.

After a second and final successful test operation early in January 1943, preparations were begun to remove and coat the 72-inch mirror. Handling this precious piece of glass was the part of the project requiring the very greatest of care. The mirror, 72 inches in diameter, 12 inches thick at the outer edge, and about 11 inches thick at the edge of its central 10-inch-diameter hole, weighs some 4400 pounds. It had never been removed from its cell since its was placed there in 1918. . . .

The glass was cleaned chemically, following the method outlined by Strong, using in turn a detergent, potassium hydroxide solution, nitric acid, distilled water, and finally, alcohol. Between cleanings, except the last two, the mirror was of course rinsed with water. The final procedure was to operate a glow discharge in the chamber when it was partly evacuated. It is perhaps needless to say that for success in aluminizing, the highest attainable degree of cleanliness of the surface is most necessary.

Finally, on February 5, 1943, the mirror was cleaned, safely installed on the base plate of the tank, the chamber closed, and the pumps started. The mechanical pump [a Cenco Hypervac] was allowed to operate all night; the next day the diffusion pumps were started, and that afternoon, February 6, the tungsten coils were heated and the aluminum evaporated onto the 72-inch reflecting surface. When the apparatus was opened up two days later, after allowing air to enter the chamber through a drying tube, the aluminum surface was found to be an excellent one. The surface showed no signs of deteriorating after exposure for a day or two, so the mirror was replaced in its cell, and the telescope was reassembled and made ready for observation by February 15.

Most remarkably, after a winter of very indifferent observing weather, commencing February 19 for nineteen successive nights with one exception only, every night was clear. Thus a very good opportunity was presented to test the performance of the telescope with the new reflecting coat on the primary mirror. It was most gratifying to find that the average exposure times for spectrograms were cut down to two thirds of their previous lengths. Also the far violet wavelength regions were considerably strengthened, thus giving a much more satisfactory intensity distribution on our plates. This means that the efficiency of the telescope in photographing stars of the usual brightness has been almost doubled, and that photographs of objects previously unobtainable with the maximum practicable exposure times can now be secured.

4

The
Mounting
and Drive

The quality of a telescope is judged by the mounting as well as the optics, and the ease of its use depends heavily on its proper mounting. Why this is so should be clear from the Introduction and Chapter 2; as the earth rotates, all celestial objects appear to move from east to west in circles about a point in the sky called the celestial pole. One of these circles, 90° from the pole, is called the celestial equator, and a telescope mounting with an axle that allows the telescope to swing parallel to the equator is called an equatorial mounting. Any telescope that may be used for photography should be mounted equatorially so that it can follow the stars smoothly while a photograph is exposed. Moreover, it is almost necessary to provide automatic motion—a clockwork "drive"—in order to keep the telescope pointed at one object for any length of time.

For simple observations—just looking at planets, star clusters, and nebulae—it is possible to use other types of mounting without a drive and to readjust the telescope from time to time. A small telescope can of course be used like field glasses—hand-held—to look at bright objects. Some portable telescopes are mounted on a bracket that can be attached with a clamp to the edge of a table or frame of a car. Others are on tripods that stand firmly on irregular ground. With such portable mountings it is often considered impractical to attempt an equatorial mounting, and the only requirement is that the telescope can swing smoothly to be pointed in any direction above the horizon; that is, it must move on two axles or about a ball-and-socket joint. One vertical and one horizontal axle form an "altazimuth mounting."

Astronomers generally use the precise term "axis" instead of the more pictorial "axle." The "polar axis" is the center line of the axle in an equatorial mounting that allows the telescope to follow a star's westward motion. Perpendicular to the polar axis is the "declination axis," the center line of an axle that allows the telescope to swing north-south. A third axis, mentioned often in the following articles, is the "optical axis" of the telescope—the line of sight from the center of the eyepiece through the center of the lens (or reflected off the center of the primary mirror) toward the stars. It is generally the center line of the telescope tube.

Equatorial and altazimuth mountings can be purchased or, as the following articles show, constructed from inexpensive parts.   — T L P

....

Mountings of Today and Yesterday

O. M. ERPENSTEIN

(Sky and Telescope, November 1952)

How to mount an instrument that is in process of construction is a problem that confronts every telescope maker of today, particularly the amateur, just as it was a problem for the old-timers, especially those ambitious enough to construct large reflectors or refractors of prodigious length. In the endeavor to arrive at a decision for myself as to the best type of mounting, I perused much of the literature, old and modern; and in the course of the investigation many unusual and interesting mountings came to light. The accompanying illustrations of small models by no means exhaust all the possible schemes, but they include the major types, as well as others that we now would never dream of using.

Model I (Fig. 30), is the conventional German, or Fraunhofer, equatorial type best suited to refractors. It requires a counterweight, and when used for a reflector, provision should be made for the tube of the telescope to be turned on its axis in order to avoid some awkward posi-

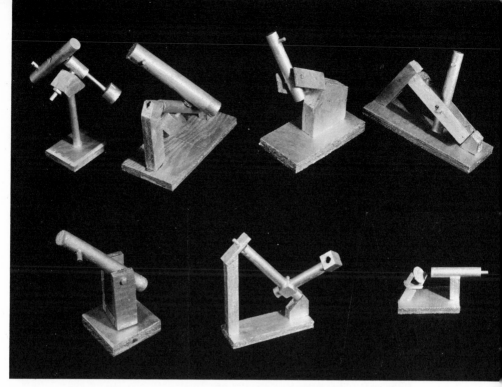

Fig. 30. The author's models of "today's" telescope mountings. At the top are Models I through IV; the German, cross-axis, fork, and yoke mountings. Below are Models V to VII, the altazimuth, coudé, and horizontal (or siderostat). The diameter of the tube in Model II is 1 inch and its length is 6 inches.

tions of the eyepiece. It has the disadvantage that when observing or photographing near the meridian it is often necessary to reverse the telescope from one side of the pier to the other to avoid striking it. Most amateur mountings are of this type. The largest refractor in the world, at Yerkes Observatory, is mounted in this manner.

Model II is nearly the same as the preceding, the difference being that the declination axis lies between the two bearings for the polar axis. In this cross-axis type a counterweight is required, but greater stability is insured than that of Model I. Unlike the German mounting, it need not be reversed upon reaching the meridian. A number of photographic instruments are mounted this way; the Jewett Schmidt telescope at the Agassiz station of Harvard College Observatory is an example.

The fork type of mounting is shown by Model III. Here no counterweight is necessary, but for general stability the fork and the polar axis must be of very generous proportions. It is proposed to mount the 120-inch reflector of Lick Observatory on a fork mounting, which will then be the largest in operation. The 60-inch of Mount Wilson is a large fork-mounted reflector.

Model IV shows the English, or yoke, equatorial. A counterweight is not needed, but of course the two side struts must be very rigid. This is the mounting used with the Mount Wilson 100-inch reflector. The mounting of the 200-inch Hale telescope is a variation of this, the upper bearing being greatly enlarged into a horseshoe so the telescope can be pointed at the pole of the celestial sphere.

Model V is a forked mounting like Model III. Indeed, the latter would assume this position of axes if it were to be used at the poles (or at the equator, with a nominal interchange of axis nomenclature). For those who are not concerned about mounting their instruments equatorially, this altazimuth mounting is the best from the standpoint of simplicity and convenience of operation at low powers.

In VI we see the equatorial coudé, or elbowed equatorial. It is in some respects similar to the well-known Springfield mounting [see p. 97], in that the observer sits under cover, always looking down through a stationary eyepiece at an angle equal to the observer's latitude. The box at the end contains a 45° mirror that is controlled from the eyepiece. In the box joining the two tubes (one of which forms the polar axis) another mirror is placed at 45°, thus providing the double reflection. The lens, or objective, is located in the square box (shown with a round hole) at the very end of the instrument. . . .

The telescope in VII is stationary, and the rays of an object are brought to it by means of a siderostat. This is, of course, one method of solar observation used to this day. . . . A disadvantage of this method is that the field of view rotates with the siderostat mirror, and when photographs are taken the plateholder must be counterrotated in order to prevent trailing of the images.

The mounting used by Sir William Herschel for his 4-foot reflector is shown by VIII (Fig. 31). This instrument was of the direct-vision type (frequently referred to as the Herschelian reflector), that is to say, the observer stood with his back to the object, and a platform that could be moved by means of a block-and-tackle arrangement supported him. This is really an altazimuth mounting, and the observer must have had quite a time in trying to locate an object with such unmanageable means. . . .

Lord Rosse, with the 6-foot Parsonstown reflector, which also was a direct-vision instrument, solved the problem of mounting such a large tube as shown by IX. The model shows that this instrument could command only a strip of sky to either side of the meridian and could not reach the zenith at all. The lower end was set in a sort of ball-and-socket joint, and the upper end rested on a support whose position, as well as the position of the tube lengthwise of this supporting bar, was adjusted with a block-and-tackle arrangement.

FIG. 31. The author built these models to show some outdated mount-ings for reflectors (VIII and IX at the top) and refractors of great focal length (X and XI at the bottom).

The last two models show methods used at the time of Huygens for managing the long refractors of that day (example: 6-inch aperture, length 90 feet). It will be recalled that such long instruments were the fashion before the days of the discovery of the achromatizing principle. Model X shows again a ball-and-socket joint near the eye end of the telescope, the position of the instrument being controlled by the ubiqui-tous block and tackle. In XI the tube was dispensed with, and object glass and eye end were joined by a rod. . . .

••

A Simple German
Mounting

HANS PFLEUMER

(Sky and Telescope, August 1955)

Illustrated here (Fig. 32) is an equatorial mounting made for a friend who bought a secondhand 3-inch refractor with a homemade altazimuth head and tripod. . . . In his back yard he erected a 4-inch heavy-duty pipe set in a fairly large block of concrete.

Heavy-duty pipe fittings were used and machined inside and out. The axes are monel and steel shafts, $1\frac{3}{8}$ inches in diameter. The polar axle is supported by two needle bearings and ball thrust bearings at either end of the wye (Y) fitting; these latter bearings are housed by sleeves fixed to the tee (T) and wye. The declination axle moves in a solid bronze bushing extending $\frac{3}{4}$ inch through the tee at the lower side.

The upper side of this tee fitting is machined down to form a brake drum leaving a shoulder. On the declination axle at the saddle plate a ring, also having a shoulder, is fastened with countersunk setscrews, forming the other half of the drum. The brake band to lock both together

Fig. 32. When mounting the equatorial head for a 3-inch refractor Hans Pfleumer made up the distance between the standard wye of 45° and the local latitude of 40°.5 north with an aluminum wedge of 4.5°. The wedge may be seen between the flanges of the pier and the mount.

FIG. 33. The telescope as it was originally completed; Dr. Custer is standing alongside. He has since made many modifications for prime-focus photography.

was built up of an eccentric ring, and a boss was fixed to the thicker side, but this could be a casting.

The saddle is 24ST aluminum. A cradle piece was bored out 3 inches in diameter, cut in half, and machined as twin pieces to insure accuracy. The counterweight consists of lead poured around a pipe bushing, the threads being recut straight to make the counterweight adjustable on the threaded declination axle.

Since this heavy head is to be left on the pedestal while the telescope is taken into the house, quick detaching is provided by a single hinged clamp band holding the tube fast in the open cradle. . . .

The Custer 12½-inch
Springfield Reflector

ROBERT E. COX

(*Sky and Telescope*, November, December 1956)

Many an amateur telescope maker builds several instruments before making his ideal telescope, the "pet" he chooses for serious observing work and in which he takes greatest pride. Clarence P. Custer, a physician and surgeon in Stockton, California, has built only two instruments, however, a 6-inch prize-winning reflector and a 12½-inch on a revised Porter Springfield mounting.

It is the latter telescope for which we shall describe the design and workmanship, in the hope that other amateurs who are contemplating the Springfield type for a large permanently mounted instrument may profit by Dr. Custer's experiences.

The photograph of the complete telescope (Fig. 33) shows the high pier that was necessary to allow the tube to clear the ground. This cork-lined tube is 16 inches in diameter and 10 feet long, of 20-gauge rolled iron. The pier, embedded in five cubic yards of concrete, has a ⅜-inch wall thickness and is filled with concrete to add mass and rigidity. Although the small counterweight (upper right of picture) weighs only 65 pounds, an additional 150 pounds of lead is concealed in the narrow end of the cone of the counterweight arm to complete the balancing of the telescope. The cone is fastened to a curved sheet of boiler iron that covers the entire end of the inside of the tube, being welded to it for greater strength. No flexure of this assembly has been detected in operation. . . .

The observing chair is conveniently adjusted, for it can be quickly moved up or down the angle-iron tracks to any set of supporting holes, where it is held on pegs bent upwards at a right angle. The seat and back are adjustable for height and distance from the pier. Ascent and descent are made by means of a stepladder.

The right-ascension assembly is provided with a slip ring, so finding objects is easy; for example, one evening in an hour's time seventeen objects were shown to a few friends with an average of only about one minute between settings of the instrument.

Dr. Custer invested 145 hours of working time on the 12½-inch mirror, over a period of 130 days. The mirror is mounted on a three-point support surrounded by a screen-covered outer cell that provides ample ventilation, permitting the mirror to come to equilibrium with the air temperature very rapidly. . . .

Light from the primary mirror is reflected to the large aluminized diagonal, which sends the light down the declination axis to the prism in the Springfield equatorial head; the prism turns the light again, so it enters the eyepiece that is located over the polar-axis bearing. . . .

The heart of the Springfield design is the equatorial head, bolted to the top of the pillar (Fig. 33). The castings were made in Toledo, Ohio, by E. S. Ensign and machined in Stockton at the Carando Machine Works. With a telescope twice the diameter of the original Porter

Fig. 34. In the type of telescope built by Dr. Custer the primary mirror has a paraboloidal figure, and it reflects light to a diagonal flat, as in a Newtonian. This flat is located at the intersection of the optical axis and the declination axis, down which the light is sent to a second flat or a prism, at the intersection of the declination axis and the polar axis. The eyepiece is in a fixed position regardless of where the telescope is pointed.

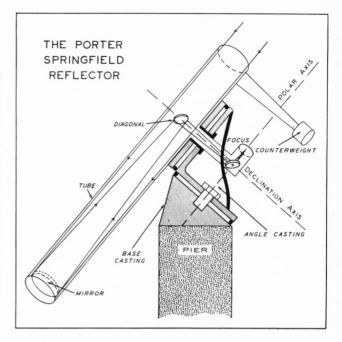

THE PORTER SPRINGFIELD REFLECTOR

POLAR AXIS

DIAGONAL

FOCUS

COUNTERWEIGHT

DECLINATION AXIS

TUBE

ANGLE CASTING

BASE CASTING

PIER

MIRROR

design and weighing 350 pounds, the scaled-up mounting may be somewhat overloaded mechanically, but it has been in constant operation since 1949 and has shown no evidence of stress or strain. . . .

Springfield reflectors have the great advantage that objects in any part of the sky can be observed while the eyepiece remains in a fixed position. The principle that allows this convenient result is illustrated in Figure 34, where it is seen that light rays are reflected three times before entering the eyepiece. The observer sits with his back to the North Star.

The construction of this useful type of telescope is more complicated than that of a conventionally mounted instrument, and the amateur who plans to make one can profit from a detailed description of a successful prototype. . . .

The side of the mounting is seen in Figure 35, with the saddle turned as if the telescope were pointed to a star high in the southern sky. The welded tube saddle is bolted onto the combination brass setting circle and worm gear for declination immediately beneath it. In the center can be seen the worm and its motor drive. The declination axis runs almost horizontally in the picture, to the right-angle prism located over the polar axle, which slopes downward to the right. The eyepiece fits in a short tube just above the prism. . . .

An equatorial mounting allows easy finding of objects in the sky. Astronomers list coordinates, right ascension and declination, that are similar to longitude and latitude on the earth (Fig. 2). The declination is measured in degrees north or south of the celestial equator, and motion around one axis in the equatorial mounting is motion in declination. A ring marked in degrees can be attached so that a pointer reads 0° when the telescope is pointing at the equator, and +90° when it is pointing at the north celestial pole (approximately at the polestar).

The right ascension is measured eastward along the equator from the vernal equinox (the position of the sun when it crosses the equator about March 21 each year). Of course, this point moves westward during the night, together with all the stars. Hence, the ring on which right ascension is to be read must move, one turn per 24 hours.   — T L P

....

A Telescope Drive with Right-ascension Circle

OWEN GINGERICH

(*Sky and Telescope*, October 1954)

Several years ago, when I decided to build a drive for my 8-inch telescope, I discovered that information on this subject is not abundant. I wrote a number of letters, made a few blunders, but finally finished the drive, which is described in this article.

A clock drive is very useful if you anticipate many visitors to your observatory, for with its aid you can follow objects without intervening every few minutes to keep the telescope tracking. In regular observing, high powers are difficult to use without a clock drive, for here especially the apparent motion of the stars is a nuisance. If your telescope is equipped with a right-ascension circle in combination with the clock drive, you will easily be able to find objects from their known positions in the sky.

Drives may be attached to portable telescopes, but their use is more limited since the mounting will not usually be accurately lined up with the celestial pole. A number of ingenious drives have been devised from alarm clocks. In most cases, the clock merely controls the power furnished by a weight or spring. Other portable telescopes have actually used synchronous motors, either with a battery and inverter or with extension cords attached to available sources of power.

With a permanent mounting, a small synchronous motor provides an accurate and convenient drive. These are generally available with

FIG. 35. The assembled
Springfield head, as seen
from the northwest side.

FIG. 36. Main cell and
yoke of Owen Gingerich's
8-inch f/6.7 Newtonian
telescope.

built-in gear reductions to about one revolution per minute (1 r.p.m.).
The R. W. Cramer Co., Centerbrook, Connecticut, supplies a small
motor (type SX) in a large selection of slow output speeds, as well as
a somewhat heavier chart drive motor (type CX) with the final reduction train set at a 15-inch-pound torque.

Many amateurs have found the heavy Telechron motors satisfactory,
from the General Electric Company, Ashland, Massachusetts. Their
styles C5 and C5M are heavier than ordinary clock motors, developing
more than enough torque for a well-balanced telescope. The Telechron
C5X is reversible, as are the more expensive K-type synchronous motors
manufactured by the Bodine Electric Company, 2254 West Ohio Street,
Chicago, Illinois. Somewhat heavier motors, series PYAZ, may be
obtained from the Barber-Coleman Company, Rockford, Illinois.

In using a 1-r.p.m. motor, a further reduction of 1440 to 1 is necessary. Most of this should be done with a large gear on the polar axis.
I learned from practical experience that a large worm gear was necessary to eliminate backlash, which was otherwise quite annoying. Worm
gears with 100 teeth (which I finally used) are regularly stocked by the
Boston Gear Works and Chicago Gear Works, and larger sizes can be
made up to order.

The remainder of the reduction can be done with spur gears. "Change"
gears of 20 pitch are stocked with every number of teeth from 20 to
120, and some smaller sizes are available. The pitch equals the number
of teeth divided by the diameter. Thus, a 20-pitch gear with a diameter
of one inch has 20 teeth, while a 32-pitch gear of the same size would
have 32 teeth, and so on. There is no objection to using gears with
somewhat higher pitch than 20, but the variety is not as great.

Assuming a 100-tooth worm gear on the polar axis, a reduction of
14.4 to 1 is still needed with the spur gears. This can be done in a
number of ways: 12- and 15-tooth gears meshing against 36- and 72-tooth
gears will do the trick. To check, write

$$\frac{36 \times 72 \times 100}{12 \times 15 \times 1} = 1440.$$

The 12- and 15-tooth gears and the worm are in each case on the
driving side of the pair.

Incidentally, worm gears and some of the synchronous motors are
available in both right- and left-hand drives; be sure to check the direction of the system. Also, many motors can be obtained in slower speeds.
Thus, with a motor of one revolution per hour, the additional reduction
need be only 24 to 1, the slower motor already providing a factor of
60 to 1 over the 1-r.p.m. motor. A pair of spurs of 50 and 12 teeth with
the 100-tooth worm gear will complete the system. . . .

FIG. 37. Closeup of the completed drive and right-ascension circle, showing the layout of the gear train, the compression spring, and the 100-tooth worm gear.

FIG. 38. An exploded diagram of the friction clutch and right-ascension circle assembly. Some of the parts may be seen in Figure 37. The outside diameter of the right-ascension circle is about 8 inches.

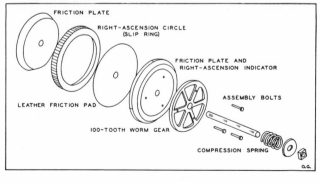

FRICTION PLATE

RIGHT-ASCENSION CIRCLE
(SLIP RING)

FRICTION PLATE AND
RIGHT-ASCENSION INDICATOR

LEATHER FRICTION PAD

ASSEMBLY BOLTS

100-TOOTH WORM GEAR

COMPRESSION SPRING

O.G.

In my own case, I had available a large number of war-surplus gears that could be assembled about as easily as an Erector set. The only problem was finding gears in the collection with the appropriate factors. I selected the compromise factor of 1436.5 [allowing for atmospheric refraction and the difference between sidereal and solar day].

The photograph of the gear train (Fig. .37) shows the Cramer SX motor, chosen because it is inexpensive (about five dollars) and yet sufficiently powerful. Beginning at the left of the motor, the gears are 20 to 52, 13 to 65, 18 to 17, 40 to 52, 50 to 45. Finally, on the worm gear, the ratio is 1 to 100. This is a 16-pitch bronze worm gear, which cost about nine dollars, including the steel worm.

The plan of the friction clutch and right-ascension circle is illustrated in Figure 38. The friction clutch is a crucial part for happy operation of the telescope, and caused some trouble until I arranged the assembly so the spring could be easily adjusted, and added a piece of leather between the cast-aluminum plates. Scrap leather costs about a cent a square inch and was readily available from a local shoe repair shop.

In operation, the telescope may be freely swung in right ascension while the drive is working. There is sufficient friction through the leather to hold the telescope steady without clamping. The right-ascension circle turns with the telescope, although it is not fastened rigidly to it. Instead, three small pins with springs set into the first friction plate provide enough friction inside this setting circle ring.

At the beginning of an evening of observation, the right-ascension slip ring must be set by pointing the telescope at a known star (for instance, Vega). Then the circle is slipped around until the chosen indicator on the other friction plate corresponds to the star's right ascension ($18^h 35^m.4$ for Vega). Now the instrument is ready for use with any other object for which the right ascension can be obtained, or the right ascension of an object to which the telescope is pointed can be read from the circle. This is because the friction plate with the indicator is bolted onto the worm gear that is driven by the motor and gear train. The indicator slowly moves around during the evening, continually reading right ascension directly and eliminating subtracting for hour-angle determinations. . . .

....

Alarm-clock Telescope
Drive

PAUL R. SWEGER

(*Sky and Telescope*, April 1954)

Two considerations led to the design of the telescope drive described here. First, for a portable telescope, a mechanical clock drive has an advantage over a motor drive in that no power supply is needed. Second, the connection between clock and polar axis should be through a worm and worm gear, since in slipping the clutch to turn the telescope to another part of the sky, the strain is taken by the worm bracket and is not transmitted to the clock. . . .

The problem in using the works of a clock was to find a shaft that would run at a suitable speed. The solution was to speed up the clock so that a 100-tooth worm gear could be used on the minute shaft. Since there are about 1436 solar minutes in a sidereal day, it was necessary for the minute shaft to make one revolution in 14.36 minutes. This was arranged by removing the balance wheel rim and gradually shortening the spokes, with frequent testing until the clock was running at the right speed. As an alternative to reducing the weight of the balance wheel, turns could have been taken from the hairspring.

On the lower end of the polar axis a collar was fastened with a setscrew, and the worm gear was placed on this axis, with a cardboard disk between gear and collar. On the other side of the worm gear I put a spring disk, made from thin steel with a central hole slightly smaller than the polar axis, and with 8 slots cut from the hole to within $\frac{1}{4}$ inch of the edge. The disk was dished by bending each of the pie-shaped pieces. On top of the tripod I made a worm bracket, pierced to take the minute shaft. With the worm in place, the minute shaft was passed through this opening and pressed into a hole in the end of the worm. Thus the clock hangs from this shaft and is kept from rotating by a projection that presses against the worm bracket. . . .

To orient the tripod, a level and compass have been fastened to it. These have proved such a convenience that their installation can be recommended to all users of tripod-mounted equatorials.

The driving mechanism of a telescope is not very powerful and will slip or stall if a large force is required. For this and other reasons, tele-

scopes must be balanced on their mountings; that is, neither end can be heavier than the other for the motion about either axis.   — T L P

<hr>

Balancing the Tube of a Reflecting Telescope

ROBERT E. COX

(*Sky and Telescope*, November 1958)

Among amateur-built reflectors, statically unbalanced instruments are the rule rather than the exception. While friction in the bearings or restraining clamps on the axis often conceal a lack of equilibrium, such a condition cannot be tolerated if slow-motion controls are to work properly or if a driving clock is to be added. . . .

It is first necessary to discuss the steps an amateur should take to balance the reflecting telescope tube and its attachments around the optical axis. If a rotating tube is planned, it would be impossible to overcome the effects of gravity in all positions of the telescope if such balance were not achieved at the very beginning.

In most reflectors, the mirror and its cell are symmetrical about the optical axis, and diagonal supports are usually symmetrical also. But every instrument must have an eyepiece base mount, with the adapter tube and eyepiece itself, all represented by E in Figure 39A. If there is a finder, it will probably be mounted at least $45°$ from the eyepiece, as shown by F. Obviously, these cause a tendency for the tube to rotate one way or the other, as shown in a and b of Figure 39A; only in a special position, c, will E and F tend to balance each other. How can we obtain an equilibrium condition for all orientations of E and F with respect to the optical axis?

Our example will be the tube shown schematically in Figure 39B, with a diameter of 8 inches and a 3-pound finder whose center of gravity is 7 inches from the optical axis. The 2-pound eyepiece assembly has its center of gravity 5 inches from the optical axis. As in Figure 39A, the angle EOF, is $45°$, and the direction of gravity is indicated by the arrow pointing downward just below the center, O.

In order to compute the moments of force of E and F around O, we first assume a particular orientation of the tube. In this example, we take angle $P'OE$ as $30°$, which makes $P'OF$ $75°$, since angle EOF has been set at $45°$. The construction lines of Figure 39B show how

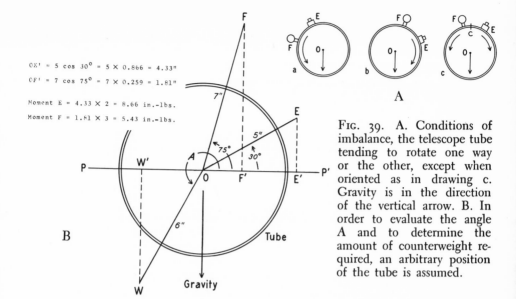

$OE' = 5 \cos 30° = 5 \times 0.866 = 4.33"$

$CF' = 7 \cos 75° = 7 \times 0.259 = 1.81"$

Moment E = 4.33 × 2 = 8.66 in.-lbs.

Moment F = 1.81 × 3 = 5.43 in.-lbs.

Fɪɢ. 39. A. Conditions of imbalance, the telescope tube tending to rotate one way or the other, except when oriented as in drawing c. Gravity is in the direction of the vertical arrow. B. In order to evaluate the angle A and to determine the amount of counterweight required, an arbitrary position of the tube is assumed.

to compute the moments, which act as if the weights of E and F were located at E' and F' on the horizontal line PP'. We shall denote the weights of E and F by E_1 and F_1, respectively. The moment of E is E_1 multiplied by the distance OE', while that of F is F_1 times OF'. The numerical results are shown in the diagram, using $E_1 = 2$ and $F_1 = 3$ pounds.

We will attempt to cure the rotational tendency by placing a counterweight of W_1 pounds at the position W, 6 inches from the optical axis, somewhere on the opposite side of the tube from E and F, as indicated by the angle A. The moment of W is 6 W_1 cos A. Equilibrium requires that the sum of the moments of E, F, and W shall be zero:

$$8.66 + 5.43 + 6 W_1 \cos A = O,$$
or
$$6 W_1 \cos A = -14.09. \tag{1}$$

But in this formula we have two unknowns, the weight W_1 and the angle of orientation A. For another position of the telescope tube, with the whole system rotated counterclockwise through 90°, the equilibrium condition is

$$-5.00 - 20.29 + 6W_1(-\sin A) = O,$$
or
$$6 W_1 \sin A = -25.29. \tag{2}$$

This condition is to be satisfied simultaneously with that of Equation 1. One method of solving these equations is to divide one by the other:

$$\frac{6\ W_1 \sin A}{6\ W_1 \cos A} = \tan A = \frac{-25.29}{-14.09} = 1.795.$$

Therefore A, which must be in the third quadrant since both its sine and cosine are negative, is 240°.9. Now we may substitute the cosine of A in Equation 1 and solve for W_1, which comes out to be 4.83 pounds.

As a check that in any position the tube will be in balance around the optical axis, the reader may wish to place the assembly in a new position and compute the moment of W against those of E and F. In some positions, however, W and E will be on one side of the tube and F on the other, and vice versa.

In actual practice, the weight W_1 will be less than the calculated value, for it is necessary to take into account the weight of the supports that hold W to the tube. Furthermore, as far as equilibrium around the optical axis is concerned, W need not be at the top (eyepiece) end of a Newtonian reflector directly opposite E and F, although many amateurs prefer it there. It can be placed anywhere along the side of the tube on a line parallel to the optical axis. This permits using the counterweight to stabilize the tube around the declination axis, which is the next step in the balancing process.

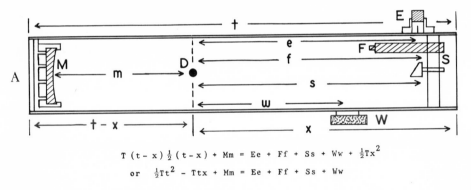

$$T\,(t-x)\tfrac{1}{2}\,(t-x) + Mm = Ee + Ff + Ss + Ww + \tfrac{1}{2}Tx^2$$

$$\text{or}\quad \tfrac{1}{2}Tt^2 - Ttx + Mm = Ee + Ff + Ss + Ww$$

FIG. 40. A. After balance around the optical axis has been achieved, the distances from the declination axis, D, to the various components may be measured as if they were located on the optical axis. The parts are pictured as if they were in the same plane. The formula for static balance around D is given below the diagram. B. The relative locations of D, W, and C in the four examples worked out in the text.

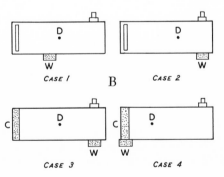

Figure 40A shows the general problem, in which the following components are indicated: eyepiece E, finder F, spider support and diagonal S, counterweight W, mirror and cell M, position of declination axis D. With respect to D, these parts are at the distances (along the optical axis) denoted by e for eyepiece, f for finder, and w for counterweight. The overall length of the tube is t, and the weight per unit length of the tube is T. The symbol x stands for the distance of D from the eyepiece end of the tube.

The condition for equilibrium is stated by the expression given in the diagram. The first moment is of the tube itself, for that part on the mirror side of D, where the weight is given by $T(t - x)$ and the distance by $\frac{1}{2}(t - x)$. For the other part of the tube, the moment is Tx times $\frac{1}{2}x$. The expression reduces to the form:

$$\tfrac{1}{2}Tt^2 - Ttx + Mm = Ee + Ff + Ss + Ww, \qquad (3)$$

and from this general equation many arrangements may be computed, according to the needs of the telescope design.

A number of special cases (Fig. 40B) are worth considering:

Case 1. Point D is centered at the midpoint of the telescope tube. Here $x = \frac{1}{2}t$, and $\frac{1}{2}Tt^2 - Ttx = 0$. Hence,

$$Mm = Ee + Ff + Ss + Ww. \qquad (4)$$

If w comes out with a negative sign, the location of the counterweight is to the left of D, on the mirror end of the tube.

Case 2. The counterweight, W, is placed at the same distance from D as the eyepiece is. Equation 3 becomes

$$\tfrac{1}{2}Tt^2 - Ttx + Mm = e(E + W) + Ff + Ss. \qquad (5)$$

If the mirror is relatively light, this construction will require a shift of the declination-axis position toward the eyepiece end of the tube.

Case 3. A combination of Case 1 and Case 2, in which D is at the tube's midpoint while W and E are at the same distance, e. In this case it is probable that an additional counterweight, C, will have to be added at the mirror end. As in Case 1, $x = \frac{1}{2}t$, and $\frac{1}{2}Tt^2 - Ttx = 0$. Therefore, we write

$$Cc + Mm = e(E + W) + Ff + Ss, \qquad (6)$$

and the value of C will depend on the choice of the distance c between C and D.

Case 4. For a fork mounting, D may be placed one third of the tube length from the mirror end. Here $x = \frac{2}{3}t$, and $\frac{1}{2}Tt^2 - Ttx = -\frac{1}{6}Tt^2$. Therefore $\quad Mm - \frac{1}{6}Tt^2 = Ee + Ff + Ss + Ww.$ (7)

Numerical Examples

To illustrate the use of these formulas, let us adopt the following values:

$M = 4$, $E = 2$, $F = 3$, $S = 1$, $W = 4.8$ lbs., $t = 48$ inches; $T = 0.15$ lb. per inch; $Tt = 7.2$; $m = t - x - 2$; $e = x - 4$; $f = x - 6$; $s = x - 3$.

Case 1. In this simple arrangement, with the declination axis in the center of the tube longitudinally, we can actually ignore the weight of the tube itself, as it is equally divided on each side of D. Since $x = 24$, Equation 4 becomes:

$$88 = 40 + 54 + 21 + 4.8w;$$
$$w = -5.625.$$

The counterweight will have to be placed $5\frac{5}{8}$ inches from D toward the mirror end.

Case 2. Suppose it is desired to have W located approximately opposite the eyepiece at the upper end of the tube, making $w = e$. Where should the tube be supported? Using Equation 5, we have

$$172.8 - 7.2x + 184 - 4x = 10.8x - 48.2;$$
$$x = \frac{405}{22} = 18.41,$$

which places D about $18\frac{1}{2}$ inches from the eyepiece end of the tube and about $29\frac{1}{2}$ inches from the mirror end.

Case 3. Since $x = 24$, Equation 6 gives

$$Cc + 88 = 136 + 54 + 21;$$
$$Cc = 123.$$

This is the unbalanced moment at the mirror end, which could be compensated by a weight of over 5 pounds at the extreme end of the tube, 24 inches from D. However, a single weight would destroy the balance around the optical axis. To prevent this, we might divide the balancing weight in half, placing the halves diametrically opposite each other. Another way would be to fit a ring around the tube, making its weight 6 pounds and placing it about 16 inches from the centered position of D. Some amateurs prefer a weight under the mirror cell, where it can be symmetrically placed around the optical axis and where it requires the least weight because it is farthest from D.

Case 4. For a fork-type mounting, the clearance of the mirror end in the fork determines the position of the declination axle. We have already assumed the support point to be two thirds of the way from the upper (eyepiece) end. We use Equation 7 to find

$$56 - 57.6 = 56 + 78 + 29 + 4.8w;$$
$$4.8w = -164.6;$$
$$w = -34.3.$$

Counterweight W would have to be placed more than 34 inches to the left of D if it alone had to balance the tube. This position is obviously impossible, but if W were placed 16 inches from D, at the extreme mirror end of the tube, its moment would be only 76.8 inch-pounds. Another counterweight is necessary, and if it were at the extreme end, its weight would be about $5\frac{1}{2}$ pounds, to furnish the additional moment of 87.8 inch-pounds. A better solution might be a ring counterweight, weighing about 6 pounds and placed 2 inches from the mirror end of the tube. In whatever way W and C are combined, they must provide a total moment of 164.6 inch-pounds.

■■

Balancing a German Equatorial Mounting

ROBERT E. COX

(*Sky and Telescope*, December 1958)

Although a telescope tube may be carefully designed to achieve balance around the optical and declination axes, further balancing procedures are necessary to insure smooth operation wherever the telescope is pointed in the sky. It must be in perfect balance around both the declination and polar axes, and provision must be made for adjusting the balance when minor accessories are added.

Imperfect balance may not show up when a new telescope is first tried out, but after some observing, it may be noticed that in certain parts of the sky the clock drive or the slow motions work erratically, or that when the tube is pointed toward the zenith it will not remain in that position. The procedures to be followed have been analyzed by G. Van Biesbroeck, of Yerkes and McDonald Observatories, for any type of mounting, including the popular German type, such as the model in the pictures (Fig. 41). He writes:

"I have heard many a telescope owner make the statement, 'I cannot

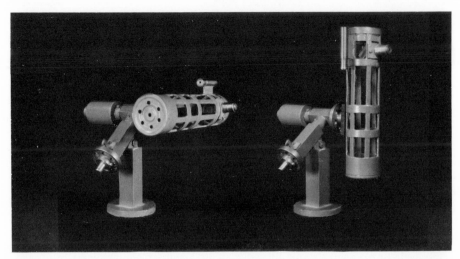

A

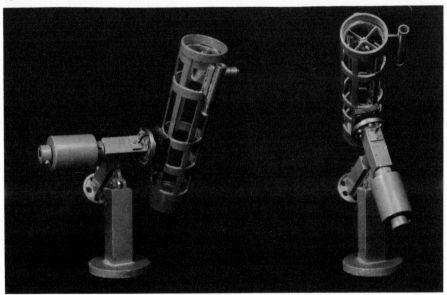

B

FIG. 41. A. The balance of a German-type mounting around the declination axis should be checked in the positions pictured here, I (left) and II, illustrated by a model 6 inches high made by Cliff Raible of the Amateur Astronomers Association of Pittsburgh. B. Balance around the polar axis should be checked in positions III (left) and IV. If in position IV the telescope tends to swing to the right (clockwise as seen from the north), an additional counterweight should be placed on the left (eastern) side of the central block of the declination assembly.

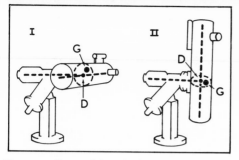
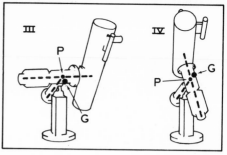

FIG. 42. In position I the center of gravity, G, is shown above and to the right of D. In position II, G is to the right and on the near side of the tube, causing its upper end to move southward. Adjusting the counterweight in position III brings the center of gravity into the vertical plane of axis P. If G is below P, then G will be on the western side of the pier in position IV. To compensate for this, a counterweight is to be placed on the eastern side of the declination housing.

get that instrument balanced in all positions.' There should not be any difficulty about this if we keep in mind that a rotating system is only balanced when its center of gravity is on the axis. In the case of a telescope, we have two axes of rotation and we have, therefore, to adjust the balance successively in four positions [see Fig. 42]."

Position I. "First, we adjust the balance of the tube in declination, pointing the telescope horizontally in the meridian. We check if the tube moves with equal ease up or down, and if necessary, shift the counterweight along the tube until that condition is obtained. Is the tube now completely balanced? It will be if the tube and its parts are perfectly symmetrical around the optical axis. But if they are not, the center of gravity (G in the diagram) may not be exactly on the axis. All that we have obtained by the counterweight adjustment in this first position is to bring G in the vertical plane of the declination axis at D. We cannot tell whether G is somewhat above or below D. Suppose it is above D; how can we check to find the actual situation?"

Position II. "By turning the telescope to the zenith. The position of G is now in front of D, as we view them here, with the result that the telescope tube will move more easily to the south than to the north. To correct this, we have to move some of the counterweight horizontally (around the tube) until G coincides with D. We can tell this is the case when the telescope moves with equal ease north or south of the zenith. It is important that the counterweight be moved only around the tube, in order not to disturb the balance already achieved in position I. Now the instrument will be in balance in declination in all positions."

Position III. "The same reasoning applies to the polar axis, and in the diagram P is the point of intersection of the declination and polar axes. Point the tube anywhere along the meridian, so the declination axis is horizontal, the tube being on one side of P and the declination counterweight on the other side. We adjust that counterweight inward or outward on its supporting shaft until the motion around P takes place with equal ease east or west. Again we ask, Is the telescope completely balanced now? No, because we only know that the center of gravity G is in the vertical plane of the polar axis. In this position we cannot tell if it is above or below P, nor how much."

Position IV.   "To check this, we move the instrument around the polar axis east or west six hours from the meridian. The center of gravity, if not originally exactly at P, has now moved east or west of it, a fact that becomes evident when we find that the instrument in this fourth position does not rotate with equal ease in both directions.

"How do we correct this? Not by changing weights on the telescope tube, for this would disturb the balance in declination. Not by changing the position of the counterweight on the declination axis, for this would have no effect, as in this fourth position it already is in the vertical plane of the polar axis. The remedy is to install a weight at right angles to the plane formed by the declination and polar axes, that is, on the east or west side of the equatorial head as it is set in position IV. A convenient position for such a counterweight may be on the equator point of a fixed declination circle, but in that case a slight final adjustment has to be made in position III.

"Not until the balance has thus been checked in the four mentioned positions can we be sure that the instrument is in equilibrium in all orientations required during observing. Most telescope makers fail to obtain that condition because they omit checking in positions II and IV. Many a good-sized instrument built by a reputable manufacturer is not free from defects in balance, owing to the neglect to test in all four positions, especially the last one."

These instructions apply also to the English cross-axis design, which employs a counterbalance on the far end of the declination axis. Fork, yoke, split-ring, and other mountings that do not have such a counterweight, should particularly be checked in positions II and IV. The last position is especially important where worm gears and their housing may be added to the declination assembly.

Some telescopes have no counterbalance on the declination axle, as the weight of the extended shaft is sufficient to maintain equilibrium. Though this may seem desirable, it does not provide for adjusting the balance when accessories are added to the tube, and the longer shaft required may get in the way of the observer and of persons waiting to observe. I prefer a counterweight of at least several pounds, not too close to the end of the shaft, with provision for clamping the weight in any position. A short shaft reduces any tendency of the counterweight to vibrate.

A practical method of determining how much counterweight is needed on the declination axle is to hang a pail about 6 inches from the end of it while the telescope is constrained in position III. Fill the pail with water or sand until the assembly stays horizontal without any restricting force. Include the mounting collar and setscrew in the pail, and weigh it carefully. . . .

5

Visual

Observations

of the Moon

and Planets

What can a telescope show us? One of the simplest objects to observe is the moon; it is relatively near (about 240,000 miles), and even a small telescope will show interesting detail on its brilliantly lit, cloudless surface. Lunar features are discussed in Volume 1, Wanderers in the Sky, together with the modern problems of landing space probes on the moon. In this chapter we are concerned with what can be seen with an earth-based telescope, with how magnification and field can be changed by selecting an eyepiece, and with the varying effect of the earth's atmosphere on what an astronomer calls "seeing." Such matters have long been understood, and the interest in a closer look dates back well before the successful use of space probes, as the next article shows.   — T L P

Exploring the Moon

WILLIAM H. BARTON, JR.

(*The Sky*, April 1938)

The moon is the nearest of all our celestial neighbors. Through the great telescopes its surface shows enough detail to stir our imagination into wondering what it would be like to visit the moon. There it lies less than a quarter of a million miles away. So near and yet so far. Galileo's feeble and imperfect "optick tube" reduced the distance to 7500 miles. With this Galileo and his students learned that the surface was not smooth, but was broken up into mountain regions and "seas." Larger telescopes brought into the picture rills, rays, clefts. Today, with the new 200-inch telescope nearly ready for use, the promise is to bring the moon to within 24 miles of our doorstep. Even then many things will be left to our imagination.

Forget for the moment the difficulties of getting to the moon, of landing successfully on its surface, and of returning to the earth. Then forget the difficulties of breathing there and of enduring the heat and cold. Then forget about food and clothing and other trifles of that sort. And let's be off—on a trip to the moon.

Perhaps the first thing we would notice would be . . . [that the] length of the day—from the rising of the sun to its going down— would, according to our earthly standards, be about two weeks. Out there in the sky our spinning earth would measure it for us. Even the day sky on the moon would be as dark as our night sky. That black dome would be studded with stars that never twinkle. There, too, would be an earth that never rises and never sets. Swinging back and forth slowly through a small arc against the starry backdrop, it would have a diameter four times that of our moon. Its face would change phase just as we see the moon change in our earthly sky. It would seem much brighter than our moon. Its sparkling oceans and glittering polar caps would reflect so much more sunlight. Over its face, drifting white clouds would add to the beauty. Not a cold, stark sight, but a scintillating object full of life and color. . . .

We would never see "shooting stars" or meteors in a moon sky. These tiny pieces of cosmic dust are made visible by their fall into the earth's atmosphere, where friction heats them to incandescence. They glow for an instant and fade out. But on the moon—no atmosphere, no friction, and no glow. Millions fall on the earth each day, and there is reason to believe that like numbers fall on the moon. With no atmosphere, these cosmic bullets would pelt down on the moon like hail from a cloudless sky. More dangerous than hail, they would have the penetrating quality of machine-gun fire. . . .

The landscape is unlike anything on the earth. The great dark plains that the early observers mistook for seas are not smooth at all, but covered with tiny craters, low ridges, and other irregularities. These great dark areas cover a large portion of the lunar surface. As seen from the earth, high peaks, casting their dark shadows on the hot rock, are

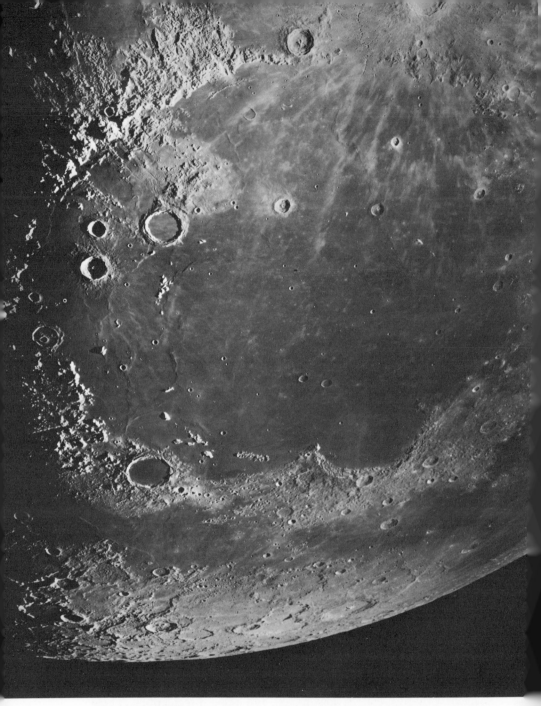

Fig. 43. The broad expanse of a lunar "sea," Mare Imbrium, bordered by tall mountain ranges, pitted by deep craters, and streaked by rays from the great crater Copernicus, 56 miles in diameter (Mount Wilson photograph).

dwarfed to tiny dots. Even great mountain ranges, towering two or three miles above sea level, if sea level is a permissible term on a sealess globe, turn into narrow dark shadows in ordinary telescopes.

Out on the plain is one of the queer features of the moon's surface—a cliff rising 500 feet above the level of the country. The sun shining brightly on the sheer face of this ridge illuminates it with great intensity, and when the shadows creep over it a dark line is the only remaining evidence.

This 2160-mile ball on which we explore is so small that its gravity is noticeably less than that of the earth, only $\frac{1}{6}$, in fact. Therefore a man weighing 150 pounds at home would reduce to 25 pounds here and be so agile that he might establish new world records without half trying. . . .

Before heading for home we shall attempt to find out how these thousands of craters came to be. Some think volcanoes are responsible and others hold to the meteoric theory. . . .

The volcanic theory assumes that the craters were formed by explosions of the lunar crust and the dropping back of the lava, which built up great cones. The low "gravity" on the moon, which allows the high jumper to reach new heights, would also permit the lava to be shot out to unusual distances and to form large craters. These are many times as great in diameter as such craters on the earth. Many of the large craters have tiny cone-shaped mountains in the center, which may have formed after the main wall, by the last feeble outflow.

The meteoric theory of crater formation describes the bombardment of the moon by large meteors. Somewhat the same kind of craters may be formed by throwing steel balls into plastic mud or plaster. In fact, shell holes in a battlefield viewed from an airplane resemble moon craters. The lack of atmosphere and moisture would preserve the topography, whereas on the earth the rain and wind constantly change the face of nature.

Which theory is correct? No one can say. Perhaps no one will ever be able to say.

It would be a real treat if geographers could visit the moon. Perhaps we should not call them geographers if they studied the moon. Geographers study the earth—selenographers study the moon. The best we can do now is look at our nearest neighbor, study it as best we can through the telescope, and dream of rocket ships to carry us there.

The various sizes of craters, mountain ranges, and maria on the moon require different magnifications in a visual telescope. In general, higher magnification shows a smaller region in greater detail. The angular extent of what can be seen in the eyepiece without moving the telescope is called the "field." Magnification refers to the increase in the angular size of an object viewed through the telescope. It surprises newcomers to learn that high-power eyepieces are short; low-power are long. The shorter-focus eyepiece allows the observer's eye to get closer to the real image (p. 20) formed by the telescope objective, and from a closer position it looks larger. Of course, the longer the telescope (the larger the focal length), the larger is the image. Hence, high magnification requires a long telescope and short eyepiece—and it gives small field. In order to find what he wants to study under high magnification, the astronomer uses a short wide-field finder telescope rigidly attached on the side of his large telescope, as noted below. Then he can conveniently "aim" the large telescope at one of the craters on the moon—or at one of the stars in a cluster, or at any point (among stars bright enough to see in the finder),—on a map of the sky and examine the selected small field at high magnification with a high-power eyepiece.   — T L P

··

Magnification, Eyepieces,
Field of View

ALLYN J. THOMPSON

(*Sky and Telescope*, June, July 1945)

Magnification.   Magnification is the effect of increasing the apparent angular size of an object. In Figure 44A a distant object, D, has an angular size at the eye equal to angle a. If its distance is reduced by half, the angular size of the object is doubled, and it appears twice as large.

In the case of very near objects, one uses a convex lens or magnifying glass of suitable focal length. In Figure 44B an object, O, distant about 10 inches (taken to be the distance of best vision) from the eye, subtends there the angle a, in this case 4°. For closer inspection it is placed 1 inch from the eye, Figure 44C. Of course, the eye cannot focus on so near an object, so a convex lens of 1 inch focal length is introduced, which produces an enlarged virtual image of the object at O′. This enlarged image subtends the larger angle a′, and the ratio of a′ to a is equal to the magnification. It follows, therefore, that the magnifying power of any single lens, or combination of lenses used as a simple

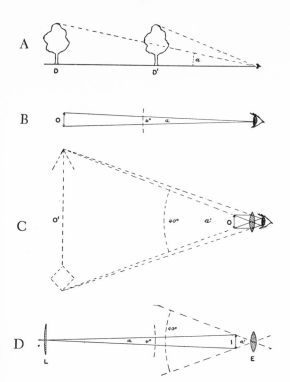

FIG. 44. Illustrations
of angular magnification.

microscope, is equal to 10/f, where f is the focal length (or equivalent focal length) of the lens in inches.

In Figure 44D an image of a distant object is formed at I by the objective lens, L. The angular size of the object at L (or at the eye, since for very distant objects the difference is negligible) is equal to angle a. The image I is enlarged by the eyepiece, E, so that it has the apparent angular size a'. Therefore the ratio of angle a' to angle a is equal to the magnification; it is easily seen that the magnifying power of any telescope is thus equal to F/f, where F is the focal length of the objective (or mirror) and f is the focal length of the eyepiece.

Eyepieces. Astronomical oculars having large apparent fields are of two types, the Huygenian and the Ramsden. Both are mounted in standard tubing of $1\frac{1}{4}$-inches outside diameter and are made in equivalent focal lengths, commonly, from $1\frac{1}{2}$ inches down to $\frac{1}{4}$ inch.

In the Huygenian ocular (Fig. 45A), which is composed of two planoconvex lenses with the convex surfaces facing away from the eye, the focal plane lies between the components, so it cannot be used as a simple magnifier; for this reason it is called a negative ocular. Spherical aberration is not eliminated in this type, so it does not perform as well as the Ramsden on telescopes of moderate or short focal ratios. In the usual design of the Huygenian, the focal lengths of the field and eye lenses are in a ratio of 3 to 1, with a separation of half the sum of the

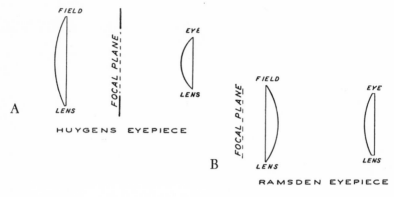

HUYGENS EYEPIECE

RAMSDEN EYEPIECE

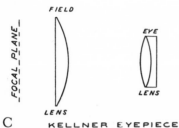

KELLNER EYEPIECE

Fig. 45. A. Huygens eyepiece, with focal plane midway between the components, where a diaphragm excludes all but useful rays. B. Ramsden eyepiece, with focal plane about ¼ inch in front of the field lens in a 1-inch eyepiece. C. Kellner eyepiece, with focal plane about ⅖ inch in front of the field lens.

focal lengths. Thus, in an eyepiece of 1-inch equivalent focal length, the focal lengths of the field and eye lenses are 2 inches and $\frac{2}{3}$ inch respectively. Their separation is $1\frac{1}{3}$ inches, measuring between the convex surfaces.

In the Ramsden, or positive ocular (Fig. 45B), the field and eye lenses are usually of equal focal lengths, with the convex surfaces facing each other and separated by a distance equal to $\frac{2}{3}$ their focal length. Thus, in an eyepiece of 1 inch e.f.l., the focal length of the lenses will be about $1\frac{1}{3}$ inches, with a separation of $\frac{8}{9}$ inch. This ocular has a good flat field, about 40° in extent, and is superior to the Huygenian for work on reflecting telescopes, which are usually of short or moderate focal lengths. While not fully corrected for color, this defect is not troublesome, inasmuch as the reflector itself is achromatic.

A modification of the Ramsden ocular in which the eye lens is formed of an achromatic combination of crown and flint glass, called the Kellner (Fig. 45C), gives a flat, colorless field about 50° in extent, as large a field as can ordinarily be used. It is excellent in low powers, where its wide apparent field can be used to advantage in variable star work, comet seeking, and so forth.

Field of view. A single planoconvex lens, used in the telescope as an eyepiece, or ocular, and held with the plane surface toward the eye,

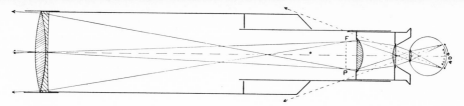

FIG. 46. The optical system of a small refractor used as a finder, of
8-inch focal length. Its 8X eyepiece has an apparent field of 40°, but the
actual field of view is 5°.

will give nice definition, but only over a very small field. One reason
for the small field will be found from a study of Figure 46. Suppose
such a lens of 1-inch focal length were substituted for the compound
eyepiece of 1-inch equivalent focal length shown in that diagram. As
the single lens would have to be placed about 1 inch from the focal
plane, *FP*, the outer rays from the objective would miss it entirely,
thereby narrowing the field. And because of the many inherent defects
that are present in a single lens, a diaphragm would have to be used,
which would further reduce the field. These defects, which are partially
or wholly corrected in the two-lens oculars, are described as spherical
aberration, distortion, coma, curvature of the field, chromatic aberration,
chromatic difference of magnification, and astigmatism. Since these
errors are increased with the distance from the center of the field, it
can be realized that the problem of increasing the useful field of view
becomes a difficult one. . . .

The 1-inch Ramsden eyepiece will take in a *real field* of view of 50
minutes in a 6-inch f/8 telescope. Multiplying this by 48, the amount of
magnification obtained, gives us 40°, the apparent size of the field seen
with that ocular. This is what is meant in speaking of *apparent field*.
Conversely, if we divide the magnification into the apparent field of the
eyepiece, we obtain the real field of view. We see, therefore, that as
magnification is increased, the real field of view becomes smaller.

On the other hand, we can increase the size of the field by the use of
low-power eyepieces having larger field lenses. . . .

Eyepieces of Interest to Amateurs

ROBERT E. COX

(*Sky and Telescope*, November 1961)

Magnification in a telescope is obtained by means of the ocular or
eyepiece—a small microscope or magnifier that enlarges the image
formed by the objective lens or primary mirror. This eyepiece ought to

be of the best quality the observer can afford. For no matter how perfect the principal optics may be, the telescope's performance will be unsatisfactory if the eyepiece is inferior.

For many decades the best oculars for astronomical use have been *orthoscopic*. This term can refer to a type of design or, as is more common today, to a standard of performance. Originally and correctly, the term indicates the design of Ernst Abbé (1840–1905), a famous optical worker and theorist, founder of the Zeiss optical company.

It is only natural that orthoscopic performance has become a standard of comparison for oculars, which may be advertised as orthoscopic even though of other design. As long as their performance is as satisfactory as a true orthoscopic, this practice should be acceptable. . . .

The writer has checked many brands, enough to give a good cross section of the available oculars. Almost all of them have met the orthoscopic standard of performance and are acceptable for astronomical work. The principal types of eyepieces available to American amateurs are shown in Figure 47. If they are carefully designed and manufactured, their observing quality will be orthoscopic, with only a few exceptions, which are noted below.

At half scale, each diagram represents the proper size of a particular kind of eyepiece of 1-inch focal length. Radii of curvature, lens thickness, spacing, and distance from the telescope's focal plane (dashed line) have all been taken into account, and can be roughly measured from the chart [multiplying all measurements by 2]. Light passes through each system from left to right. The kinds of glass are indicated by hatching, which slopes downward to the right for crown, and upward to the right for flint.

In the following comments, *angular field* refers to the angle subtended at the eye by an object filling the field; on the average this is about 40°. In each case mention is made of the smallest focal ratio of the main telescope for which the eyepiece is suited. For focal lengths still shorter in proportion to aperture, the convergence of the light rays is too rapid for the eyepiece to accept them without introducing serious aberrations.

A. Orthoscopic. The basis of this design is a cemented triplet lens followed by a positive meniscus. Its angular field is 30°, and it gives excellent results on f/6 instruments. It is sometimes found with the single lens planoconvex, a design attributed to Mittenzwey. A third form, shown in the diagram, has the front element of the triplet with a plane surface, and the single element is planoconvex. This is called a Hahn eyepiece. . . .

B. Symmetrical. Known under a variety of names including symmetrical, Steinheil, and Plössl, this eyepiece has a pair of achromatic

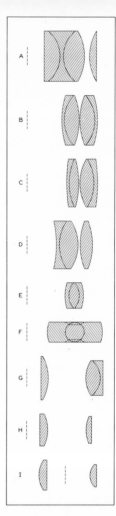

Fig. 47. Half-scale diagrams of the principal types of eyepieces available to amateur astronomers. A. Orthoscopic (Hahn). B. Symmetrical (Plössl). C. Abbé. D. Erfle. E. Triplet. F. Monocentric. G. Kellner. H. Ramsden. I. Huygens.

lenses, usually identical in size, glass types, and construction. The crown elements face each other and are air-spaced a small distance apart. The first two named above are early models and have angular fields of 35° to 40° at f/6. The Plössl, using modern glass and design techniques, is a French ocular with a field of up to 50° at f/6. This is the eyepiece illustrated. Although they appear to be touching, the two lenses are separated at their centers by $\frac{1}{500}$ inch.

It is possible with a pair of carefully chosen war-surplus achromatic lenses to construct a very passable inexpensive form of symmetrical eyepiece of relatively long focus.

C. Abbé. Although it contains two achromatic lenses, the Abbé is not symmetrical. The front, or field, lens has a focal length $1\frac{1}{4}$ times that of the rear element. The air space is also greater than in the symmetrical ocular, but much smaller than in a Kellner eyepiece (G). This is probably the eyepiece which surplus houses offer as the Kellner, but the lens spacing indicates a design nearer to the Abbé type. The angular field is 40°, but use with faster telescopes than f/6 is not recommended.

D. Erfle. This popular item was originally made as shown here. Newer Erfles consist of an achromat for the field lens, another for the eye lens, and a simple double-convex element in between them. In this later form, the Erfle can cover a field of 60° with good definition at f/6.

The giant Erfle, used on Moonwatch and other amateur telescopes for exceptionally large fields of view, consists of three achromats. It is limited in its application to short-focus instruments only by strong astigmatism at the edges of the field and will cover an apparent angle of 65° at f/6 with good results.

E. Triplet. This loupe, or magnifier, is a derivative of monocentric forms and is credited to Steinheil. It makes an excellent eyepiece, but its design must be aplanatic, that is, corrected for spherical aberration; otherwise, definition can be mediocre or poor. It has fine achromatism, a long working distance from the telescope's focal plane, and excellent eye relief. It operates at a focal ratio of f/6 with an angular field of 20° to 30°. There are a number of triplet lenses on the surplus market, but I have been unable to find one that performs well as an eyepiece.

F. Monocentric. Although not at present offered on the American market, this eyepiece has been included because of its high-quality images and performance. Its basic design is that of Steinheil, who used it in spectrometers and spectroscopes because of its excellent color correction. Many optical workers consider it a highly corrected form of solid eyepiece. It has three cemented lenses that are *monocentric*, all four surface radii having one common center·at the middle of the assembly.

At focal ratios below f/6 the performance is not quite satisfactory. In actual construction the central ball is cut down, as shown by the dashed lines in the diagram. This reduces mass and internal reflections, and limits the field so that excessive curvature, beyond a 25° maximum angular field, does not detract from otherwise fine images. The normal field of excellent definitions is 16° to 20°, the ocular's only drawback.

After one has worked with a standard eyepiece or a wide-field Erfle, using a monocentric gives the impression of looking through a tunnel or tube. Yet for lunar and planetary observing, on an equatorially mounted telescope with a good slow-motion or clock drive, this eyepiece performs splendidly. It was widely used by astronomers in the late 1880s and is still found extensively in Europe today.

G. Kellner. In the original design, the field lens of this eyepiece was double convex, but today it is usually planoconvex, as drawn. This is the old achromatic Ramsden. It has an apparent field of 30° to 40° at f/6, but extending it beyond this limit will give poor edge definition, just as in the orthoscopic.

H. Ramsden. This and the Huygens (I) ocular are simple, efficient, and inexpensive. Their performance is not orthoscopic, but if properly designed and mounted, they can give good results on small telescopes— Ramsdens for reflectors, Huygens for refractors.

Originally the Ramsden had both of its planoconvex elements of the same focal length and size. However, better performance results if the field lens is of slightly longer focus than the eye lens, as shown in our diagram. Although the lenses are similar to those of the Huygens, turning their plane surfaces outward places the focal plane in front of the ocular, as with all the eyepieces mentioned earlier. The Ramsden is therefore a *positive* ocular. Its spherical aberration is roughly $\frac{1}{8}$ that of the Huygens, and it performs well at focal ratios of f/8, even down to f/6 without serious harm. The angular field is between 30° and 40°.

Designed for relatively steep cone angles, however, the simple Ramsden is not as suitable for long-focus reflectors or refractors as are the orthoscopic-quality oculars already described. In fact, it is inferior to the Huygens arrangement in such cases.

I. Huygens. The convex surfaces of the lenses face the incoming light, and the focal plane lies between them. Since this design cannot be used for a simple magnifier, it is a *negative* eyepiece. In the case illustrated, the front lens has $1\frac{3}{5}$ times the focal length of the rear one, the combination yielding a field of about 30°.

The Huygens is used on low-cost refractors or compound telescopes where the long, narrow cone angle in the focal plane favors its performance. At less than f/10, spherical aberration becomes most serious, and a Huygens should never be used with short-focus instruments or the standard Newtonian reflector.

Our list by no means exhausts the varieties on the market today, but it does represent the major types and indicates what to look for in selecting eyepieces for your telescope.

Recently I tested a *zoom* eyepiece on a 12-inch reflector. With this revolutionary device, focus can first be obtained at a low power, then easily zoomed to a high power by the turning of a knurled barrel. The ocular tested varied in focal length from 21 mm to 8.4 mm, giving a range of $2\frac{1}{2}$ to 1 in magnification. Although the highest power needed a slight retouching of the rack and pinion, the image was clear and sharp. A focal length of 16 mm was dialed, and the definition and field were compared with a standard ocular of orthoscopic performance—it was difficult to decide if any difference existed between them.

Not only does a zoom ocular do away with a battery of eyepieces, but it makes any focal length or size of field available between wide extremes. The power can be chosen to fit the object under observation, and can be varied at will as seeing and other observing conditions change.

■■

Determining the Field
of an Eyepiece

JOSEPH ASHBROOK

(*Sky and Telescope*, June 1956)

Every observer finds it useful to know the angular width of the field of view for each of the eyepieces of his telescope. For a low-power eyepiece, a simple but rough method is to estimate the size of the field in terms of the apparent diameter of the sun or moon, both of which average about 30 minutes of arc.

A better procedure, widely used, is to time the interval for a star to drift centrally across the field when the telescope is stationary. If the interval is t seconds, and D the field diameter in minutes of arc, then

$$D = \tfrac{1}{4}t \cos \delta,$$

where δ is the declination [see p. 14]. If the star is within a few degrees of the celestial equator, as in Orion's Belt, the factor $\cos \delta$ can be considered equal to one. This second method is only approximate, as the star may not follow a path that is exactly central across the field.

To some extent, the "power" or magnification most suitable for visual observation depends on the seeing. There is no advantage in using high power if the image is fuzzed out by atmospheric conditions. Sometimes such poor seeing is caused by conditions nearby and can be reduced by moving a portable telescope away from drafts of warm air. With a large telescope it sometimes helps to reduce the aperture by means of a diaphragm over the objective lens or mirror. Nights of good seeing are generally windless and follow a day of fairly uniform temperature. After some experience, astronomers all learn to make full use of such nights—they are all too rare at most locations. —TLP

....

Astronomical Seeing

FRANK VAUGHN

(*Sky and Telescope*, November 1959)

Every observer with a 3-inch telescope or larger is uncomfortably aware that on some nights the moon, planets, or close double stars do not yield satisfactory images. The user of binoculars, however, generally has sharp, clear views, even when his colleague with a powerful telescope complains of poor seeing.

The term *seeing* is used to indicate the departure of the telescopic image from its ideal form. A commonly employed seeing scale ranges from 0 (hopelessly blurred) to 10 (perfect in every way). Thus, seeing 5 characterizes average conditions, in which a fair-sized amateur telescope will show considerable detail on Mars or Jupiter, but with enough atmospheric disturbance to prevent fully efficient use of a good optical system. However, all experienced planetary observers will bear poor-to-average seeing for hours on end in order to enjoy the brief moments when the image steadies down, permitting full exploitation of the telescope.

Ideally, a lens or mirror brings rays from a point on a distant object to a point in the focal plane of the telescope. Air, being a refracting medium, affects the path of the light rays according to its density and is as much a part of the optical system as the telescope itself. Anything that alters the homogeneity of the long column of air through which the telescope looks will distort the path of the light rays.

For the purposes of the visual or photographic observer, three distinct types of seeing (I, II, and III) may be distinguished, but they can also occur in combination. This threefold classification is helpful in analyzing what can be done about seeing, for it is one of the knottier problems facing the practical observer.

In poor seeing of Type I, the image changes rapidly, and small objects such as stars or Jupiter's satellites occasionally appear double or triple. On the moon or planets, the disk may show two or more distinct boundaries rapidly moving or vibrating, and surface detail seems jumpy. In addition, an out-of-focus image of a bright star shows boiling or moving streakiness.

The cause of these phenomena is air currents within or very close to the telescope, with a wavelength of about one tenth to one half the diameter of the mirror or objective. These moving inhomogeneities within the optical path prevent rays from all parts of the mirror or objective from reaching the focus simultaneously. The effect is much as if the telescope consisted of several small mirrors in relative motion. When this trouble is present, photographic work of any delicacy is out of the question, no matter how short the exposure.

Type II seeing is characterized by images that are steady but blurred or fuzzy. There is poor contrast on extended surfaces, and star images appear swollen, often to several times their theoretical size.

Usually, Type II poor seeing results from air currents outside the telescope tube, but low-lying and often in fairly rapid motion. The wavelengths of these disturbances are small, perhaps less than half the diameter of the mirror or lens. These conditions may arise during the night cooling of air, when stable temperature layers dissipate in the presence of natural or artificial objects having different cooling rates (houses, rocks, pavement). A change of wind direction with increasing altitude may produce the same effect if the vertical temperature gradient is steep. The passage of weather fronts often produces violent Type II disturbances. Under such conditions lunar or planetary photography would be hopeless for any observer.

Finally, in seeing of Type III the images are sharp but somewhat unsteady. A star image is crisp and clear, yet in motion; the edge of the moon ripples to some degree, although it is sharply defined. These are the effects of high-level atmospheric inhomogeneities, whose wavelengths are large compared with the aperture of the telescope, perhaps three or four times as large, or more. When poor seeing of this type is present, there can be appreciable positional errors on photographs, since image points separated by only a few seconds of arc may be differently refracted.

Something can be done to combat the first two varieties of inferior seeing, but not the third. Seeing of Type I generally results from faulty telescope design (for example, an uninsulated metal tube), heat from the observer's body, or air currents in or just above the tube. With a reflector, on very still nights, it is well to open the vents at the bottom of the tube for a while to get an approximation to thermal equilibrium; then close them to avoid slow convection currents in the interior of the tube. On windy nights leave the vents open, as the gusts will prevent the formation of appreciable temperature gradients in the interior of the tube.

In any event, telescope tubes are best made of material with low heat conductivity and low heat capacity, to keep rapid local variations of outside air temperature from being transmitted to the tube interior and to minimize the amount of heat so transferred. It has often been found that the performance of a telescope with a metal tube is improved by applying an interior layer of insulation, a favorite material being sheet cork.

An open or latticework tube may be helpful if it is rotatable, so that if the wind is behind the observer on a cool night, the tube can be turned to prevent his body heat from causing poor seeing of Type I. However, the asymmetry of such a tube invites temperature gradients, as its material loses heat by radiation, becoming cooler than the surrounding air.

Poor seeing of Type II can sometimes be cured by moving the telescope to a better location. Removal of the instrument from a downslope site will avoid the typical night drainage of turbulent cold air. Getting away from a heated building may help. Other remedies will occur to the reader who considers his own observing situation.

While nothing can be done about inferior Type III seeing, it often does not hinder delicate visual work. Photography is possible when these high-level disturbances are not too pronounced, if the exposure time is kept short compared to the period of rippling.

In summation, it is plain that seeing of Type I is to a large extent remediable, that II may sometimes be ameliorated, and that III is frequently not serious enough to impair visual and photographic observation. Of course, it will often happen that the seeing, despite all efforts, is just not good, in which event it is as well to go to bed and get a good night's sleep!

After the moon, planets are generally the most rewarding objects for visual study. The view is disappointing at first, because the image is small and suffers by comparison with published photographs (which are usually selected from among the best obtained with large telescopes). The blur due to generally poor seeing will be noticeable, but the visual observer can "catch" detail during moments of good seeing, whereas a photograph is blurred unless the seeing is good for the full exposure. Mars is a typical and interesting planet; note the advantages to be gained by the use of colored filters, described in the following article. Other planets showing a good deal of detail are Jupiter and Saturn.   —T L P

■■

Observations of Mars

THOMAS R. CAVE, JR.

(*Sky and Telescope*, November 1958)

. . . This year Mars at its nearest will show a disk 19.2 seconds of arc in diameter, compared with 24.8 in 1956. But its declination will be $+19\frac{1}{2}°$, as against $-10°$ then, placing Mars about 30° higher when on the meridian for Northern Hemisphere observers. This increased altitude will hardly compensate, however, for the disk diameter being 22 per cent less.

Good telescopes of small aperture will show the larger orange deserts and dark "seas" of Mars, but at least a 6-inch telescope is needed for observation of finer details. Most students of Mars agree that a first-rate 10-inch telescope reveals considerably more detail visually than do the best photographs.

From my more than twenty-three years of observing experience, I have found little difference between good reflectors and good refractors of equal aperture. On nights of better than average seeing, reflectors usually provide better image contrast, with sharpness equal to that in refractors. With only fair seeing, refractors have somewhat steadier and prettier images, but with subdued contrast.

To see much of the Martian surface markings, the amateur needs patience and persistence. Observations should be attempted on every night when seeing conditions are favorable. I find it a good plan to observe the planet for at least fifteen minutes before beginning any sketching. This preliminary watch enables the eye to become fully adjusted to the glare of Mars and makes delicate features easier to detect.

Color filters are helpful; I use a Harrison-Duraline No. 2 RD4 orange filter or a Wratten 23A red filter to increase the visual contrast between the desert and mare regions, and also to lessen irradiation. An Eastman Kodak deep blue filter makes the Martian disk faint but enhances the polar caps and the mists surrounding them and helps show white areas near the limb and terminator. It is useful in detecting visually any occurrence of the famous "blue clearing."

Drawings of Mars should be of generous size, with the planet's disk at least two inches in diameter. Beginners often use too small a scale. The drawing should always contain only what is actually seen through the eyepiece, and not what some map may show.

My observations of Mars in 1958 began during the mornings of late April, but the red planet was far from the earth, and the brilliant south polar cap was the only conspicuous marking. The telescope used for all my work so far this year is an 8-inch f/7 Newtonian reflector with electric drive, setting circles, and rotating tube.

No drawings were attempted until June 21, when the angular diameter of Mars was 8 seconds. The dark band about the south cap was conspicuous, and the maria appeared of normal contrast.

By the beginning of August the diameter was 10 seconds, about the minimum for serious study. On several occasions, the extensive areas Hellas and Elysium apeared very white when seen near the limb. Mare Cimmerium and Mare Tyrrhenum were very dark along their northern borders (see Fig. 48). The tip and western side of Syrtis Major were among the darkest portions of the planet. In the northern deserts, Trivium Charontis and Cerberus were very obvious, and I even saw them on two nights in early September with a 3¼-inch Brashear refractor at 250X (magnification 250).

From August 10 to about 22, the south cap looked hazy, as if partially mist-covered, but was brilliant though small during the remainder of the month. While the dark band was not seen with certainty after August 10, on three occasions since September 13 a very narrow dark band was suspected surrounding the tiny remnant of the south polar cap. . . .

All the "canals" I saw during the early part of the 1958 apparition of Mars seemed rather wide and diffuse, except for those in the desert north of Sinus Sabaeus. These were narrow and dark, being described on August 27 (see Fig. 48) as very well defined. . . .

Near dawn on September 16, Walter H. Haas reported a large cloud over Ausonia, part of Mare Tyrrhenum, and part of Syrtis Major. Unfortunately, I could not observe this region the next morning. On September 20, I saw a small, very bright projection on the terminator —probably a cloud high in the Martian atmosphere. It was first visible at 7:07 UT, and was very plain at 7:52, when fog over Long Beach, California, halted observation. On the next night, when the same region of Mars was again on the terminator, a close search revealed no trace of this projection.

The blue clearing is the occasional abnormal transparency of the Martian atmosphere at short wavelengths. When it occurs, blue-light views show the surface markings instead of just a featureless disk. Until 1954, the blue clearing was thought to occur only at the time of opposition, but cooperative observations obtained evidence of it on several dates considerably earlier. In 1956, G. de Vaucouleurs, observing

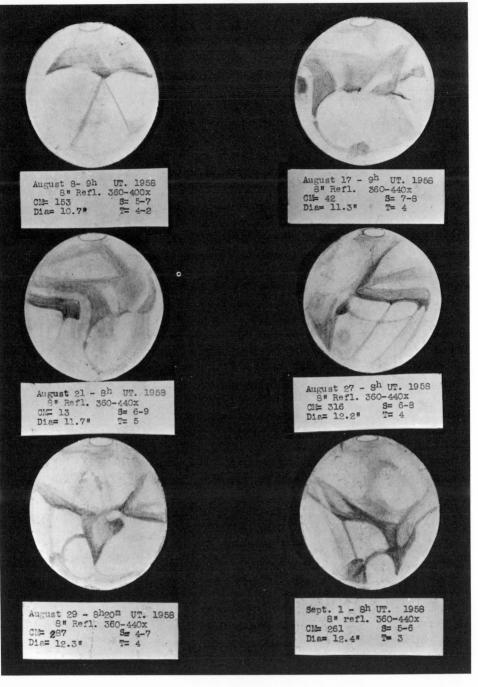

August 8- 9h UT. 1958
8" Refl. 360-400x
CM= 153   S= 5-7
Dia= 10.7"   T= 4-2

August 17 - 9h UT. 1958
8" Refl. 360-440x
CM= 42   S= 7-8
Dia= 11.3"   T= 4

August 21 - 8h UT. 1958
8" Refl. 360-440x
CM= 13   S= 6-9
Dia= 11.7"   T= 5

August 27 - 8h UT. 1958
8" Refl. 360-440x
CM= 316   S= 6-8
Dia= 12.2"   T= 4

August 29 - 8h20m UT. 1958
8" Refl. 360-440x
CM= 287   S= 4-7
Dia= 12.3"   T= 4

Sept. 1 - 8h UT. 1958
8" refl. 360-440x
CM= 261   S= 5-6
Dia= 12.4"   T= 3

FIG. 48. Thomas R. Cave, Jr., made these drawings with an 8-inch Newtonian reflector using powers from 360 to 440. Under each drawing is given: CM, Martian central-meridian longitude; Dia, image diameter in seconds of arc; S, seeing, on a scale of 0 to 10.

in Australia, found that the blue clearing is not always planet-wide, as had been believed, but may occur over only a part of one hemisphere.

Since early August, every night that I observed Mars I inspected the planet through a Kodak deep blue filter to look for the blue clearing. Ordinarily this showed only the south cap and some vague white areas near the north limb. On August 29, I suspected a clearing, for Syrtis Major was faintly visible through the filter. On September 19 and 20, Solis Lacus and its surroundings were definitely visible in deep blue light and, in the darker mare, detail was quite easily seen.

In early September, R. S. Richardson took photographs with the 60-inch Mount Wilson reflector showing definite evidence of a blue clearing, and visual observations of the phenomenon were made by Alika K. Herring of South Gate, California.

The very favorable 1956 opposition of Mars was disappointing to many observers because of the apparent faintness of the dark markings. When Mars was closest to the earth, in September that year, much surface detail was obscured by a great yellow cloud, the most extensive and long-lasting in the history of Martian observations. My studies this year consistently show that better views of the dark maria can be expected through the coming autumn and winter months, for in general they appear of normal contrast and intensity.

Saturn and Its Rings

PERCY W. WITHERELL

(*Sky and Telescope*, January 1942)

Saturn, the wonder planet (Fig. 49), is now favorably situated for observation in the southeast evening sky in Taurus, near the Pleiades. Known to the ancients as one of the wandering stars, it remained for Galileo with his planoconvex and planoconcave telescope to discover in 1610 that Saturn was not of a simple form, as commonly supposed. But his crude instrument showed only a peculiar triple form, and it was not until 1655 that Huygens demonstrated the form of the ring. Then, in 1675, Cassini discovered that the ring was double. In 1850, Bond of Harvard revealed the presence of a third, inner dusky gauze, ring, so thin that the body of the planet and its satellites were sometimes visible through it. Later, Encke showed that fine dark divisions appeared under

Fig. 49. Saturn, photographed by E. E. Barnard with the 60-inch reflector at Mount Wilson.

Fig. 50. The rings of Saturn appear turned at different angles to observers on the earth although they maintain their inclination of 27° to the ecliptic. At intervals of 15 years, Saturn's rings appear alternately opened out and edgewise, causing the apparent brightness of the planet to vary considerably. (Drawing by Christiaan Huygens, *Systema Saturnium*, 1659.)

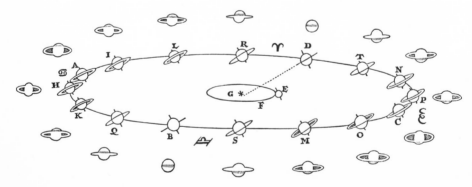

favorable seeing conditions in the outer ring, and Lowell observed a division 1000 miles wide between the middle bright and the crepe rings.

One of the remarkable features of these rings is their extreme thinness, as very clearly shown at 15-year intervals when their relative position to the earth places them edge-on to us. At these times they are invisible for a few days, even in large telescopes, and appear as only a fine line before and after the critical days.

Although the outer ring is 171,000 miles in diameter, it is less than 10 miles in thickness. . . .

Saturn appears yellowish-white in the equatorial regions and greenish-blue at the poles, with the edges slightly darker than the center. Its surface markings are so ill-defined that its period of rotation is not certain, but Barnard gives 10 hours and 38 minutes as the period at latitude 36° north in 1903.

The equatorial diameter is 74,100 miles and the polar diameter 66,300 miles. . . .

At a mean distance of 887 million miles from the sun, with a variation of 100 million miles on account of the eccentricity of its orbit, Saturn takes 29.5 years to go around the sun, so that its apparent position in the sky changes very little each year.

Its brightness varies as much as 70 per cent, due to the relative position of its rings toward the earth and the variation in its distance from us (745 million to 1027 million miles).

Satellites to the number of nine were discovered between 1655, when Titan was found by Huygens, and 1898, when Pickering noticed tiny Phoebe with its retrograde revolution. . . .

A globe 22½ inches in diameter, surrounded by a ring of the thickness of paper, placed at a distance of 2 inches from the surface, 12½ inches wide, with an outside diameter of 51½ inches, would be a model of the system. The nearest satellite would be in an orbit 35 inches from the center of the globe and the outer satellite 200 feet from the center. The sun might be represented by a globe 23 feet in diameter at a distance of 4 miles.

Saturn offers one of the best views with a small telescope and can be seen far more clearly than was possible in Galileo's day. Saturn's moons are not easy to identify, and it is the moons of Jupiter—also seen by Galileo—that best illustrate how planets move around the sun. The four brightest can easily be followed for several nights in a small telescope, and can be studied in detail with a larger instrument. — T L P

■■

Jupiter's Satellites

(*Sky and Telescope*, July 1961)

With a dozen known satellites, Jupiter is the center of a minature solar system. No other planet has so numerous a retinue of secondaries (if we omit the tiny artificial bodies circling the earth and the host of moonlets that make up the Saturnian ring system). The runners-up are Saturn with its nine moons and Uranus with five.

Jupiter's satellites are of two sharply contrasting kinds. Four of them are giant moons, comparable in size to the earth's satellite or to the planet Mercury, and are bright enough to be seen readily in binoculars. They were among the first objects discovered with the newly invented telescope in the winter of 1609–10, independently by Galileo in Italy and by Simon Marius in Germany. . . . Together, these bodies are often referred to as the Galilean satellites; individually, they are designated I, II, III, and IV, in the order of increasing distance from the planet. The corresponding names, Io, Europa, Ganymede, and Callisto, were introduced by Marius.

The remaining eight satellites are small and very faint. With the 36-inch Lick refractor in 1892, E. E. Barnard discovered V, a little point of light even closer to Jupiter than I, orbiting in only 11 hours 57 minutes. Because of the overwhelming glare of the planet, this difficult object is observable only in very large telescopes. Satellites VI to XII are faint moons moving far outside the others and were discovered photographically between 1904 and 1951. Their magnitudes range from 14 to 18. Remarkably, four of them (VIII, IX, XI, and XII) are moving around Jupiter in the opposite direction from all the others. The outer satellites are so remote from the planet that their motions are subject to large disturbances from the sun's attraction, posing difficult problems for specialists in celestial mechanics.

The four Galilean satellites, on the other hand, present a variety of interesting phenomena for amateur observers. Because of their relative proximity to Jupiter, I, II, and III on every revolution pass in front of the planet's disk, behind it, and through the Jovian shadow cone. In addition, the shadows of the satellites themselves move across the disk. But IV, in its larger orbit, shows these phenomena only during about 5 years out of every 12, at other times passing north or south of the disk and shadow cone. . . .

Predictions of these events are published yearly in the *American*

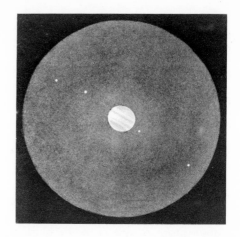

FIG. 51. Jupiter and its four Galilean satellites as they appear in a small telescope. (From *Astronomie* by L. Rudaux and G. de Vaucouleurs, Paris, Libraire Larousse, 1948.)

Ephemeris. The predicted times are only rough approximations, and sometimes differ by several minutes from observation. Certain rare events, such as the eclipse of one satellite by another, are not listed there, but are forecast in the *Handbook* of the British Astronomical Association. . . .

The angular diameters of the Galilean satellites are, according to E. E. Barnard's micrometer measurements with the Yerkes 40-inch telescope: I, 1.05 seconds of arc; II, 0.85; III, 1.51; and IV, 1.43. The disk of the largest moon, Ganymede, can be made out with a 4-inch telescope under very favorable conditions. R. T. A. Innes, who made regular observations of these satellites from 1908 to 1925 with a 9-inch refractor in South Africa, reported that 700X would always show him the disks, but that this was not the case with 400X. On many occasions, a satellite entering eclipse appeared dichotomized, that is, like a tiny quarter moon.

Surface features on the satellite disks can be usefully observed only with very large apertures. Barnard with the 36-inch Lick refractor at 1000X found that I has a bright equatorial belt and dark polar caps, while III and IV have bright polar caps and conspicuous though vaguely shaped dusky markings. The easiest of these features is III's bright cap, which has been definitely seen with a 12-inch telescope. . . .

The outer satellites of Jupiter and Saturn, and all the fainter objects of the solar system, appear starlike in most telescopes. Their positions among the stars can be charted, and this allows them to be identified by a visual observer, but the most convenient mode of observation is photographic. Many observations of the asteroids (minor planets that move around the sun between Mars and Jupiter) are needed in order to keep track of these numerous objects. — T L P

■■■

The Observation of the
Minor Planets

H. E. WOOD

(*Sky and Telescope*, July 1944)

During the last thirty-three years a considerable amount of work on the observation of minor planets has been carried out at the Union Observatory in Johannesburg. This was the result of the gift to the observatory in 1909 of the Franklin-Adams star camera with its powerful photographic triplet lens of 10-inch diameter and 44.6-inch focal length, and aperture of f/4.5.

A condition of the gift was that a number of the southern plates for the Franklin-Adams star chart of the sky should be repeated, as some of the plates of this series taken earlier at the Cape were not up to the high standard required. The completion of these plates was naturally the first work undertaken with the telescope when it was erected at Johannesburg. These plates were 15 by 15 inches in size, cut from specially selected glass, and were given an exposure of two hours so that images of stars to about the 16th magnitude could be obtained. Before any negative was passed, it was carefully examined to see that the guiding had been good, that the star images were as round as possible, and that the limiting star magnitude had been reached. When the region photographed was near the zodiacal belt occasional short trailed images were noticed on the plates. These were the images of minor planets which, of course, had moved a little during the two hours of the exposure.

It was then recognized that the Franklin-Adams star camera was an ideal instrument for the discovery and observation of minor planets. The lens had a very large field, so that a considerable area of the sky could be photographed at a time; it also had a very powerful light grasp, so that the trails of quite faint asteroids were visible. So, when the Franklin-Adams chart plates were finished, plates were exposed along the zodiacal belt for the observation of minor planets. After exposure in the telescope, a reseau was printed on the plate, so that the negative was divided up into small squares. Each square was then scrutinized with a magnifying lens to detect among the many round images of stars the short trail of a minor planet. When such trails were found, the position of the planet was roughly measured in right ascension and declination and then reference was made to the ephemerides [predicted positions] of minor planets prepared by the Astronomisches Rechen Institut in Berlin. If the position agreed fairly well with the ephemeris position of a known asteroid, and if the magnitude also agreed, then the identification was accepted, subject to confirmation to be supplied by a later photograph. Frequently, it was found that the trail on the plate could not be so identified with any known minor planet, and then it was marked as a possible new planet. . . .

[The author next discusses the difficulties involved in finding faint trails on photographs showing many fixed stars. He describes the stereocomparator, an instrument used to compare two photographs by viewing first one, then the other, in rapid succession.]

The examination of a pair of plates in the stereocomparator was very much less tiring and much more thorough than the examination of a single plate would be, because with the instrument everything that was common to the two plates was unnoticed by the eye, and only the points of difference drew attention to themselves. Thus the stereocomparator was equally efficient in picking out minor planets and variable stars. If the brightness of any star had varied between the taking of the two plates being compared, then the eye would be caught by the swelling and shrinking of its image as seen in the stereocomparator.

When the pairs of plates had been examined and the minor planets found on them had been marked, the work had only just begun. The right ascension and declination of each planetary image had to be measured as accurately as possible. With the help of the *Astrographic Catalogue* [a list of accurate star positions] the star images nearest to the planetary images were identified so that they could be used as reference points for measurement. . . . By selecting a triangle of three reference stars around the image of a minor planet, the position of the planet could be obtained with a sufficiency of accuracy and a minimum of labor. . . .

Very few other observatories in the Southern Hemisphere have participated in this work, and from 1911 to the present time most of the observations of minor planets south of the equator have been obtained at the Union Observatory. Many new planets have been discovered there, and the list of names of the minor planets will be noticed to contain many associated with South Africa. The name of the donor of the telescope used in this work is commemorated in the asteroid 924 Franklina.

6

Observing
the
Stars

Although most stars are as large or larger than the sun, their great distances make them appear only as points of light in even the largest telescope. "Looking at a star" therefore has little to offer in comparison with observations of the rich detail on the moon or the hazy forms of planets. Clusters of stars, particularly the globular clusters, are interesting objects to study visually, and close doubles offer striking views, sometimes with marked color contrast. A look at single stars provides a useful check on the focus of the telescope and the seeing (p. 129), but little else of immediate interest.

However, there are star-brightness measurements of scientific importance that can be made visually with small telescopes. Many stars are variable; some because they pulsate in size and temperature, others because of eclipses in a close pair. In order to learn more about such variable stars, astronomers need a plot of brightness versus time—a "light curve."

Brightness is measured in terms of "magnitude," a number that increases by 5 each time brightness decreases by 99 per cent. The brightest stars in the sky are of "first magnitude," the faintest visible to the naked eye are about 100 times fainter, or sixth magnitude (6 mag.). A 3-inch telescope shows stars 100 times fainter yet (11 mag.) and a 30-inch reaches 16 mag. or more (10,000 times fainter than visible to the unaided eye).

Other measurements can be made also: of the colors of stars, of the motions of double stars (one around the other) and of spectra (see Chapter 7). The present chapter starts with simple naked-eye observations that help an astronomer find his way among the thousands of stars visible in the sky and proceeds to the more detailed telescopic observations. —T L P

■■■

The Constellations

MARIAN LOCKWOOD

(The Sky, July 1937)

The origins of the sky pictures which we know today as constellations are lost somewhere back in the obscuring mists of antiquity. No man knows just when or where the visible night sky began to be subdivided into such fantastic groups as the Big Bear and the Little Bear, Cassiopeia and Andromeda and Cetus, Coma Berenices and the Northern Crown. We do know, however, that there must have been a definite plan for the dividing-up of the stars into groups, but where that original plan came from is still a mystery. Authorities are more or less united in believing that the early cradle of astronomy was in the valley of the Euphrates. We know that in ancient Persia men believed in the four "Royal Stars" —Regulus, Aldebaran, Antares, and Fomalhaut—which were supposed to rule over four equal sections of the sky, while in ancient Peru it was said that all living creatures were represented among the stars of the sky.

Whatever the origin of the constellation figures, they have proved to be a convenient way of dividing the sky into small sections, and today each star has its place in some constellation and is easily indicated by name or number as a member of that particular group. In the days of Ptolemy, the famous Alexandrian astronomer who lived about A.D. 150, there were only forty-eight recognized constellations. A great part of the sky at that time was uncharted, partly because not all the sky could be seen from those latitudes, and partly because those stars which did not fit conveniently into the constellations already decided upon were simply ignored and "left out in the cold," so to speak. In modern times, the entire sky is completely charted or mapped, and there is no small or faint star, no matter how insignificant in appearance, which does not have its place in some one constellation. In all, today, there are eighty-eight of these groups.

Any given star rises four minutes earlier on each succeeding night, and therefore the constellations pass in a constant procession around the sky during the changing seasons. In the autumn, for instance, we see the great figure of the colossus Orion appearing during the evening over the eastern horizon. By the spring months, Orion is near the western horizon in the early hours of the evening and soon to disappear, not to return until the following fall.

And so, during the summer season this year, we watch for old star friends to reappear—friends we have not seen since last summer. Just as Orion is almost "a sign and a symbol" for the winter sky, so does the great curving line of Scorpius symbolize the summer season.

Anyone wishing to learn how the sky is divided up and just which stars are included in the different constellations can progress most rapidly by studying a good star chart. . . .

Astronomers ordinarily do not consider of much significance the myths and legends about the star groups which have come down to us from antiquity. They do, however, form an interesting cultural background for the more detailed and scientific knowledge of the individual stars, and it is fair to say that no person could call himself well versed in star lore who had not at least a slight conception of the mythological background of the heavens.

In considering the constellations, it is interesting to discover that they range themselves in groups, not only the stars, but the constellations themselves. In the northern sky we find, for instance, Ursa Major, the Great Bear, Ursa Minor, the Little Bear, and Boötes, the Bear Driver. These three constellations are linked together in one of those age-old "sagas" which originated we know not where nor when. The great figure of the Bear Driver seems to be driving the bears constantly in their circuitous route around the pole. . . .

It is interesting in this connection to note that our word *arctic* comes from the Greek word *arktos*, which means bear. The arctic regions, therefore, are those which are near the Bears; the antarctic, those which are opposite the Bears. From this same origin also comes the name of the star Arcturus, literally the Bear Watcher, which is the Alpha, or brightest star, of Boötes.

The constellation Hercules is one of the interesting groups to be observed in the sky during the summer season. It is distinguished easily by the great letter H which marks it, and which we can almost imagine to be the signature itself of the Greek hero. The Hercules saga of constellations, if we can refer to it in this way, is a lengthy one. Hercules, as all the world knows, was a son of Jupiter by a mortal maiden and from his birth was destined to be a hero of surpassing courage and strength. Because of his origin he incurred the enmity of the ever-watchful Juno. Juno, by her machinations, arranged twelve seemingly impossible tasks for Hercules to perform—the twelve labors of Hercules. Two of these labors are immortalized in the sky in the figures of Hydra and Leo the Lion. The Hydra was the great nine-headed monster which ravaged the land of Argos, and which Hercules was commanded to kill. The hero struggled valiantly, but for every head that he succeeded in cutting off, two more heads grew. At last Hercules hit upon the plan of searing the injured portions of the creature's anatomy with a white-hot iron and in this way prevented the growth of any more heads. One of the heads, however, proved to be immortal, and this Hercules disposed of by burying it beneath a great rock. Juno, in her rage at seeing the Hydra being overcome and her plans for Hercules' death foiled, sent the Crab, an enormous creature, to annoy Hercules during the fight. The Crab nipped Hercules on the foot, causing him severe pain. The hero merely crushed the unlucky crustacean beneath his heel, however, and fought on to victory. Juno saw to it that the figures of both the Hydra and the Crab (Cancer) were placed among the stars in the sky. The constellation Serpens appears to be, according to some legends, the very serpent which attacked Hercules when he was a baby—that same serpent which the precocious infant strangled with his bare hands. The Serpent Bearer, Ophiuchus, is holding the forepart of the snake with his left hand and the hindpart with his right hand, so that it can no longer threaten the hero, who is placed nearby in the sky. The constellation Gemini, the Heavenly Twins, also has a certain relation to Hercules, since both Hercules and the Twins, Castor and Pollux, were members of that famous Argonautic expedition which set out to recover the Golden Fleece, the fleece which we see shining brightly in the sky in the constellation of Aries, the Ram.

Then, again, we can link together the constellations Cassiopeia, Cepheus, Andromeda, Cetus, Pegasus, and Perseus. Cassiopeia was said to be a queen of Ethiopia many, many centuries ago. This queen was beautiful and vain. Tactlessly, she boasted that her beauty was greater even than that of the sea nymphs. Naturally this offended the sea maidens, and they insisted that their king, Neptune, should punish Cassiopeia. Neptune, yielding to their entreaties, sent a great sea monster (which we identify as the constellation Cetus, the Whale) to ravage the country of Ethiopia. At last, after an enormous amount of damage had been done, Cassiopeia humbled herself sufficiently to appear before Neptune and plead for peace. Neptune agreed to call off the sea monster

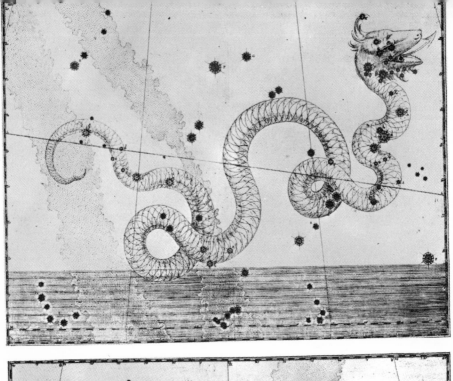

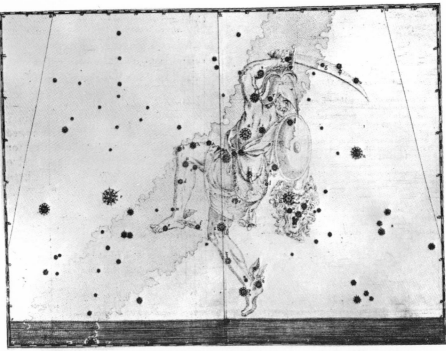

FIG. 52. A. Serpens, the Serpent, from Bayer's *Uranometria* (published in 1603). B. The constellation Perseus as depicted in Bayer's drawing of the mythological hero. In his right hand Perseus holds the head of the Gorgon. Notice the double cluster (h and χ) in the hand holding the sword.

on one condition—that Cassiopeia's beautiful daughter, Andromeda, should be chained to the rocks on the seacoast of Ethiopia and left there as a sacrifice to be devoured by the sea monster. Heartbroken, but forced to obey, Cassiopeia and her husband, King Cepheus, left Andromeda to the mercies of Cetus. However, just as the fair maiden was about to be devoured, the hero Perseus descended from the heavens (some say upon the winged horse, Pegasus) and rescued her from the monster's jaws. Cetus, Perseus turned to stone by showing to him the snaky head of the Gorgon, which he had recently decapitated. And they say that on a certain seacoast in Ethiopia the petrified body of Cetus may still be seen, a shapeless pile of great black rocks.

■■

Testing Your Telescope
by Observations

R. R. LA PELLE

(*Sky and Telescope*, February 1951)

In the course of visiting many amateur astronomers and astronomical groups, the writer has frequently been asked for an opinion as to the worth of an amateur-made instrument. Occasionally, this has been in conjunction with exhibits at conventions and on other occasions.

A thorough test of any optical instrument requires the equivalent of an optical bench and auxiliary test equipment. As an alternate to or in the absence of such equipment, the writer has worked out, by trial and error, a series of tests that serve at least to rate assorted telescopes in a comparative way. If a comparison instrument is available so an independent rating can be assigned to the observing conditions, the test allows a very fair appraisal of the instrument under inspection; in the absence of such a standard telescope, the tests are still of considerable value.

Of course, it is realized that observing conditions vary widely at different places, and that seeing and transparency continually change at one place. This makes an absolute appraisal, from observing tests alone, impossible, which is why the standard comparison instrument mentioned above is necessary. The following conditions should be met:

1. The moon must be absent, or low in the sky, and either younger than the first or older than the last quarter.

2. The seeing must be at least 7 on a scale of 10, with 10 perfect; thus, fair steadiness of the telescopic image is required.

3. The transparency must be 3 to 4 on a scale of 5, with 5 perfect. This means not too much haze or smoke or glare from city lights.

If these conditions cannot be met, the tests may still be made, but some of them will be difficult or impossible.

Color and Spherical Correction.   Observe Jupiter or Saturn at about 100X, examining the image carefully for color effects and fringes. Observe detail on the planet's surface, noting the number of zones and belts visible, as well as spots, swirls, and other markings. In the case of Saturn, look for details in the rings, for Cassini's division, the shadow of the ball on the rings, and the shadows of the rings on the planet.

Many refractors fail in color correction, which will show up in this test. A lack of fine detail also indicates poor correction of the objective or eyepiece. A change in eyepiece will usually indicate where the blame should be placed. In a reflector, of course, any color effects must be in the ocular alone, since mirrors are inherently achromatic. Warning: Any telescope will show color fringes when the planet is low in the sky, as a result of refraction by the atmosphere; hence the test should be performed when the planet is near the meridian.

Field Size and Vignetting.   Using a very low-power ocular, giving about 25X to 35X, with a field of over 1°, examine the clustering of stars in some rich star field. In the summer the field east and west of Gamma Cygni is excellent. In the winter the field near Iota Orionis, or the double cluster in Perseus, may be used. Note particularly the number of stars visible. Move the telescope so the stars near the center of the field move to the edge. Watch for any sign of dimming of the stars as they approach the edge. If such vignetting occurs in a reflector, the secondary mirror may be too small. Watch for distortion of the star images as they reach the edge of the field. The images should be small round circles throughout the field, without any sign of flare or coma or of irregularity of shape.

Astigmatism.   Center the telescope on Epsilon Lyrae, the well-known double double, using a power of about 100X. With an instrument of 4 inches aperture or larger, the two pairs of images should each split cleanly and without difficulty, and at the same focal point. An astigmatic mirror or lens will usually require a slightly different focus for each pair and will not show both split simultaneously. Warning: Such a defect in figure may be caused by errors in either the primary or secondary reflections but may also result from a "pinched" mirror (either primary or secondary), in which the mounting may be distorting a perfectly good mirror into an astigmatic shape. It is also sometimes, but not often, due to poor optical alignment of the mirrors or to a poor eyepiece. Therefore, before condemning the mirror, try another eyepiece and check the cells to make sure the mirrors are perfectly free.

Light-gathering Power. Unless magnitude charts are readily available, make use of the globular clusters. The great globular cluster in Hercules, M13, contains many stars of visual apparent magnitude about 13.4 or 13.5. A 6-inch telescope should readily reveal these stars on a good night at about 100X, showing multitudes of individual stars. The stars in M3, in Canes Venatici, are about half a magnitude fainter, suitable for an 8-inch or a 10-inch instrument. M15, in Pegasus, is of about the same brightness, but more condensed; a 10-inch shows it very well at about 125X.

Resolving Power. This is, of course, the acid test of any telescope. For a 6-inch, during the summer months, Zeta Herculis is a good test. This is a double of 1 second of arc separation, the stars being of magnitudes 3.0 and 6.5. The difference in brightness makes this a very severe test, but not beyond a satisfactory instrument on a good night, at about 200X to 250X. In winter, Eta Orionis, magnitudes 4.0 and 5.0 at 1 second separation, is an equally good test, in part because of its more difficult southern position in the sky.

The ultimate test for a 6-inch, requiring an excellent instrument and exceptionally good seeing, is probably Gamma Coronae Borealis, 4.0 and 7.0 magnitude at 0".7 separation. It should be seen double readily with a 10-inch. The ultimate for a 10-inch or 12-inch might be the blue star of the wide yellow-blue pair known as Gamma Andromedae. This is itself a close double. About 250X to 300X should resolve this blue star, provided both the seeing and the instrument are extremely good.

Dawes's rule that the resolving power in seconds of arc equals 4.56 divided by the diameter (in inches) of the primary mirror or lens may be taken as a working approximation, based on yellow stars of equal brightness. The resolving power of most instruments is better for blue stars than for yellow ones, and it is worse for red stars. In the case of Gamma Andromedae, note that the yellow star seems the larger of the two, even though it is single and the blue one is double.

While these tests are not definitive and do not separate, by themselves, imperfections in the objective from imperfections in the eyepieces used, they have proven to the writer more practical than the method using inside- and outside-focus images usually given in textbooks. Try the above tests on several good nights, and if you possess a really good instrument, you will have the great satisfaction of having proved its worth by direct observations.

■■

Limiting Visual
Magnitudes for Small
Telescopes

FRANK J. KELLY

(*Sky and Telescope*, August 1953)

The standard formula for the determination of the limiting magnitude that may be seen with a telescope of diameter D (clear aperture of mirror or lens) is given in Dimitroff and Baker's *Telescopes and Accessories* as:

$$m = 8.8 + 5 \log D.$$

For instance, the computation for a 4-inch objective indicates that such a glass cannot see beyond magnitude 11.8.

The writer has been an observer of variable stars for several years, however, and it has been his experience that stars of magnitude 11.8 are very easy to see with a 4-inch instrument. This cannot be caused by his acute vision or excellent local seeing conditions because he is gifted with neither of these.

In fact, on reasonably transparent nights, stars of magnitude 12.9 have been seen, and verified by comparison with the estimates of fellow observers in the American Association of Variable Star Observers. Therefore, to fit such an observation, the formula ought to read approximately:

$$m = 9.9 + 5 \log D.$$

With this formula, for a 2-inch aperture the limiting magnitude is 11.4. This result encouraged me to purchase and assemble a 2-inch refractor of 23.5 inches focal length, in the hope that if such a magnitude could be reached, an instrument of this convenient size could be transported to observing spots without the trouble that attends moving the larger refractor. This proved to be the case, for an 11.2 comparison star to the variable RZ Scorpii was seen without much effort, and in the field of RU Librae one of magnitude 11.4 was seen.

Therefore, I am of the opinion that a good 2-inch refractor, especially if the lenses are fluoride coated, is perfectly suited to the instrumental requirements of variable star work, refuting the common belief that nothing smaller than a 3-inch glass can make a serious contribution to this branch of astronomy.

···

Notes on "Limiting Visual Magnitudes for Small Telescopes"

JAMES G. BAKER

(*Sky and Telescope*, August 1953)

The aperture of the fully dark-adapted eye is, nearly enough, 0.3 inch, and the limiting magnitude to which it can see is commonly accepted to be 6.2. On a strict area basis, a 1-inch telescope should see 2.6 magnitudes fainter, for it has more than 11 times the area of the dark-adapted eye. Adding 6.2 and 2.6 gives the constant 8.8 in the original formula. When the equation is applied to any instrument, three assumptions are being made:

1. That 6.2 is the limiting magnitude for the dark-adapted eye.

2. That in going to an ideal telescope of 1-inch aperture, there is an increment which is calculable on a strict area-to-area basis.

3. That in going to larger apertures all telescopes are 100 per cent efficient.

The first assumption seems to be reasonable, although there is no doubt that there will be minor variations between individuals. I have experimented with the stars around the north pole of the sky to determine how faint I could see on the best nights. When my maps were reduced by another astronomer, it was found that I had seen only to magnitude 5.9; in the west I would expect to see probably to magnitude 6.1 or 6.2, but certainly not to the 7.3 magnitude that would be called for in Mr. Kelly's revised formula.

Thus, the eye does not appear to behave in the ideal manner of a simple optical system, and in the case of the second assumption the characteristics of the eye have to be taken into account. There are two phenomena that reduce the efficiency of the eye for star images when the pupil is at maximum size. One is the spherical aberration of the eye, which, as in any optical system, increases with the pupil size and spreads the image on the retina, probably causing a decrease in visual acuity. The second is the Stiles-Crawford effect,[1] whereby light passing

[1] Stiles, W. S., and Crawford, B. H., *Proceedings* of the Royal Society, 1933, B112, 428, 1934, B110, 55.

through the peripheral regions of the pupil is not as effective in activating the cones of the retina as is light which passes through the center of the pupil. . . .

When we use a telescope, there is usually sufficient magnification to make the exit pupil quite small. In the case of Kelly's 2-inch telescope, a 1-inch eyepiece would give 23.5 power and an exit pupil $\frac{20}{235}$, or 0.085 inch in diameter. The Stiles-Crawford effect would be absent, and the spherical aberration negligible. This would lead to the situation Kelly describes.

On the other side of the picture, large telescopes are not as efficient as small ones. The lack of adequate color correction in large refractors and the coma in reflectors both tend to diminish the amount of light reaching the eye. Thus, the increase in limiting magnitude with increase in aperture is probably not quite as rapid as the term $5 \log D$ would indicate. For relatively large telescopes, the two discrepancies would tend to compensate, and the standard expression $8.8 + 5 \log D$ would give a more nearly correct value than for smaller instruments. Atmospheric seeing, which is a function of focal length rather than aperture, also tends to reduce the efficiency of large telescopes. . . . If Kelly were to use a very low-power eyepiece on his 2-inch refractor, he could bring the deficiency of the eye into play. . . .

[After reading Baker's Note, Kelly reported further: "A 2-inch telescope with a focal length of 8 inches fitted with an eyepiece of $1\frac{1}{2}$ inches e.f.l., has an exit pupil 0.375 inches in diameter and assures complete use of the pupil of an average observer's eye when opened to its largest size. When the field of R Ophiuchi was explored with such an arrangement, the stars were apparently much more brilliant than usual and had a clearer background, and it seemed obvious that the faintest stars in the field could be seen. Nevertheless, a star of magnitude 9.8, previously seen quite comfortably with a $\frac{1}{16}$-inch exit beam, could now only be detected with the greatest difficulty. . . .

The results of these observations show that the amateur cannot be like the camera enthusiast, who always uses a smaller opening to gain sharpness but is considered something less than expert if he uses a smaller diaphragm opening to take pictures under twilight conditions. The camera can make full use of its larger apertures because of skillful grinding of curves to accommodate them, but the eye is like a mirror with a poor edge. The brilliance of the field with a large exit pupil is apparently a diversion rather than a contribution to the problem of seeing faint stars."]

....

Variable Stars

PERCY W. WITHERELL

(*Sky and Telescope*, March, April, May 1943)

Although Tycho saw a nova in 1572, the first observation of a typical variable star was of Omicron (*o*) Ceti, when, in 1596, Fabricius listed a star that did not appear on previous charts. Bayer listed it again in 1603. It was not until 1638, however, that it was recorded that sometimes the star was visible and at other times invisible. Holwarda made this sensational discovery when he noticed that Mira varied through 5 magnitudes, or 100 times in brightness. The 11-month period was established in 1660.

The next discovery was that Beta (*β*) Persei, known to the Arabs as Algol, the Demon Star, faded for several hours on every third night. A century passed before the mystery of Algol's light fluctuations was cleared up by the theory that this was a binary system of two stars rotating about a common center of gravity, which caused a periodic stellar eclipse.

Two more variables like Mira were the next to be found. Chi (*χ*) Cygni with a period of $13\frac{1}{2}$ months, was discovered by Kirch in 1686, and R Hydrae, period, 17 months, was found to be variable by Miraldi in 1704. The first varies 10 magnitudes, or 10,000 times in brightness; the period of the latter star has shortened 3 months since its discovery.

Near the end of the eighteenth century, another long-period variable like Mira was found, R Leonis, in 1780, and an eclipsing binary like Algol, Beta (*β*) Lyrae.

FIG. 53. When near its maximum brightness Mira (Omicron Ceti) makes Cetus appear as shown at the left, whereas near minimum the variable is not visible to the naked eye (right).

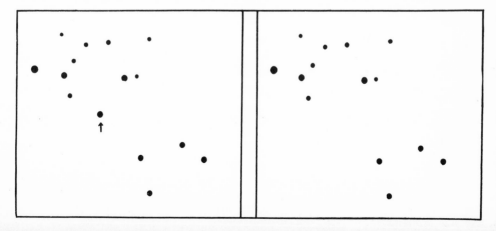

A new class of variables was next observed—stars with a period of less than a week and a change of a little less than 1 magnitude. The first was Delta (δ) Cephei with a period of 5 days, and the second, Eta (η) Aquilae, which completed its cycle in 7 days. This was the beginning of the list of Cepheids, which stars are so useful in the determination of distances, and which have so enlarged our conception of the distances of other galaxies.

Three more classes were begun when, in 1795, Sir William Herschel noted the small, irregular fluctuations of Alpha (α) Herculis, and when R Coronae Borealis, with its peculiar changes, and R Scuti, with semi-regular periodicity, were added to the list.

At the beginning of the nineteenth century, 16 variables were on record: 4 long-period Mira-type stars, 2 Algol eclipsing variables, 2 Cepheids, 1 irregular, 1 peculiar, and 1 semiregular variable, and 5 novae. After U Geminorum was found (of a class later known as the SS Cygni-type stars), the visual discovery of new types practically ceased. It is worthy of note that these early naked-eye variables have been and are today the object of thousands of painstaking observations, and their light curves are given the most careful study.

Groups of enthusiastic amateurs were formed to observe the light variations of these inconstant stars. When memberships became world-wide, someone was on watch all the time to "spot" any changes in brightness. Two of the largest organizations are the British and American Associations of Variable Star Observers. The American Association has turned in to its recorder over 800,000 observations. One of the most notable sets is the more than 50,000 observations of SS Cygni made over a period of 46 years.

With the fainter stars recorded by photographic plates, the convenience of studying many stars on one plate in comparison with a plate of the same region taken at some previous time, and the improved optical methods of detecting light changes, the number of recorded variables has increased by leaps and bounds. By the end of the nineteenth century, the number of known variables was over 1,000. This total has since jumped to about 20,000.

One convenient method which has resulted in the discovery of hundreds of variables is to superimpose a positive and a negative plate of the same region taken by the same camera at different times. The black dots on the negative show up on the white spots of the positive. It is very easy to detect when one of a pair is absent; it is evident that the star was not of the same brightness on the two dates of the exposures.

Another efficient method uses the blink microscope, or stereocomparator [see p. 141], in which each plate is alternately and rapidly flashed into the field of view. Any variation in the intensity of the two images produces a flash as the brighter image replaces the fainter one. . . .

Binary eclipsing variables are conveniently observed by taking multiple images on the same plate. This can be done by moving the telescope or the plateholder slightly in declination between successive exposures. Any variation of brightness is easily seen as a change in the size of the image on the plate.

An indication that the number of variable stars was not expected to be large is the fact that they were designated by the letters from R to Z in the order of their discovery in any constellation. As the number increased, these letters were doubled and combined (RR, RS, RT, etc.), then followed by AA, AB to AZ, then BB to BZ, and so on, omitting the letter J. QZ was thus the 334th variable in any constellation. The next is marked V335, and numbers then continue the sequence. The Variable Star Commission of the International Astronomical Union assigns the names after a proper verification of a star's variability and the determination of its period and type. Until the final designations are adopted, provisional numbers are used, such as 2.1943, which indicates the announcement of the discovery of the second variable in 1943, or a serial number is given in a list of the discoveries made at a large observatory such as Yerkes or Harvard.

The first observers estimated the changes of magnitude of a variable in comparison with a nearby star that was believed not to change. A good observer was able to note a change of 0.1 magnitude under favorable circumstances. A standard sequence of circumpolar stars was established by photometry at Harvard Observatory, and later, similar comparison stars were listed in regions covering nearly the whole sky. An observer can now usually observe directly the differences between a variable and comparison stars of slightly different magnitudes conveniently located in the same region. As photographic plates easily show stars 1 million times fainter (at the sixteenth magnitude) than a first-magnitude star, and photometric estimates are now made to 0.01 magnitude, the importance of an accurate standard is evident. . . .

The observations of a variable are arranged in a graph with the magnitudes plotted vertically and the corresponding times horizontally. Such a *light curve* of an eclipsing system of stars can be used to determine the relative sizes and shapes of the components and of their orbits in terms of the diameter of one of the stars. As some of these systems are near enough to allow their distances to be measured by parallax, the dimensions of the system can then be calculated.

The range of size is staggering. At the lower limit are the invisible companions whose presence is detected by their effect on the orbit of their larger companions, such, for example, as the third (and possibly a fourth) companion of Algol.

At the upper limit is S Doradus in the Large Magellanic Cloud. According to Sergei Gaposchkin, this system consists of twin stars about 1800 million miles in diameter (the diameter of Saturn's orbit) which revolve about a common center of gravity in about 40 years. The system's actual brightness is about 600,000 times that of the sun, but as it is 95,000 light years from us, it is only recently that the above data have been computed. . . .

It has often been stated that if any other star had planets revolving around it as does the sun in our solar system, we could never verify it. K. Aa. Strand has shown that the orbit of 61 Cygni, long known as a visual binary with a period of 720 years and a separation of its components of 10 billion miles, has small, regular deviations. This suggests the presence of a third body. Consider an object about 16 times the mass of Jupiter and revolving around one of the components in 5 years, in a very eccentric orbit which allowed an approach within 65 million miles of its master. Such an arrangement would account for these perturbations. As this object is only $\frac{1}{60}$ the mass of the sun (the "lightest" known stars are about $\frac{1}{10}$) and at its nearest to its primary is only $\frac{2}{3}$ the distance of the earth from the sun, is it not a fair inference that this is a "planet"? . . .

At the beginning of the present century, man was rather pleased with his knowledge of the extent of his galaxy. When its dimensions were compared with the universe's supposed extent a hundred years previously, there really was ground for such complacency. There did not seem to be much chance of greatly extending the early twentieth-century boundaries, until some brilliant minds noticed the Cepheids, and used the peculiar relation of their magnitudes to their periods to expand our knowledge of the size of the universe to an almost unbelievable extent. . . .

The typical light curve of a Cepheid variable [see Fig. 54A] is quite different from that of an eclipsing variable [Fig. 54B]. From minimum light, the increase in brightness is comparatively rapid, while the fall from maximum is more gradual and somewhat irregular. The minimum is usually of longer duration than the maximum. *Cluster-type* Cepheids are those of extremely short periods—they go through their cycle of phases in less than a day, and in some instances, the light doubles in less than an hour. Zeta Geminorum is representative of a few Cepheids whose rise and fall are of about equal speed.

The visual range of Cepheid luminosities is usually less than 1.5

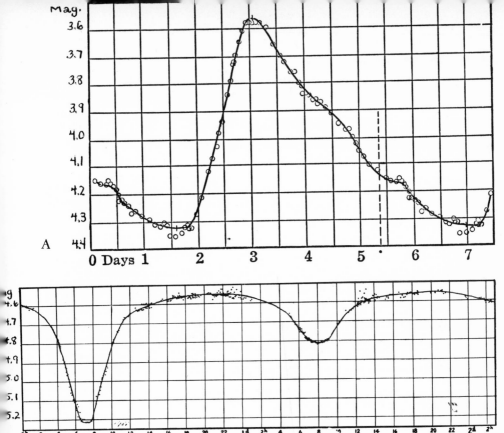

FIG. 54. A. The light curve of Delta Cephei by Joel
Stebbins, then at Washburn Observatory. This curve is
repeated every 5.3 days. B. The light curve of 68u Herculis, which has a period of a little over 2 days, is typical
of close eclipsing double stars. This is a photoelectric
curve with very small scatter of the individual observations.

magnitudes, and the variation of those of very short period is often only
a few tenths of a magnitude. Usually, Cepheids are redder at minimum
than at maximum, changing their spectral class simultaneously with their
changes in brightness. . . .

At present we are more interested in the relation between the period
of a Cepheid and its total luminosity. The real brightnesses of these
useful stars show a progressive increase, first discovered in 1912, when
Henrietta Leavitt noted a relationship between the apparent magnitudes
and the periods of 25 variables in the Small Magellanic Cloud.

These stars all had light curves similar in form to that of the well-
known variable Delta Cephei. . . . The Cloud was assumed to be so
distant that all of its stars could be assumed to be about the same

distance from us; consequently, the *relative apparent* magnitudes could be considered as giving the *relative absolute* magnitudes. . . . The importance of Miss Leavitt's discovery was that she showed Cepheids to have a peculiar characteristic—those of longer period had greater intrinsic luminosities than those of short period.

Then, Harlow Shapley made a series of studies of Cepheids, including those in globular clusters, and in 1918 published the visual *period-luminosity* curve; 11 points on this curve were fixed by our knowledge (by other methods) of the absolute magnitudes of 11 comparatively nearby Cepheids. . . .

As a consequence of this remarkable correlation, a Cepheid, wherever it may be in the universe, telegraphs us the clue to its real brightness by the period of its light fluctuations. If a Cepheid is identified as such in some distant cluster or galaxy, and its period can be determined, this period-luminosity relation gives its absolute magnitude. Knowing its absolute magnitude and observing its apparent magnitude, the star's distance can be easily computed. By this means, the distance of the nebula in Andromeda has been set at about 700,000 light years, and the distances of thousands of other galaxies and clusters have been obtained. The greatest extent of our own galaxy is found to be more than 100,000 light years, and the Magellanic Clouds are nearly that far away. The uniformity of Cepheid behavior everywhere in the universe seems to be amply confirmed.

Cepheids have periods ranging from 1 to about 20 days, and the cluster-type Cepheids display their cycle in less than a day. Neglecting for the moment some variables with periods in the 20- to 40-day range, let us consider the large group known as *long-period variables.*

A long-period variable, of which Mira (Omicron Ceti) is the original example, may be defined as a red star with a period of more than 40 days. . . . The long-period variables and Cepheids may be considered as related groups rather than a continuous series. . . .

Long-period variables are supergiant stars, but of lower temperatures than the Cepheids. Mira is supposed to have a very dense core, but an atmosphere of low density fills a sphere with a diameter about the size of the orbit of Mars.

In addition to the classes of variables already mentioned, there are several other interesting groups of intrinsic variables. . . . Each of the stars varies continuously in brightness, color, temperature, and diameter. This means also a continual change of pressure, and consequently, of density inside the star.

The pulsation of a variable may be briefly explained thus: In an ordinary star there is an internal equilibrium between the inward pressure of the weight of the outer layers and the outward pressure of the gas and radiation. Suppose the star were forced to contract, the internal pressure and temperature would increase, and the star would be forced to expand. If it expanded to a larger diameter than its normal size, the pressure would be lowered and the gravitational pull would cause the star to contract. Once started, such an oscillation would continue indefinitely. The rise of internal temperature due to compression will take a little time to reach the surface, which agrees with the observation of maximum luminosity at the time of approach. The greatest changes in light and velocity occur with the greatest amount of pulsation. The period of pulsation varies with the mean density of the star. The contraction is about 5 to 10 per cent of its radius.

Visual Observing Programs for Amateurs

DAVID W. ROSEBRUGH

(*Sky and Telescope*, April, May, December 1950; January, February, March, April 1951)

It is estimated that thirty thousand amateurs have made their own telescopes, but that only three hundred amateurs are engaged in any systematic program of observation in which their results are carefully recorded and submitted for study to scientific bodies.

Probably the fact that most of us have a deep urge to make things with our hands is primarily responsible for this ratio of one hundred to one. However, it may be caused in part by the misconception that visual instruments are outmoded. It may also be caused by the fact that thousands of pages of instructions on how to make telescopes have been published in the last twenty-five years, but probably not more than a few hundred pages which describe the use of telescopes for visual observers.

Therefore, this is the first in a series of articles devoted to removing the above misconception and to giving instructions in visual observing. The need for visual observations by amateurs will probably increase as professional astronomers find more objects in the sky which require watching. The advantage of visual work is that it can be easily and quickly done without spending the money or time required to take photographs and study them afterwards.

At present, visual observations by amateurs are of value in work concerned with variable stars, novae, occultations of stars and planets by the moon, sunspot counting, manifestations of sudden increases in solar activity, the foreshortening of sunspots, the granulation of the sun's surface, the presence of E-type groups in the sun's center zone, auroral statistics, migratory birds crossing the sun or moon, lunar and planetary details, the varying brightnesses of planets and some asteroids, telescopic meteors, the search for meteors hitting the moon, meteor counting, the zodiacal light, halos, and probably other phenomena of which the writer has no knowledge. I have been assured that many of these lines of visual research must be carried forward for a century or more, if for no other reason than to derive the full advantage of the work which has already been done on them in past decades.

Actually, of course, new problems are continually presenting themselves. Professional astronomers are now not only concerned with the variations but with the "variations in the variations" of variable stars. Judging the future from the past, a century is too short a time in which to secure the data to solve such problems. The American Association of Variable Star Observers now has charts on Luyten's newly discovered "flame star" in Cetus and two others in Aquarius and Leo. These vary so rapidly and unexpectedly that it will take at least a portion of the observing time of each of a score of the AAVSO observers to follow these stars as they must be followed before their visual light curves can be determined. The coronagraph and other new devices have made it possible to study the sun in more detail than before. It is therefore more important than formerly for professional astronomers to know when any sudden activity occurs on the sun. The members of the Solar Division of the AAVSO have taken on this duty as "watchdogs of the sun." (This does not make us sundogs!)

The above examples are typical of the new lines of study which are continually opening before the eyes of amateurs.

Thus it is evident that visual observations with small telescopes are not outmoded. . . .

Variable Star Observing

If the heavens were conveniently studded with variables of naked-eye brilliance, it would be easy to start variable star observing by eye, but in practice we must turn at once to large binoculars or our telescopes. True, there are a few variable stars that can be seen with the naked eye, but mostly they are more suitable for special work by experienced observers than for the untrained eye of the beginner. My eye can just detect with some uncertainty a change of 0.1 magnitude or a 10 per cent change in a star's light. Most of us, therefore, will do well to spend the greater part of our observing time on stars which change a couple of magnitudes or more in brightness. This qualification eliminates most eclipsing variable stars, such as Algol, Cepheids, and slightly irregular stars like Betelgeuse and Gamma Cassiopeiae. It leaves us with the long-period variable stars and the special stars which are the backbone of the observing program of the AAVSO and doubtless of other variable star groups and associations on other continents. A few of these stars reach naked-eye visibility at times, such as 021403 Mira, 184205 R Scuti, and 194632 Chi Cygni, but most of them, even at maximum, require binoculars at least and 3-inch to 12-inch telescopes in general.

The numerous details which now confront us may be considered under six different headings. These are: 1. Charts and observing instructions. 2. Locating a variable star. 3. Estimating its brightness. 4. Organizing our observing program. 5. Reporting observations. 6. What is done with the observations that we report?

1. Charts and observing instructions. Some instructions and practice charts are included in the *Observer's Handbook* of the Royal Astronomical Society of Canada. The British Astronomical Association and the New Zealand Astronomical Society have variable star sections. However, those who wish to undertake a serious program of variable star observing and who live in the Western Hemisphere would do well to get in touch with the recorder of the AAVSO, at Harvard College Observatory, Cambridge, Massachusetts 02138. The AAVSO furnishes at cost to its members an instruction booklet, report forms, and star charts. If you have a friend nearby who is a reporting variable star observer, an evening spent with him may be helpful, but I regret to say that there are scarcely more than a hundred such observers in North America, and in any case doing the work oneself is the only way to learn it.

2. Locating a variable star. If you have a telescope with circles in good adjustment, on a pier, these may be of minor assistance in locating a variable star. But even so, to identify the star definitely you must refer to a chart and pick out the star by its geometrical orientation with regard to its neighbors. Most of us do not have or need circles. The stars themselves act as reference points and lead us to whatever variable star we want to find.

Let us practice on the long-period variable star 210868T Cephei. This star has a suitable magnitude range from about 6 to 10 and a period of 387 days, exhibits the interesting property of a still-stand on the way to maximum, and is located near enough to the north celestial pole so as

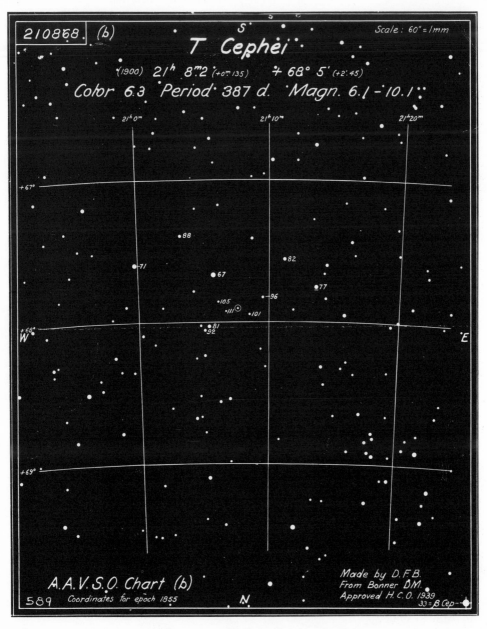

FIG. 55. AAVSO "b" chart for T Cephei.

to be observable at some time of every night in the year in midnorthern latitudes. We need AAVSO "a," "b," and "d" charts of the field of T Cephei; a finder chart for T Cephei or a detailed star atlas showing stars to the eighth, ninth, or even tenth magnitude; an AAVSO *Atlas* or equivalent showing stars to the 6th magnitude and the locations of many variable stars; and a 3-inch telescope or larger, with a finder of 8 or 10 power and a $1\frac{1}{4}$-inch or $1\frac{1}{2}$-inch objective lens. We also need a pocket flashlight small enough to be held in the teeth, and we take it and all our charts and atlases with us to the telescope. [Only the finder chart and AAVSO charts "b" and "d" for T Cephei are reproduced here (Fig. 55 and 56). Chart "a" showing brighter stars would not be needed.]

The first four figures, 2108, in the designation of the star indicate that at epoch 1900.0 [in January 1900] the star was at right ascension 21 hours 08 minutes, and the last two figures, 68, indicate that its declination was 68° north. (If these two figures had been underlined, or the entire number had been in italics or in bold face, it would have indicated that the star was in south declination.) . . .

The AAVSO *Atlas* shows us that T lies southwest of Beta Cephei. We look for Beta Cephei in the sky and point our finder at it. Then we refer either to the AAVSO finder chart or to some star atlas showing stars to the eighth, ninth, or tenth magnitude, and to the AAVSO "b" chart of the field of T Cephei. We find that T Cephei lies near three other stars of tolerable brightness which form a right-angle triangle with sides approximately 24, 32, and 40 minutes of arc in length. As shown by our T Cephei "b" chart, these stars are of magnitude 67, 71, and 81 (actually 6.7, 7.1, and 8.1 magnitude, as the decimal points are omitted on the chart for fear they might be mistaken for stars). Thus, at least the two brighter stars will be visible in our finder and, of course, quite bright in our main telescope, though in the latter we may see at one time only two of the three stars forming the triangle because the asterism may be too large for us to see all of it at once.

If we can locate this triangle, we shall have no difficulty in finding T Cephei in the telescope, as we see that it lies near the shorter side of the triangle. By looking at our finder chart or our detailed atlas we note that there is a curved line of eight stars, of around the eighth magnitude, extending from Beta Cephei to the 67-magnitude star shown on the "b" chart. As we have already pointed the telescope at Beta Cephei, we use the finder or the main telescope with a low-power eyepiece (of 20X or 30X), whichever is the most convenient instrument to look through, and follow our trail of stars to 67, located at the right angle of the triangle. Then we look through the main telescope.

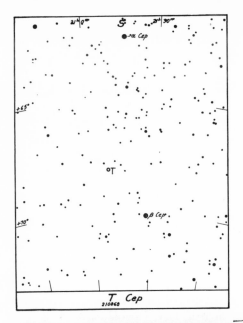

Fig. 56. A. The AAVSO finder chart for T Cephei (reduced from its original size) shows stars to about eighth magnitude. B. The central portion of the AAVSO "d" chart for T Cephei. The coordinates are centered on the star, and the heavy square is half a degree on a side. The variable star is circled, as in Figure 55. Numbers beside star images are their visual magnitudes multiplied by 10.

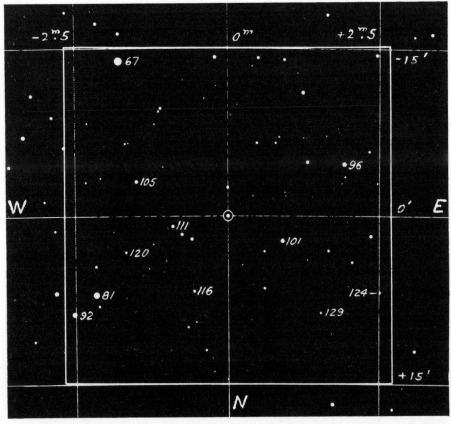

But now we are puzzled. T Cephei is marked so plainly on its chart that we certainly expected to see our three triangle stars and T Cephei as well, or four bright stars in total, but we only see three stars. Can we have made a mistake? No—we check again starting from Beta Cephei and arrive again at our little triangular asterism. Then we suddenly remember that, since T is a variable star, it may not be bright, but may be faint. We put in a slightly higher-power eyepiece, say 40X. Sure enough, after careful scrutiny we see a faint star in the location where T ought to be. Can it be T? We notice a 101-magnitude (10.1) and a 105-magnitude (10.5) star on our T Cephei "d" chart, one lying on either side of where T ought to be. If we can see these in the sky, and if the star that we suspect is T lies in the right relation to them, then our identification is certain. We do see them in the sky, and their relative positions are correct. We check again, comparing the sky against our T Cephei variable star chart, for this is our first variable star, and finally become convinced that we have cornered T.

This same general method can be used to locate any variable star, but it must not be supposed that this process is easy at first. The first variable I ever observed, 052404 S Orionis, took me an hour to locate. Now it would take me but a few seconds, for I am familiar with its field. However, nowadays I can locate and observe a star totally new to me in about six minutes.

Certain difficulties will arise. Until we get used to our own instrument, we will not have any idea how bright stars will appear. For instance, we cannot tell from looking at our charts how bright the 6.7-magnitude star near T Cephei will appear in our finder or our main telescope. Will it look like Sirius does to the naked eye, or more like Polaris? (Probably even fainter than the latter.)

We have no idea of the scale of size of asterisms in the sky. Are those three stars we see forming a triangle on the "b" chart of T Cephei close together when seen in the finder or far apart? (The answer probably is that they will seem about one quarter as big as the bowl of the Big Dipper does to our eye.)

When we move from the finder to the main telescope can we see all the asterism we are looking for, or half of it, or only one star of it, or on the other hand does it occupy only a small area in the field of view? (Probably we can only just take in the entire asterism in our field of view at 40X, and when we move the telescope so as to center it on T Cephei we will only see the two nearest members of the triangle.) . . .

We are troubled too by the orientation of objects in the sky. Should we hold our charts upright as they are printed, that is, with south on the chart toward the zenith, or at some other angle? In the case of refractors, hold the chart in such a position that south points toward Polaris. When you are using binoculars, north should be pointed toward Polaris.

With reflectors the situation is more complicated. If you have a New-tonian, on an equatorial-type mounting, with the polar axis pointing roughly towards Polaris, and if the eyepiece points in toward the polar axis, and the eyepiece's optical axis is parallel to the declination axis, then the orientation is as follows: When looking into the eyepiece, hold the chart up against the telescope tube with its north and south line at right angles to the tube, and the south end of the chart toward the north side of the tube; what you observe in the eyepiece will then appear at the same angle as what you see on the chart. If, however, the reflector is not mounted equatorially, or if the polar axis does not point fairly close to the north celestial pole, or if the tube is rotated so that the eyepiece's optical axis is not parallel to the declination axis, then the field may assume almost any angle in the eyepiece, and the observer will have to figure things out for himself on the stars by trial and error.

When you use a Springfield-mounted telescope the field may assume almost any angle. Cassegrainian telescopes have the same orientation of the field of view as refractors. Modified Cassegrainians have a re-versed field of view. . . .

3. *Estimating the brightness of a variable.* As the preceding descrip-tion of how to find a variable star implies, each AAVSO chart contains its own magnitude scale. Near the variable are comparison stars whose brightnesses have been carefully determined, and they are used as a scale. When we identified T Cephei in the sky we did so using its orientation with regard to stars marked 105, 101, and so on, meaning that these stars are of magnitude 10.5, 10.1, and so on, respectively. [Throughout the rest of this article, magnitudes are given as printed on the AAVSO charts; ten times the true visual magnitude.]

As we look at T Cephei through our telescope, and check it with the AAVSO "d" chart, we ask ourselves, Is it brighter than 105? Yes. Than 101? Possibly. Than 81? No, it is quite definitely fainter than 81.

At this point we search our chart for other comparison stars and find 96 not far away. T is definitely fainter than 96, but after careful review we believe it is brighter than 101. Hence, we estimate it at magnitude 98, for it seems nearer to 96 than to 101.

We jot this observation down on our log sheet, together with the time and date, and our first variable star observation is made!

Now the logical question confronts us: Suppose instead of being faint, at magnitude 98, T Cephei had turned out to be quite bright, what then would we have done for comparison stars? The AAVSO issues several different types of charts. In our example we have been using both the "b" and the "d" chart. The "b" charts are most useful with a 3- to 6-inch telescope with low power, not exceeding 40X, and a wide field of upwards of a degree. The T Cephei "b" chart shows comparison stars to magnitude 111. The "d" chart is more useful when the star is faint and with 4-inch or larger telescopes, using powers of 40 and higher. The T Cephei "d" chart shows comparison stars to magnitude 129. But if the star is bright, say about magnitude 65, we shall need to use an "a" chart, which shows some 30° of the sky each way, and comparison stars down to magnitude 74. This "a" chart is erect, as one sees the sky by eye or binocular, and if T Cephei is bright, we shall need to use either our wide-angle finder or a binocular to compare its brightness with such comparison stars as magnitude 49, 54, 55, and 60, all located some 5 or 6 degrees away from T Cephei. It will be difficult if not hopeless to use our main telescope for comparison purposes when T is above magnitude 67, for if we have to hunt up comparison stars several degrees away we will inevitably lose track of T Cephei itself. . . .

Sometimes the atmosphere is so jumpy that stars will appear to vary erratically in brightness and no estimate is possible. Such a condition occurs in New England about once a year during a cold wave.

Red stars are very troublesome. As one gazes at them they seem to rush upwards in brightness, a half magnitude or more. This is due to the physiological phenomenon called the Purkinje effect. To counteract it, try looking quickly at the stars and then away—the "quick glance" method. . . .

As in the case of finding a variable star, we must not suppose that estimating its brightness is an easy process at first. When I started the work, I sometimes took as long as twenty minutes determining the magnitude of a variable. Nowadays, even with a strange star, I would not take over a minute, for I am of the opinion that confident first impressions are more accurate than doubting second impressions, because the eye soon tires. Beginners should start with comparison stars which are very definitely brighter and fainter than the variable star in question and move in on it from both directions. As Sir William Herschel pointed out long ago, "If one cannot decide which of two stars is the brighter, then they are equal."

4. Organizing a variable star program. Members of the American Association of Variable Star Observers can secure a chart catalogue from AAVSO Headquarters, 187 Concord Avenue, Cambridge, Massachusetts, 02138. From this they can select charts covering suitable stars for their own conditions, giving due regard to the part of the sky that is seen best, the faintest stars visible in available instruments, and the time of year observing is begun.

It will be noted that variable stars tend to congregate along the Milky

Way; indeed, it is sometimes considered that the study of variable stars is essentially a study of Milky Way evolutionary and distance problems. There are two periods of the year when variable stars present themselves in great profusion, September and October, and February and March, when the Milky Way is overhead at dusk. At other times of the year, the sky presents fewer variable stars, at least for the amateur who must do his observing in the early evening hours.

Some observers like to keep their charts filed by constellations, but I use 48 folders. In the first are charts numbered 000451 to 001909, in the second those numbered 003179 to 005840, that is, by half hours of right ascension. A wooden wedge may temporarily take the place of a chart which is in use at the telescope; this facilitates refiling. It is convenient to paste the finder charts on the backs of the larger comparison charts; the "d" charts are best for this purpose.

To record your observations either use a ledger sheet for each star or enter all observations serially on a nightly log sheet. The ledger system permits easier completion of the monthly report in which all observations of a star are grouped together, and it permits easier plotting of light curves if one feels so disposed. The log system may result in more accurate observations, for the observer will not have noticed (on a ledger sheet) how bright a star was the last time it was observed. The log system is speedier on nights when observing is good; it is better to leave desk work to cloudy nights.

At the telescope, use a flashlight small enough to be held in your teeth. I prefer the C-cell size. You can cover the lens with red paper or cellophane to decrease glare on the charts. . . .

5. *Reporting variable star observations.* Until you obtain a Julian Day calendar, report your observations in standard time. However, the monthly report form calls for the Julian Day and decimal thereof to express the time of each observation. January 1, 1951, is Julian Day 2,433,648 (beginning at noon), which may be written 3,648 for brevity.

Group all the observations of each star together chronologically and list stars in numerical order. For instance, all the observations of 021403 Omicron Ceti should come first, then those of 023133 R Trianguli, and so on.

Reports are sent to AAVSO headquarters, Cambridge, Massachusetts 02138, on the monthly report form which the AAVSO provides its members. If you are interested in becoming a member of this society, write to headquarters for an application blank.

6. *The use of the variable star observations.* Our estimates, say of T Cephei, will be entered in a 10-day ledger, together with all the observations received on that star for the same 10-day period. The average

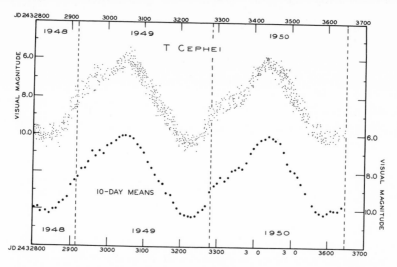

FIG. 57. The upper portion of this graph shows the observations of T Cephei reported by individual AAVSO observers. Below is plotted the light curve that results with 10-day means of the same observations.

of the observations is considered the brightness of T Cephei for that particular period. Later, a light curve [see Fig. 57] will be drawn, showing brightness plotted vertically against time plotted horizontally. Perhaps the entire history of T Cephei will be studied statistically by some astronomer for its period, shape of light curve, and other correlations.

We cannot discuss in detail here the many types of variable stars, but the new observer does desire some knowledge of the kinds of objects on the AAVSO observing program. The majority are long-period variables that become bright and faint rhythmically, but never do quite the same thing twice. The "variation in the variation" of such a star is perhaps the principal interest at present.

Then there are the SS Cygni stars, which are ordinarily faint but which occasionally brighten up quickly by several magnitudes, only to fade away again after a few days. Some astronomers consider these stars as repeating novae of small range. The four brightest stars of the R Coronae Borealis type are on the AAVSO lists. These stars are ordinarily bright, but sometimes fade away by perhaps 6 or 8 magnitudes, for months at a time. Novae are immediately added to the AAVSO program when they occur.

During the past year, additions included Luyten's flare star 013618 in Cetus, the odd star 092720 in Leo, and the sporadic, suddenly brightening variable 203501 AE Aquarii. And there are the familiar but little understood irregular stars, such as 115158 Z Ursae Majoris and 184205 R Scuti, which are continually doing the unexpected. Seldom a week goes by that one or more of the variable stars on an active observer's list does not do something exciting.

Books on variable stars include *The Nature of Variable Stars* by P. W. Merrill (Macmillan, 1938), *Variable Stars* by C. Payne-Gaposchkin and S. Gaposchkin (Harvard College Observatory Monograph 5, 1938), and *The Story of Variable Stars* by L. Campbell and L. Jacchia (McGraw-Hill, 1941).

Most variable stars change slowly, and observations need be timed only to the nearest day and hour. Some change more rapidly, and it is necessary to say as exactly as possible just when a measurement was made. A good observer always records the times of astronomical observations, and in some cases (eclipses, occultations of stars by the moon, positions of planets and asteroids) tries for an accuracy of 0.1 second, which can be estimated between 1-second "ticks" of a clock, or measured with a stop watch. The clock ticks are broadcast by short-wave radio stations such as WWV (2.5, 5, 10, 15, 20, and 25 megacycles per second) in Washington, D.C., and can be picked up by an inexpensive radio receiver. Such time signals can be used to check a clock or to start a stop watch at a known instant. In the observations described in the following article, however, such high accuracy of timing is not involved.

— T L P

Why Observe Stellar Eclipses?

ALAN H. BATTEN

(Sky and Telescope, June 1960)

Total eclipses of the sun have for a long time afforded astronomers their only chances of observing certain solar phenomena. Even though coronagraphs and other special instruments have been developed, solar eclipses still provide opportunities for many important observations. Likewise, for the past half century, eclipses of stars have been recognized as a source of much useful information.

Since the orbital plane of the moon is only slightly inclined to that of the earth, the moon can pass in front of the sun from time to time, producing a solar eclipse. Similarly, stellar eclipses result when the orbital plane of a binary star system is so oriented in space that each component can alternately obstruct the other's light on its way to the earth.

Just as eclipses of the sun can be total, annular, or partial, so can those of the stars; and, as with the sun, total stellar eclipses are the most useful ones to observe. There is one difference, however. For any given binary system, the kind of eclipse is fixed by the position of the orbit in space. Thus, we always observe either successive partial eclipses or total and annular eclipses; in the latter cases the larger star of the pair is first in front of and then behind the smaller one.

Viewed from the earth, these eclipsing systems appear as single stars; how, then, can they be recognized? It is obvious that eclipses must cause variations in the total light that we receive from each pair. Eclipsing binaries, therefore, are usually discovered in the course of any systematic search for variable stars. The characteristic nature of their light curves distinguishes eclipsing stars from other kinds of variables.

In the ideal case, the light of the system is constant for a considerable part of each orbital revolution, because both stars are shining unobstructed. (Only rarely is either component a truly variable star.) Then, as an eclipse begins, the system's brightness gradually decreases, for one

FIG. 58. In this schematic diagram, five varieties of eclipsing-variable light curves are interpreted. For each case, brightness increases upward, and time toward the right. The hotter star has the greater surface brightness, so the deeper eclipse always occurs when it is behind the other one. The hotter component may be either the larger or smaller of the pair. In the fourth example, the stars are brightest at their centers, darker at their edges.

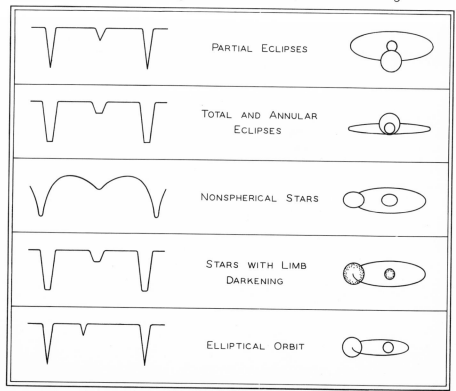

PARTIAL ECLIPSES

TOTAL AND ANNULAR ECLIPSES

NONSPHERICAL STARS

STARS WITH LIMB DARKENING

ELLIPTICAL ORBIT

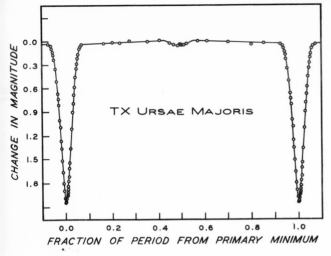

star is cutting off the light of the other. If the eclipse is total, there is another time of constant, but fainter, light; then, as the second component emerges from behind the first one, the light of the system increases until it regains its former level.

When the smaller star is in front of the other, the eclipse is annular instead of total. On the other hand, during an eclipse that is only partial, the light varies continuously and increases again as soon as minimum is reached. Light curves of these different possibilities are illustrated here.

Most eclipsing systems go through a complete cycle of two eclipses in a few days; these are stars that are close to each other and so are traveling quickly in their orbits. Many have periods of less than a day. On the other hand, a few eclipsing systems have periods of some years; the stars may be widely separated in proportion to their sizes, but their orbits lie very nearly in the line of sight, that is, at right angles to the plane of the sky. . . .

The details of the light curve depend on the geometry of the eclipsing binary system. Thus, the duration of each eclipse, measured as a fraction of the period, must depend on the dimensions of the two stars relative to the diameter of the orbit as well as on the angle between our line of sight and the orbital plane.

The problem of analyzing a light curve is to calculate these various quantities from the observations. Then a scale "model" of the system can be made, in which all relative dimensions and the orientation of the orbit are known. However, the absolute size of the orbit is unknown, and the geometrical problem is complicated by various physical considerations. . . .

Since so many factors influence the shape of a light curve, it is not surprising that unraveling the various effects presents a complex problem. In a strict mathematical sense, it has no exact solution, because some properties of the system have to be assumed before others can be derived. To obtain any solution at all, we have to find the ratio of the radii of the two stars, and the limb-darkening coefficient, which expresses the amount by which the eclipsed star is darkened at the limb. The problem is simpler for a light curve displaying a total eclipse. We can tell immediately which star is the hotter, as it is being eclipsed during the deeper minimum. The relative depths of the primary and secondary eclipses can then be used to give the ratio of the radii. An annular eclipse allows the limb darkening to be determined, for there is a slow variation of light during the annular phase.

In a partially eclipsing system neither of these aids is available, and it is often necessary to start with an outright guess of these two quantities. Fortunately, the solutions possess the property of convergence. That is to say, if values of the ratio of the radii and limb darkening are assumed, certain information can be derived about the binary system, including improved values of these quantities. Employing them, a new solution can be made. But even this method is useful only if both eclipses are deep and have been well observed. Otherwise, a light curve of a partially eclipsing system is practically useless.

If knowledge can be obtained from stellar eclipses only with so much difficulty, why is so much time spent observing them? The answer is that they are the principle source of many kinds of much needed information. From eclipsing binaries a great deal can be learned about the sizes and masses of stars, the structure of stellar atmospheres, and even about the internal structure of stars.

It has already been indicated that relative dimensions of an eclipsing variable may be obtained from its light curve, providing, in effect, a scale model of the system. If the binary has been observed spectroscopically, the radial velocity measurements should give the actual orbital speeds of the component stars in kilometers per second. From these values, all the linear dimensions of the scale model can be obtained, that is, the actual sizes of the two stars and their distance apart. Furthermore, masses of the components may be determined from a generalized form of Kepler's third law of planetary motion. In addition, the stars' surface temperatures may be estimated from their spectral characteristics. These, combined with their actual dimensions, lead to their intrinsic luminosities, or absolute magnitudes, and to an estimate of the distance. . . .

Perhaps it was obvious that eclipsing systems should provide data about the sizes and shapes of their component stars. It may seem surprising, however, that they should also prove to be a source of facts concerning physical conditions in the atmospheres and deep interiors of stars. It is this wide range of information that makes stellar eclipses so important.

It may well be that there are more double than single stars in the sky. Of course, only a tiny fraction of these will be observable as eclipsing binaries, but even this number is so large that there is no hope of discovering all such systems as are believed to exist. And among these, many different types of stars will be found. Thus, from a comparative study much may be learned about stellar evolution—a further reason for observing eclipsing variables.

Observations of periodic variables, such as the ones described above, can be planned, but the irregular variations of some stars can pose problems; the brightness may change when no one is looking! (For instance, the observations of novae cannot be planned in advance.) There is an increasing number of stars known to vary irregularly—some with sudden changes—and these should be watched by many observers. The American Association of Variable Star Observers (p. 161) is well organized for this purpose and needs more observers on programs now under way.

Another type of measurement—the relative motion of two stars in a close pair—can usefully be made with telescopes of all sizes. Visual double stars are more widely separated than eclipsing binaries (which are so close that only one image is visible). In both cases, one star moves in an orbit around the other, very like a planet moving around the sun (see Vol. 1, Wanderers in the Sky). The smaller the distance between them, the faster is this orbital motion. Of course, the separation of the two star images in a telescope (see Fig. 60) depends on the distance of the pair from us, and the focal length of the telescope. Measures of the changing separation (in seconds of arc) and the changing direction of the line between the two stars (the "position angle" measured in degrees from a north-south line) can be used to plot the orbit, which is very useful to astronomers. In cases where the distance of the visual binary can be measured, the masses of the two stars can be calculated from the orbit. The micrometer used for such measurements is described in the next chapter.

Thousands of visual binaries are listed in catalogues such as R. G. Aitken's Catalogue of Double Stars, available in university science libraries. Some of the double stars are actually triples and quadruples, and a few are not really close together; one star just happens to be lined up with a much more distant one. Orbits have been measured for only a few per cent of the doubles, and more observations are needed to "weigh the stars." Of course, some of the stars are too close to be resolved by a small telescope. Higher magnifying power (shorter-focus eyepiece) will help somewhat, but even under the best conditions a 6-inch telescope cannot resolve two stars closer than about 1″. This "resolving power" is better for a 12-inch, which can show stars separated by as little as 0″.5 (half of a second of arc).

Some of the well-known doubles easy to observe with a small telescope are Beta Cygni, Gamma Virginis, Alpha Geminorum (Castor), Zeta Aquarii, and Zeta Ursae Majoris (Mizar, at the bend of the handle of the Big Dipper). These are all fairly widely separated and move very slowly in orbit, but they offer wide contrasts in color and brightness.

—TLP

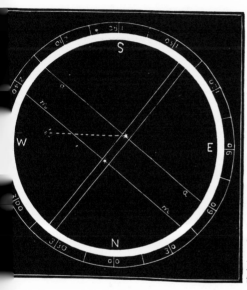

Fig. 60. A double star in the inverted field of view of a position micrometer. The fixed and movable wires (a and m) are set on the component stars to measure their distance apart. The parallel wires indicate position angle, which is here about 320°. The arrow shows the direction in which the star drifts when the driving clock is stopped; therefore this is west. (From *Astronomy* by H. N. Russell, R. S. Dugan, and J. Q. Stewart, Boston, Ginn, 1945.)

7

Telescope

Accessories

At this point it must be clear that a number of accessories are desirable on a telescope used for measurements. In discussing them, we first ask, What measurements are possible on a beam of light from an astronomical object? The most obvious are direction and brightness (magnitude). Detailed analysis of the colors of light—the spectrum—is a third type of measurement, and polarization is a fourth (not discussed here; see Vol. 2 in this series, Neighbors of the Earth).

In order to measure direction, or accurate position in the sky, it is necessary to provide a marker that can be seen in the eyepiece, so that the telescope can be pointed accurately at a star or other object. The marker generally used is a pair of fine wires or hairs at right angles mounted at the focus of the telescope objective. When the image of a star is seen on the cross hairs, the telescope is accurately pointed. Of course, a "finder telescope" of low magnification is generally mounted on the side of a large telescope that has a small field. Then the general background of stars can be seen in the wide field of the finder, and the telescope pointed so that the object to be studied is seen on the cross hairs in the finder. If the finder is properly lined up, the object of study is then nearly centered in the main telescope.

Small differences in direction, such as the angular distance between two stars in a pair, can be measured with two sets of cross hairs, one set being moved away from the other by an accurate screw. Turns of the screw measure the distance between the two cross hairs, and the device is called a micrometer. By turning the whole micrometer, distance can be measured from one star to another in any direction, and if the direction can also be measured (in degrees of arc east or west of north), the device is called a position micrometer. — T L P

....

How to Make a Position Micrometer

ROBERT MILLER

(*The Sky*, August 1937)

To many stargazers, observational astronomy has an added interest because they watch the heavens through instruments of their own manufacture and measure stellar positions with devices they themselves have made. Previously on these pages, readers have been given instructions for the construction of small telescopes, and it is the purpose of the present article to aid them in making and using an important telescopic accessory—the position micrometer.

Work is done solely at the telescope's eyepiece, and the first thing to do is to select one that gives a moderate magnification. A 1-inch is about the best for general use in the work we are about to do. If the eyepiece is of the so-called negative type, the cross hairs we are to use will be placed *between the two lenses;* if the eyepiece is positive, the hairs will be placed *in front of the field lens.* The cross hairs, of course, are placed in the *focal plane* in both cases. Constant reference should be made to the accompanying diagrams.

It is only fair to warn the reader at this point that since there is no simple method of illuminating the hairs or wires when the instrument is in use, it is only practicable in the vicinity of a bright star or planet, or on a moonlit night. However, even with this drawback, many moments of interest and fun can be spent in measuring a planet's motion in relation to the position of a nearby star and in making other, similar observations.

The cross hairs which form the essential part of the micrometer may be built into the telescope as follows: A small flat metal ring is made to fit snugly into the eyepiece tube (in the case of the negative eyepiece) or into the adapter tube of the telescope (in the case of the positive eyepiece).

The inside diameter of this ring should be equal to the diameter of the diaphragm-hole in the negative eyepiece; or as large as the focal image of the object-glass when using a positive eyepiece. This ring can very easily be made from a piece of tin, a thin piece of galvanized sheet iron, or heavy-gauge celluloid (see Fig. 61A).

It is not important to make the spaces between the parallel hairs of any particular width. In fact, it is better to vary them because this will greatly simplify matters when you use the instrument to judge the separation of two objects. The lone vertical hair and the central horizontal hair should be perpendicular to each other, and they can be made so by use of the circle scratched on the flat ring (see again Fig. 61A).

Divide the circle into four equal sections. Four points, evenly spaced around the circle, will result at the boundaries of these quarters. Place a straightedge across each opposite pair of points and use a needle to make a scratch running through these points and the diameter of the circle. Lines drawn through each set of scratches will prove perpendicular to each other, and they will be of great aid in fastening the hairs to the ring.

And now we come to a consideration of what we shall use for the hairs. In the first place, they should be as fine as possible; and they should also be strong and of uniform thickness. The finest obtainable magnet wire (which can be purchased in electrical shops) answers our needs remarkably well. Of course, if one has enough patience and skill to handle the material, he may use spider's thread; but this is difficult to work with, and it is also hard to see on a dark night.

After the foundation scratches have been made on the ring, as described previously, it is time to fasten the wires to it. To make certain that the wires will be set in the ring at the proper tension, secure a piece of thin bamboo about twelve inches long. Twist one end of the piece of wire around one end of the bamboo, and the other end of the wire around the other end of the bamboo—bending the bamboo so that it forms a bow and stretches the wire.

Now that the wire has been stretched tightly by the bow, it is laid across two corresponding scratches on the ring and fastened to the ring by a drop of shellac or liquid solder. When the shellac or solder has dried, the bamboo may be removed and the extra length of wire clipped away. The process is then repeated for all the other parallel and cross wires.

When all the hairs have been fastened to the ring they should be protected by a cardboard ring. The outside diameter of this protecting ring should be slightly smaller than the first ring, and its inside diameter, slightly larger.

The ring, with its cross hairs firmly in place, is now fitted into the eyepiece in a position determined by whether the eyepiece is positive

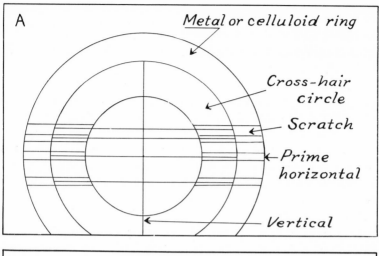

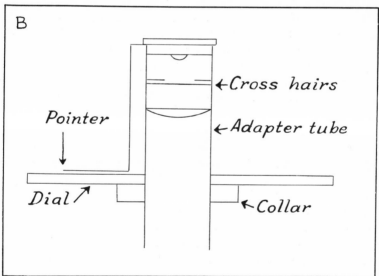

FIG. 61. Diagrams of a position micrometer. A. Top view. B. Side view.

or negative, as has already been explained. And when the eyepiece has finally been fitted with a fixed micrometer, a dial is needed so that visual observations may be translated into standard units of distance.

The outside diameter of the dial can be of any convenient size, but the inside must fit snugly to the adapted tube. It may be made of wood or cardboard; it should be either shellacked or painted, and it is then divided into degrees. In marking the degrees, you have only to remember that there are 360 degrees in every circle and to mark the circumference of the dial accordingly.

To determine its position, refer to Figure 61B and note the distance from the eyepiece at which it is placed in order to allow the observer to put his eye to the lines. A collar placed in back of the dial around the circumference of the telescope tube will serve to keep the dial in place.

Used with the dial, the eyepiece pointer helps to give the exact position. It may be made of tin, and one end should be attached to the eyepiece cap, but since the exact method of installation depends upon the nature of the eyepiece this procedure should be determined by the individual. The completed instrument is shown in Figure 61B, and a careful analysis of this diagram will make the construction and arrangement of parts clear.

When the instrument is completed, it is essential to determine the distances separating the parallel hairs. To do so, direct the telescope at a star that is as close as possible to the celestial equator.

Adjust the eyepiece so that the vertical hair is parallel to the equator, and then move the telescope back and forth from east to west. This will cause the star selected to make a fine trail of light from one side of the field to the other. The vertical hair will, of course, also be parallel to this line of sight. Now move the telescope until the star is at the extreme eastern side of the field, and let it remain so. As the star advances toward the west, it crosses each hair.

Make a note of the time intervals between these crossings. The distance between each crossing is equal to the separation of the hairs in seconds of time, and to convert this reading into seconds of arc multiply the number of time seconds by 15.

Figure 62A shows an example of how the micrometer may be put to use. The diagram shows the planet Jupiter; a nearby star is also in the field.

The first problem is to find the position angle, or line of Jupiter's declination, to the star. The horizontal wire is adjusted to run through the planet, and the eyepiece is turned until, as the planet moves from east to west, it is bisected always by that wire. The base line is thus established, and now the dial is turned, the eyepiece remaining fixed,

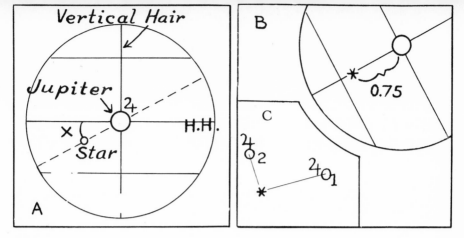

FIG. 62. Use of a position micrometer to measure Jupiter's position relative to a nearby star. A. Vertical hair north-south. B. Vertical hair adjusted in position angle.

until the mark o is indicated on the eyepiece pointer. Leaving the dial fixed, the eyepiece is now turned until the central horizontal hair ("H.H.") bisects the star and the planet. The reading of the dial at this point is equal to the angle X in Figure 62A, in this case about 25°.

After this, the next observation is to determine the distance from Jupiter to the star in units of arc. The eyepiece is turned until the vertical hair bisects the star and the planet, the horizontal hairs being used as a micrometer (Fig. 62B); the planet is bisected by the prime horizontal hair, and distance to star is judged in relation to separation of the two hairs.

In the drawing, the star is about 0.75 of the distance between the cross hairs; we have but to multiply 0.75 by that value to obtain the distance from the comparison star. The other hair can be used in the same way.

Having two position observations (angle and distance between planet and star) it is an easy matter to plot the planet's motion with a ruler and protractor as in Figure 62C.

<hr>

The Construction of a Filar Micrometer

CHARLES E. WORLEY

(*Sky and Telescope*, September 1961)

One of the most useful accessories for a well-mounted telescope is a micrometer, for it allows the patient, practiced observer to make a sub-stantial contribution by measuring visual double stars [see p. 174].

The bifilar (two-wire) micrometer is a classical astronomical instrument that has been used for more than a century to make accurate measures of small angular distances on the celestial sphere. The heart of the device consists of two fine wires placed in the focal plane of the telescope, with provision for determining both the distance between the wires and their orientation. Of the many types of micrometers that have evolved over the years, the bifilar is still perhaps the most versatile.

To realize its full potential, however, the instrument must be used with a suitable telescope. A very sturdy, carefully aligned equatorial mounting and an accurate clock drive are absolutely necessary. Further, a long focal length is desirable, to give a large scale. In an accurate micrometer, one of the wires is fixed and the other movable by means of an accurately machined screw. Both wires are held in a carriage so that together they may be turned around the optical axis of the telescope until the fixed wire is superimposed upon both components of a double star to indicate the position angle.

To illustrate the construction of such an instrument, we have chosen the compact and convenient, yet accurate, micrometer of the 12-inch Lick refractor (Fig. 63). The position-angle circle is divided into degrees and half-degrees, and may be read by estimation to 0.1 degree. The square plate is the base on which the micrometer box slides. This base is secured by a circular flange, invisible beneath the position-angle circle, which permits the box to rotate freely. The zero point in front, and another on the back, indicate the position angle on the circle when the box is rotated. This rotation is controlled by the knob just to the right of the eyepiece in Figure 63 which may be locked at any desired position by means of the small screw clamp behind it. . . .

Above the base plate is centered the head, or nut, for the long tangent screw on the near side of the box, with a control knob at either end. With this screw the whole box may be moved left and right, carrying the eyepiece and both wires across the star field viewed in the telescope.

On the right of Figure 63 is the micrometer screw, the most important unit in the entire instrument. The screw is held stationary in the box, and turning it causes the central brass plate to move. Two springs inside the box maintain proper tension. To eliminate backlash when a measure is taken, the screw is always turned against the spring tension. In any bifilar micrometer, the screw should be at least 1 inch long and have 40 to 80 threads per inch. It is convenient to have a drum reading in hundredths of a revolution, so that thousandths can be estimated. Combined micrometer heads and screws may be purchased at reasonable cost from such firms as Tubular Micrometer, Brown and Sharp, and Starrett.

It should be mentioned that in most commercially available microm-

Fıg. 63. A filar micrometer removed from the Lick 12-inch telescope's tailpiece.

eter units the head is held stationary and the screw moves. In such a case the springs must be attached to the side of the box nearest the drum. Instead of the U-shaped brass assembly, a rectangular piece should be used. The screw, pressing against a ball bearing set in this piece, and held tense by the reversed springs, will then provide the required motion equally well.

Near the midpoint of the central plate the central wire is glued, extending across the gap under the eyepiece. For illuminating the wires, a light in the tube at the extreme left shines through a slit in the end of the box, its intensity controlled by a rheostat. . . .

The eyepiece unit, carrying the fixed wire, is attached to the micrometer box. . . . The fixed and movable wires must be as nearly in the same plane as possible, yet must not interfere with each other. Therefore, great care is necessary in spacing the eyepiece unit slightly above the moving-wire assembly.

In the past, micrometer "wires" have been obtained from spider webs or cocoons. If long, even strands can be obtained, this material is perfectly satisfactory. But modern technology provides a convenient, if expensive, substitute in the form of annealed tungsten wire of 0.0002-inch diameter, obtainable from Sigmund Cohn Manufacturing Company, Mount Vernon, New York. This wire is now used in the 12-inch micrometer, and has proved exceedingly satisfactory. It has great uniformity, high tensile strength, and is very easy to attach.

Micrometer wires may be installed by placing rosin or some other sticky material on the points of a pair of calipers. We attach one end of the wire to a point of the calipers, draw out a sufficient length of wire, and catch it on the other point. Then we spread the calipers gently until the wire is taut, and lay it across the grooves, cementing with a small amount of dilute glue. When the glue has set, the ends of the wire are carefully snipped free from the calipers and trimmed. . . .

Before the instrument can be used for double star measurements, the value of one revolution of the micrometer screw in seconds of arc must be determined, and the north point (zero) on the position-angle circle must be found [see p. 180].

When several angular distances are to be measured in one field of view, it is often desirable to take a photograph with the telescope and measure the photograph later. Moreover, the photograph allows measures of the brightness (from blackening of the negative), and it provides a permanent record of the observation—sometimes an artistic show piece (some astronomers make attractive lampshades from several enlarged transparencies of their favorite astronomical pictures).

The professional astronomer generally takes photographs with the film or plate at the focus of the main telescope objective. This blocks the view through the eyepiece, and arrangements must be made to watch a nearby star past the edge of the film in order to keep the telescope pointed ("guided") properly during the exposure. An amateur astronomer often fastens a separate camera to the tube of his telescope and uses the telescope for guiding the smaller camera. Alternatively, he can photograph through the eyepiece of his main telescope and guide with the finder, as the next two articles describe.   — T L P

■■

Astrophotography for the Amateur

HANS PFLEUMER

(*Sky and Telescope*, January, February, March, April 1956)

Many amateur astronomers want to photograph what they observe, and perhaps use their pictures to make slides to show to their friends. The writer has developed methods for obtaining negatives suitable either for standard-sized lantern slides or those used in 2-by-2 projectors.

The various objects in the sky may be divided into four groups, each requiring a different plate scale. The first consists of large areas of the sky, including such extensive constellations as Ursa Major and Orion. The next includes smaller star groups such as Cassiopeia, Lyra, and the

Hyades. The third is comprised of most individual open star clusters, nebulae, nearby galaxies, the double cluster in Perseus, the Orion nebula, and so on. Finally, requiring the largest plate scale of all, are the planets, portions of the moon, the ring nebula in Lyra, and most galaxies.

My experience is based on photography with my $5\frac{1}{2}$-inch refractor, which has an f/15 objective. It has a good sidereal drive, which is a prime requisite for successful photography. For this work a good 4-inch to 6-inch telescope is needed, and a separate camera.

For the first group of sky objects, an f/3.5 lens of 3-inch focus is about right to obtain negatives that will make 2-by-2 slides directly. A simple camera is attached to a dovetailed bracket near the front end of the telescope tube. The dewcap is removed to avoid obstructing the field. The telescope is used for guiding, and since the exposures with fast lenses such as a Zeiss Tessar are short (10 to 15 minutes) the strain of guiding is bearable.

For the second group, the same arrangement is used, with a camera having a f/4.5 lens of 6-inch focal length.

To open and close the camera shutter, I use a short cable release, the button of which is inserted in a barrel fastened to the dovetail bracket on the telescope and held in by a knurled and threaded bushing around the cable. Into the other end of the barrel there is fixed a $\frac{1}{8}$-inch brass rod that extends to the eye end of the telescope through holes in the saddle pieces. Near the barrel, the rod has an adjustable split stop-ring that determines how far the rod can be pushed—this protects the cable release from strain. The shutter is set at a bulb; pushing the rod opens the shutter; pulling the rod closes it—no mistake possible.

The field of good definition for a long-focus refractor permits excellent focal-plane photographs to be taken of the third group of objects by means of a special attachment which is exchanged for the observing tailpiece of my instrument. It is made up of a triple-leaved shutter (see Fig. 64), pressure-vacuum operated for $\frac{1}{30}$ second and time exposures. The field of view is 3 inches in diameter on $3\frac{1}{4}$-by-$4\frac{1}{4}$ cut film.

Since at f/15 the exposures are relatively long, guiding is important. Therefore, the finder is converted to a longer focus by means of a Barlow lens.

Using this prime-focus camera for objects in the fourth group is very difficult. Mars, for instance, has an image $\frac{1}{5}$ millimeter in diameter, and Saturn's ring is only half a millimeter. Therefore, recourse has to be taken to projection through an eyepiece. . . .

A simple projection camera, such as described here, can be made at home with a little skill; only three parts require some lathe work. It can be quickly attached to the standard rack-and-pinion focusing tube

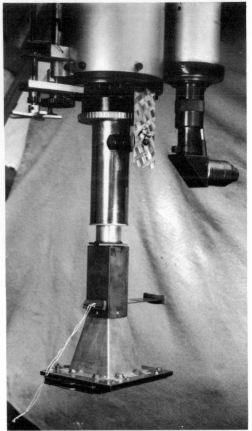

Fig. 64. The shutter attachment for taking direct pictures of the third group of sky objects.

Fig. 65. The camera for eyepiece projection photography, attached to the 5½-inch refractor. The guiding telescope is seen at the upper right. Next to it on the main tube is the stainless-steel plate for locking the focus of the camera. The twin-slide filmholder is in place at the bottom of the picture.

on the telescope. The construction should be substantial but light, in order not to strain the focusing device. With a Graflex double film-holder for 3¼-by-4¼ cut film, the attachment weighs 2 pounds. The distance from the eyepiece to the film plane is 4 inches.

Figure 65 shows the device attached to the telescope. At the center, the adapter tube slides into the telescope; it carries a square Bakelite baffle. In the square tube is seen the shutter, equipped with sponge-rubber stops. The shutter is pulled by the cord, but may be rubberband loaded for instantaneous exposures.

Below center in Figure 66, a photograph of partly disassembled equipment, the adapter tube for a 1¼-inch diameter eyepiece holder is seen again. On the larger end are soldered two collimating rings 1¾ inches apart, which have been machined true to fit tightly into the square tube. The Bakelite baffle slides between the first ring and a clamp that is adjusted with a screwdriver.

In attaching the camera, the square tube, 1¾ inches wide and 4 inches long, is pushed against the light trap, the clamp taking care of the variation of projection. The stainless-steel sliding shutter has a $\frac{3}{4}$-inch hole in its center (see Fig. 66), and it rides in two narrow slits $\frac{3}{4}$ inch from the other end of the square tube. The slits should be just large enough to allow the shutter blade to slide smoothly. In the equipment shown in Figure 66 two small screws at the ends prevent the shutter from falling out; sponge rubber may be used instead (as shown in Fig. 65). The small clip on the shutter shown in Figure 66 is attached to hold it open.

The main camera body is a pyramidal section of thin aluminum sheet riveted along one edge. The small opening of the pyramid is slit at the corners for $\frac{1}{2}$ inch, pushed into the square tube, squared on, and bolted. As can be seen (Fig. 66), the larger end of the pyramid has $\frac{1}{2}$-inch wide flanges, and it is fastened to the camera back with 6-32 countersunk brass screws, washers, and nuts. . . .

The 1-inch high-quality eyepiece shown gives a sharp field. Using it, the projected image can be varied between $4\frac{1}{2}$ and 5 times the scale of the prime-focus image; larger and smaller plate scales are obtained by using other eyepieces. . . .

Tracking must be even more accurate when the main telescope is to be used for prime-focus photography, and correct drive speed is of utmost importance. In this case guiding is accomplished with the finder, whose magnification is increased by the insertion of a Barlow lens. Figure 67B shows the results. . . .

The moon is an easy object at the prime focus, giving an image $\frac{3}{4}$ inch across. The intensely bright full moon requires short exposures, about $\frac{1}{100}$ second; if a high-speed shutter is not available, exposure time can be lengthened by using a panchromatic emulsion and a filter. A gelatin filter can be placed near the film plane, but for a glass-mounted filter, remember that the focus must be extended by one third the thickness of the glass.

One problem in photographing the moon near its quarter phases is that if correct exposure is given for the bright limb, the neighborhood of the terminator will be underexposed. I find that with the projection camera good results can be obtained if the shutter in the square-tube section is moved part way back and forth to increase the exposure of the terminator relative to the limb. The shutter opening comes from the terminator side and is stopped by a small clip from passing the full-open position; the shutter slide is then pulled back to its starting position. Of course, after a negative of the moon is developed, during the printing of enlargements the method of *dodging* may be used to control the relative intensities of the limb and terminator regions.

The projection camera, also used for planetary work, normally pro-

Fig. 66. Pfleumer projection camera partly disassembled. At the left is the focusing frame, and behind the camera is the filmholder. The magnifier with its prism is at the extreme right, next to the eyepiece in the adapter tube, which is lying in the center foreground. In front is the focusing stop, of stainless steel. In the square-tube part of the camera, the shutter has been pulled out to show the circular central hole.

vides about five times the scale of the prime-focus device. Since the exposure times do not exceed a few seconds, guiding is not necessary, but the drive rate must be accurate. Sharp focusing is necessary, but often is difficult because the image seen through the ground-glass screen is faint. Rubbing the rough side of the glass with glycerin helps, and the image is examined with a 5X magnifier resting on the glass. A fine cross made on the ground side with a sharp No. 6 pencil is used to adjust the magnifier for its sharpest focus. . . .

The proper length of exposure for projection photography varies as the square of the projection factor. For Saturn on Super Panchro Press film (type B, rating 125) I use an 8-second exposure with the f/15 objective and a $\frac{1}{2}$-inch eyepiece $4\frac{1}{2}$ inches from the film plane. This arrangement gives 9 times the prime-focus scale, and the image of Saturn is $3\frac{1}{4}$ millimeters in diameter.

The general procedure in taking a photograph is first to start the driving clock and to place the object on the finder cross hairs. Next the image is focused on the ground glass. After closing the shutter and installing the filmholder, the placement of the object in the finder is checked. The drive is allowed to run for a minute to take out any slack, and then the shutter is carefully opened to begin the exposure.

FIG. 67. A. In this 10-minute exposure of the constellation Orion made with the 6-inch camera, the three belt stars are in the middle, with the sword and Great Nebula below them. Because it is a red star, Betelgeuse is relatively inconspicuous in the upper left. The development was 8 minutes in D–19; enlargement 3 times. B. This picture of Orion's sword was made at the prime focus on January 18, with an unguided exposure of 54 minutes, representing three turns of the driving worm of the 5½-inch refractor. A print nearly contact size (upper left) has fairly acceptable images, but enlargement to about 3½ times reveals their faults. (All photographs in this article courtesy Hans Pfleumer.)

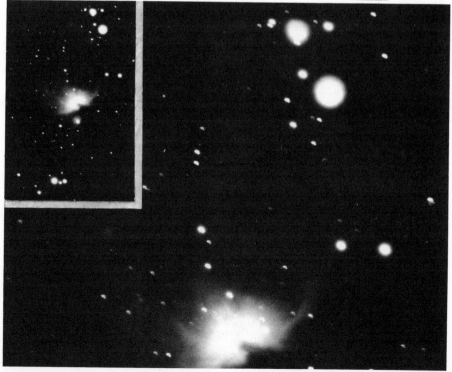

I use high-speed film (generally Super XX Pan), contrast-developed for 9 or 10 minutes in D-19. Glass plates are not necessary, for cut film is inserted in its packet in such a way that it curls against the filmholder and is held in the focal plane. I find that film scratches during development can be avoided by using a deep round-cornered tray of kitchenware, of such a size that it supports the four corners of the film but does not let it touch the bottom. Such a tray is also used for washing.

....

High-resolution
Photography

THOMAS POPE AND THOMAS OSYPOWSKI

(*Sky and Telescope*, January 1965)

A moderate-size telescope of high quality shows a breathtaking amount of lunar and planetary detail visually. But when an attempt is made to capture this fine detail on film the result is inferior more often than not. Over the past five years, we have carried on an extensive program of lunar and planetary photography to improve our techniques. Other amateurs with 8- to 16-inch telescopes may find our field-tested procedures useful.

There are five essential requirements in high-resolution astronomical photography:

Excellent optics. The telescope should be ·of the highest quality optically. A mediocre mirror or objective will spread light that blurs out fine detail, reducing image contrast. Dirt on the optical surfaces gives a washed-out view by scattering light.

As members of the Milwaukee Astronomical Society, we have been using the 12½-inch Newtonian reflector at its observatory. The well-corrected f/9 primary mirror from Cave Optical Company, combined with a 1¾-inch diagonal, gives excellent definition and image contrast.

Perfect focus. Particularly when eyepiece projection is used, focusing must be critical. One of the most convenient arrangements for the amateur is a 35-mm reflex camera body attached to the eyepiece holder with extension tubes. The ground-glass screen in such cameras as the Miranda, Exakta, or Nikon F can be replaced with clear glass and a cross-hair pattern. When both the image and the cross hairs are sharp in the camera's viewfinder the telescope is properly focused. This system is far superior to using ground-glass or "focusing" screens.

In designing an adapter for the camera body, provision should be made for introducing a highly corrected projection eyepiece or Barlow lens into the optical train. Mostly, we have used eyepieces, since they seem to give better results at high amplification.

Recently, we have experimented with movie-camera lenses, because of their superior definition. They can be purchased secondhand for from five to fifteen dollars. An 8-mm camera lens will fill 35-mm film if the image is projected six or seven times the normal focal length of the lens. A lens from a 16- or 35-mm camera will cover a 35-mm frame more adequately.

Our simple camera adapter was made of parts from an M70 telescope. As shown in Figure 68, it has two tubes that thread into each other. The forward tube is machined to a 1¼-inch outside diameter to slip into the telescope's eyepiece adapter, while a projection eyepiece fits in the other end. At the rear of the second tube, either the camera back or additional extensions can be mounted. This tube is slotted to allow a small black card to be flicked across the light path, creating a handy vibrationless shutter.

Accurate guiding. A 12½-inch telescope can theoretically resolve detail less than half a second of arc. Therefore, with this instrument, *unguided* exposures on the moon and planets must be kept shorter than about $\frac{1}{30}$ second. If longer exposures are needed, a smoothly running clock drive is indispensable.

Even with a sidereal drive, exposures of the moon should not be longer than about one second, because of the moon's eastward motion relative to the stars. Fortunately, even slow films rarely require longer exposures than this.

The Milwaukee Astronomical Society's telescope has an excellent drive, allowing us to record one second of arc detail on Jupiter with time exposures of up to 20 seconds. Such driving accuracy calls for a carefully balanced telescope—we hung a folding chair on the counterweight to compensate for the camera's extra weight.

FIG. 68. An exploded view of the camera adapter. The projection eyepiece slips into the forward tube; all other parts screw together.

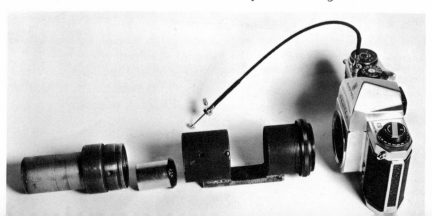

During the exposure there must be no vibration, and the biggest source of trouble will probably be the camera shutter. As previously mentioned, we use a small black card to make the exposure. The camera shutter is set on "bulb" and opened with a cable release; vibrations are given a few seconds to damp out; the card is removed from the optical path for the desired time and then replaced; finally, the shutter is closed.

Proper film and f-ratio combinations. The film must be capable of resolving all the detail a telescope can show. Film resolution is usually expressed as the number of lines per millimeter that can just be distinguished separately on it. Manufacturers' test charts have high contrast, such as alternate black and white lines, but the contrast on the moon or planets is much more subtle. For this reason, the film should have a theoretical resolution about three times that of the telescope.

To determine the number of lines per millimeter (R) a telescope can resolve, we have used the formula,

$$R = \frac{1450}{f} ,$$

where f is the effective focal ratio of the instrument. Note that the resolution in lines per millimeter depends on the effective focal ratio, rather than on telescope aperature.

Some suitable films for several f-ratios are given in Table 3.

TABLE 3.   SUITABLE FILMS FOR HIGH-RESOLUTION PHOTOGRAPHY

f	R	Film
20	72	Adox Dokupan
		Kodak High Contrast
		Copy Film
40	36	Kodak Panatomic-X
70	21	Adox KB14
80	18	Plus-X, Tri-X
160	9	Any film

Adox Dokupan is actually a copy film, but with greater speed and much more controllable contrast than Eastman's counterpart. The Adox film also has extremely fine grain and very high resolution. One of our negatives of the moon taken on Dokupan at the prime focus of the 12½-inch revealed craters less than two miles across. A 30X enlargement was needed to bring out all the detail.

Generally, we prefer to use the slower films; their finer grain and higher contrast make more acceptable enlargements. The choice of developer is mostly personal preference. FR X-22 is a handy product

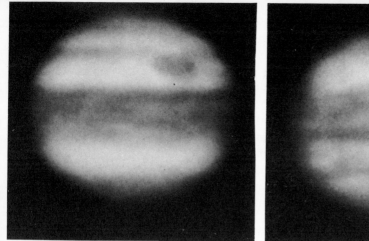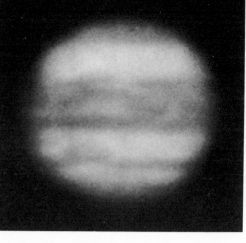

FIG. 69. In different colors, Jupiter's appearance changes greatly. At the left is a white-light picture made September 3, 1962, at 6:13 UT. At the right is another exposure, made at 6:20 with a red filter (Wratten 25A); note the disappearance of the Red Spot. Both 2-second exposures were at f/70 on Adox KB14 film.

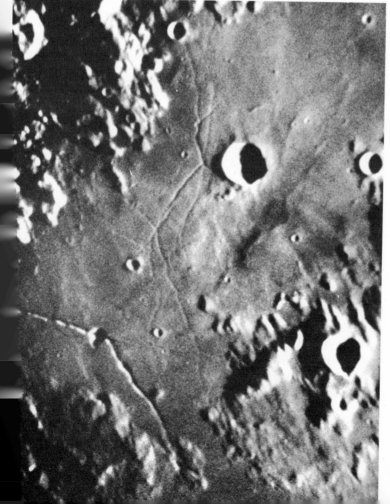

FIG. 70. Taken with a 12½-inch telescope, this enlarged picture of crater Triesnecker and its delicate rills has remarkable resolution. Notice how clearly the small 2.2-mile crater left of Triesnecker is resolved. At lower left is Hyginus and its wide, bent rill. The 1-second exposure was made at f/64 on Kodachome-X at about 10:20 UT on August 20, 1964.

to work with, and film contrast can be varied from high to low by diluting the stock solution with water from one part in ten to one in twenty.

Color film can be used to advantage, especially on the planets, provided the proper emulsion is chosen. We have obtained the "truest" color with Kodachrome-X, a medium-speed film. Color details on Jupiter, such as the Red Spot, the brownish belts, and the currently yellow Equatorial Zone, were very faithfully recorded in our pictures, as judged by a number of experienced visual observers of the giant planet.

By trial and error, we found that the exposure times given in Table 4, expressed in seconds, give consistently good results.

TABLE 4. EXPOSURE TIMES GIVING BEST RESULTS

Film	Gibbous Moon		Jupiter	Saturn
KB14	$\frac{1}{60}$ at f/9	$\frac{1}{2}$-1 at f/64	2 at f/90	4 at f/64
Dokupan	$\frac{1}{15}$ at f/9	1 at f/32	2 at f/32	8 at f/32
Plus-X	$\frac{1}{250}$ at f/9	$\frac{1}{4}$ at f/90	$\frac{1}{2}$ at f/90	2 at f/90
Kodachrome-X	$\frac{1}{60}$ at f/9	$\frac{1}{2}$-1 at f/45	4 at f/90	8 at f/54

Excellent seeing. If details at the limit of telescopic resolution cannot be observed visually due to bad seeing, they can't be photographed. Fine details must remain visible at least long enough to be captured on the film. The image as a whole must also remain motionless in the field, or the picture will be blurred. . . .

Color in Astrophotography

GEORGE T. KEENE

(*Sky and Telescope*, August 1963)

In recent years more and more amateur astronomers have turned to color photography. Sometimes the results have been quite successful, but often the color rendition has been disappointing. Photographs of the planets by amateurs usually show realistic tones, but the color of an aurora or a bright nebula often differs from that recalled by the photographer. Why is color film sometimes successful and other times not?

For many years astronomers have used spectrograms—records of light intensity at different wavelengths—as a valuable tool for studying stars, nebulae, and galaxies. Although the usual black-and-white spectrograms can be analyzed to tell the color of an object, astronomers are often more interested in such properties of the spectrum as the positions and widths of the lines. While of the greatest importance in astronomy, spectrograms do not effectively describe the visual appearance of celestial objects in terms most of us can appreciate.

A picture closely resembling the visual appearance of a heavenly body can be gained from a set of photographs on black-and-white film taken through red, green, and blue filters. This technique, used frequently in planetary photography, gives images from which the colors of the original subject can be reconstructed. There are many difficulties in this method, however, including registration and the selection of filters and dyes. The biggest problem is the relative amount of exposure to give each color record in the camera and in the printing.

A more direct method is to use modern color films, such as Kodachrome, Ektachrome, and Anscochrome, which employ three thin layers, each sensitized to a different band of the spectrum [color of light]. The speed of each layer is such that with normal exposures the film will produce a neutral scale of grays from neutral objects. Reproduction of colors is then fairly satisfactory for most subjects found in nature, but the film may easily give wrong answers for objects that radiate a line spectrum or when the exposure time is substantially longer than for a normal snapshot, which is often the case in astronomical photography.

Color film consists of a transparent support, about 0.005 inch thick, on which are coated as many as ten separate layers. These include the emulsions sensitive to red, green, and blue light, plus a yellow filter layer, interlayers, and protective overcoats. It is most remarkable that the total thickness of all these coatings is only 0.001 inch or less, yet each layer is controlled in thickness to within 5 per cent.

Amateur photographers are probably most familiar with reversal color films—those processed to produce dyes that give direct positive transparencies ready for viewing. Some of these, like Ektachrome film, include half of the dye-forming agent in the film. The dye is produced in a relatively simple process in which the other half of each dye molecule is supplied to all three images by a single color developer. Kodachrome, on the other hand, is essentially a multilayer black-and-white film, with all the color-forming agents contained in the solutions needed for its complex processing. In both systems, a negative silver image is first produced; the film is reexposed to light and a positive silver-and-dye

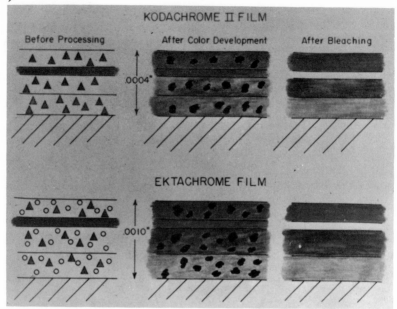

FIG. 71. The layers from top to bottom in both types of film are yellow, a yellow filter, magenta, and cyan. Triangles represent silver-halide grains, circles are dye couplers, and irregular shapes are developed silver grains.

image is developed. After the silver is removed by bleaching, the film is fixed and washed and is ready for projection.

A color picture is reconstructed by the filtering action of the cyan, magenta, and yellow dyes formed in the film. Each dye controls selectively the amount of red, green, or blue light passing through the film, and thus the apparent color of each point on the screen. The amount of dye formed is approximately inversely proportional to the intensity of light that fell on that particular point on the film during exposure in the camera. Many factors, however, modify this proportionality. Most important are chemical interactions between the light-sensitive layers during processing and the effects of different exposure times on speed and contrast.

This last complication, the failure of the reciprocal relationship between light intensity and necessary exposure time—referred to as *reciprocity failure*—is of great concern to astronomers. With an ordinary black-and-white film, for example, we might expect that two stars differing by 10 magnitudes or 10,000 times in brightness would give similar images if the fainter were exposed 10,000 times as long as the brighter. But in general the two images will not be similar, because both the contrast and the sensitivity of the film will be different with the longer exposure; film is "faster" for short exposure times.

The loss of speed for exposures of several hours duration is so great that astronomers often must use emulsions specially made to minimize this drawback. Thus, films and plates of the Kodak Spectroscopic 103a type are a common choice for photographs requiring long exposures.

For color film, reciprocity failure may affect in different ways the responses of the individual light-sensitive layers. The resulting picture is distorted in color balance and contrast. Sometimes these shifts can be partially corrected by color filters used during long exposures, and reciprocity effects are reduced if the film is exposed at low temperatures.

The combination of reciprocity failure and sensitivity effects would seem to make color films a rather poor tool for astrophotography. In a one-hour exposure, however, we can restore the color balance of High-Speed Ektachrome film by using a CC20 red filter. Then the colors of faint objects that radiate a continuous spectrum will be correctly rendered. The planets, shining brightly by reflected sunlight, also have a continuous spectrum, but are photographed without a filter, using short exposure times. But the faint nebulae, nearly colorless to the eye, appear red in photographs. Even with the correcting filter, the Orion nebula photographs bright red, although visually it appears slightly bluish green. This difference can be understood from the diagram (Fig. 72) in which the nebula's radiation is represented by the four vertical lines. These are two hydrogen lines, at 6563 (red) and 4861 angstroms (blue-green), and a pair of oxygen lines at 4959 and 5007 angstroms (blue-green).

The spectral response curve of the eye at low levels is indicated by the dashed curve. The dark-adapted eye sees the blue-green lines with nearly its peak sensitivity, but is virtually blind to the red hydrogen line.

The three humped curves labeled B, G, and R are the relative sensitivities of the three emulsion layers in High-Speed Ektachrome. The green lines of the nebula to which the eye responds fall in the dip between the peaks of the blue- and green-sensitive emulsions. On the

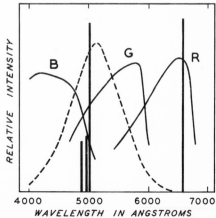

FIG. 72. Spectral response of eye and of film.

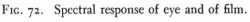

other hand, the red hydrogen line lies very near the peak of the response curve for the red-sensitive layer in the film; hence it predominates in the color photograph.

What then is the true color of the Orion nebula? If we were close enough to see its colors without a telescope, it would appear as a peculiar pearly pink—a curious blend of the red and blue-green wavelengths that our eyes and color films record with such very different results.

While nebular photography requires a telescope, the aurora offers colorful displays over a wide field of view and may be recorded by amateurs with ordinary cameras. With modern color films, use exposures running 10 to 60 seconds at f/2 or f/2.8, depending on the motion and brightness of the display. Exposures can be further increased for arcs and bands and other stationary forms. Be sure the camera is motionless during the entire exposure.

The aurora is caused in our outer atmosphere by the fluorescence of nitrogen and oxygen that have been energized by particles from the sun. As with nebulae, auroral radiation is confined to certain lines and bands in the spectrum, so that it is difficult to catch on film hues that match those seen by the observer directly. Nevertheless, color pictures of the northern lights generally give pleasing results.

Because they are brighter and have continuous spectra, the planets offer more satisfactory results in color to the amateur who has the proper telescope and camera equipment. Images of Mars, Jupiter, and Saturn are discouragingly small in amateur telescopes, even with effective focal lengths of 600 to 700 inches. Image brightness at f/50 or f/70 is low, so a fast (and more grainy) film must be used.

With a daylight speed index of 160, High-Speed Ektachrome allows Mars' colors to be recorded in $\frac{1}{2}$ second at f/50. Exposures for Jupiter run about 1 second and show considerable color detail in the various belts and zones, and in some years the giant Red Spot is prominent. If you observe where the air is very steady, Kodachrome-II (speed 25) or Kodachrome-X (speed 64) may be useful, their fine grain favoring resolution of planetary details. Shorter exposures of smaller images should also be explored on these films.

My method of photographing planets is to project their images through a microscope objective or eyepiece onto the 35-mm color film held in a single-lens reflex camera. The camera lens is removed and an extension tube inserted to hold the film perpendicular to the optical axis, with focusing on the camera ground glass. Usually, I take two pictures of a planet on each frame, and at least ten or twenty pictures are taken at each observing session. Almost invariably, one or two of them will have superior detail, the rest being more affected by air turbulence,

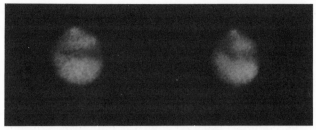

FIG. 73. Photographs of Mars originally taken in color, 1¼ hours apart, by the author on August 25, 1956. He used ½-second exposures at f/51 (with eyepiece projection on his 12-inch reflector) on Ektachrome E–2 film.

camera or telescope motion, or poor focus. Image motion can be reduced by setting the camera shutter for a time exposure and manually removing a cardboard shield to admit light to the telescope tube. A clock-driven equatorial mounting helps, and is essential when focal lengths of 600 inches are used with exposures of ½ second or more.

For color prints, I first make 3X enlargements onto Kodachrome film. Since the brightness range of a planet image is limited, the camera film may be underexposed, appearing dark on projection. The shorter exposure times give maximum image sharpness. Enlarging and rephotographing brings the pictures to normal brightness and raises the contrast substantially. Prints made from these enlargements include further enlargement and increase the contrast and color saturation, with pleasing results.

NOTE: Further information on astrophotography in color is given by William C. Miller in the December 1962, *Publications* of the Astronomical Society of the Pacific. For an album of a dozen celestial color prints taken by Miller on Super Anscochrome with the giant Palomar Observatory telescopes, order "Ansconian Color Photographs" for 80 cents from the Hayden Planetarium Book Corner, New York, New York 10024.

Color photographs of astronomical bodies make fine displays and have proved helpful to astronomers in noting details and overall patterns missed on black-and-white photos. Small objects (planets) must be taken through the eyepiece ("in projection") in order to show any detail. Large, faint objects, such as nebulae or galaxies, require long exposures on color film, and it is advisable to try first with ordinary black-and-white film.

For quantitative measurements of star colors, professional astronomers generally take two or more photographs of the same field through colored filters on black-and-white films or plates. The brightness measured on a "red photograph" (through a red filter) will show reddish stars relatively brighter than bluish ones. On a "blue photograph" the effect is opposite, and the difference between the two is a measure of color.

More detailed analysis of the colors of light from a star can be made with a spectroscope (in which the colors can be seen, spread out in a spectrum from red to blue) or with a spectrograph (in which the spectrum can be photographed). As shown below, these instruments must be attached to the telescope in place of the eyepiece, with the entrance slit at the focus of the objective lens or mirror, so that light from only one star gets through the slit.   — T L P

Make Your Own
Spectroscope

EARLE B. BROWN

(*Sky and Telescope*, September 1942)

. . . Spectroscopy plays such a large part in modern astronomy that the amateur astronomer ought to be in a position to learn something about it firsthand, especially when it is not so difficult a job to build a spectroscope of considerable power.

The requirements are a dispersing element, two small achromatic lenses, an eyepiece, and a few odd pieces of metal, plus a little mechanical ingenuity.

The dispersing element can be either a prism or a diffraction grating. A replica grating of about 15,000 lines per inch can be purchased at a scientific supply house for two or three dollars and will give excellent spectra, quite satisfactory for anything except quantitative work. If the amateur can secure a 60° flint glass prism, it will probably be more satisfactory, since the diffraction grating is too wasteful of light for use on stars with anything less than a 12-inch telescope, and then only on the very brightest. For the sun, the grating is much superior. If desired, the instrument may be constructed so as to be interchangeable for prism or grating.

The lens should be of short focal length, since if the instrument is to be mounted on the telescope, it must be kept as compact as possible. It is not absolutely essential that the lenses be achromatic, but there may be some difficulty in focusing if they are not. The eyepiece should be of about $\frac{1}{2}$-inch focal length, since we want considerable magnification but must not reduce our field too much. The lenses should be equal in diameter to the width of the prism face—not greater, since we would then waste much of the light. It is better to have them too small. Larger lenses can be diaphragmed down to the proper size.

There will be five principal parts to our spectroscope: slit, collimator, prism or grating mounting, view telescope, and spectroscope mounting.

Slit. This will be the most difficult part to make. The two "leaves," or "jaws," should have perfectly straight, smooth edges and must be mounted parallel. One of the leaves should be so mounted as to be adjustable for varying the width of the slit. It is not possible for the amateur to make the slit leaves smooth and straight in the original cutting operation. They must be mounted side by side, and the edges carefully ground until they can be closed light-tight without pressure. A good device is a piece of cloth impregnated with fine carborundum. The actual surface of contact of the two leaves should be very nearly, but not quite, a knife edge. Steel is probably the best material.

Collimator. Use the lens of shorter focal length for the collimator. A metal tube is prepared so that the slit can be mounted at the opposite end from the lens, and at its principal focus. The collimator tube should be carefully blackened inside with *flat* black paint. If the inside surface is roughened in some way, the effect of the blackening will be enhanced. The collimator is attached rigidly to the mounting of the instrument.

Prism or Grating Mounting. The dispersing element, whether prism or grating, is mounted immediately in front of the collimator, and in approximately the position shown in Figure 74. In the case of the grating, rotation should be permitted through at least 90°. The axis of rotation should intersect the optical axis of the collimator and be perpendicular thereto. The grating itself should have its center on the optical axis, and have its lines in a vertical plane.

View Telescope. Use the lens of longer focal length for the view telescope. The view telescope is merely an ordinary refracting telescope, with the eyepiece at principal focus, and the objective placed close

Fig. 74. Optical system of the spectroscope. A is the angle of incidence to make D the angle of minimum deviation. The position of a grating in place of a prism is shown by the dashed lines. Detail of the slit is not shown.

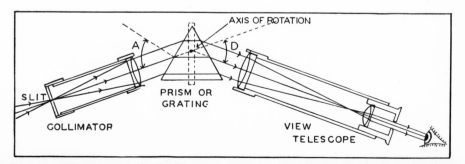

to the prism or grating. It is preferable if the view telescope is mounted so as to swing about the axis of rotation of the prism or grating, but this feature is not essential. If the view telescope rotates, the prism or grating need not do so. In this case, the grating is mounted perpendicularly to the optical axis of the collimator, and the prism is mounted at the angle of minimum deviation, which is, for a 60° prism, about 50° (the angle between the normal of the prism face and the entering ray). The view telescope, of course, must be blackened inside.

Mounting.   No general type of mounting can be given. It will be up to the individual to mount the instrument so that it is readily attachable to his telescope, with the slit in the center of the telescope's focal plane. The instrument will weigh several pounds, and so must be counterbalanced.

Using the Instrument.   In use, the image of a star, or the sun, is focused on the slit, and the spectrum is observed through the eyepiece of the view telescope. If a grating is used, the entire spectrum will not be visible in the field of view, and the view telescope or grating must be rotated slightly to bring the remainder into the field.

When the light of a faint planet, star, or nebula is spread out into a spectrum it becomes too faint to see (hence the use of a spectrograph). The sun provides much more light—so much as to be dangerous at the focus of a telescope—and offers the interesting features described below.   —T L P

....

Observing the Sun

DAVID W. ROSEBRUGH

(Sky and Telescope, May 1951)

Unlike variable star observing, which is an austere activity little likely to attract neighbors to your telescope, solar observing is prone to take on the aspects of a children's party, with adults on the outer fringe asking, Can you tell if it's going to rain tomorrow?

Caution! Caution!

Be sure that neither children nor adults damage their eyes by looking through the finder, which, of course, is not equipped with a solar eyepiece, or by pressing their eyes to the exit rays from the Herschel wedge in the solar eyepiece. Don't leave an unattended, uncapped telescope and finder sitting on a mount in such a location that a youngster can point it toward the sun.

Be sure that your solar eyepiece assembly is entirely safe to use. It is imperative to have at least one reflection off unsilvered glass before allowing the sun's light to reach the dark filter and eyepiece. I have two friends who developed scotomas in their eyes while observing the sun when their dark filters cracked. A scotoma is a burned-out spot or streak on the retina which produces an impression like an intermittent shadow hovering before the eyes.

I have had two dark glasses crack in my own telescopes—when I foolishly omitted the reflection off unsilvered glass because I thought the sun was too low in the sky, in one case, and because I had dia-phragmed down my objective in the other. Fortunately, I had stepped back each time, so my eye was not damaged, but this was just dumb luck. I have had two crossed Polaroids burn out before my eyes, but this change took some minutes, so it did not do any damage to my eye.

Of course, if one is studying the sun by projecting its image on a white surface, the reflection off the unsilvered face of the Herschel wedge is not required.

It would seem needless to caution observers against looking at the sun with the naked eye. But the late Dr. William L. Holt, the AAVSO observer who sent in the millionth observation on variable stars in 1946, told me that he had had at least one patient who had permanently damaged her eyes while looking at a partial eclipse of the sun. So everyone should be cautioned against looking at the sun with the naked eye unless his eyes are shaded by a suitable dark glass or filter of high density.

Solar Observing Programs

The regular observations of the sun made by members of the Solar Division of the American Association of Variable Star Observers may be grouped for convenience into those of a statistical nature, those which deal with manifestations of unusual solar activities, and collateral studies.

Statistical studies include sunspot counting, estimation of the granulation of the sun's photosphere, measurements of foreshortening of sunspots, and measurements of the solar constant of radiation (made with an electric-eye type of radiation meter).

Unusual solar activities include color in sunspots, and sudden or unusual growth in the activity of any portion of the sun's surface. Also included in this category are studies of evidence of rotation in sunspots and studies of prominences with a monochromator.

Collateral studies include reports of aurorae and of migratory birds seen crossing the sun's disk during solar observations.

The backbone of the first three subdivisions of the statistical studies listed above is sunspot counting. The Solar Division has a supply of "Instructions for Reporting Visual Sunspot Observations," which describes this procedure.

Let me warn you, however, that these observations are not easy to make. Don't think you can go out and count sunspots as you would roses in your garden. Before you can count sunspots intelligently, you must have some idea of the diversity of appearance which spots, and especially groups, may present, and you must learn to orient the sun so that you know where east, west, north, south, and the solar equator lie. In addition while the casual observer of variable stars can and often does contribute observations of use, only the regular and reliable sunspot observer is of value in the Solar Division program.

Great statistical reliability is required, and your observations at first will be used merely for establishing your reliability weighting, W_i, and your observatory constant, K_i (i means individual). There may be an opportunity for very useful study here for anyone who is statistically inclined, to help in the problems that face the determination of the American sunspot number.

As is well known, Schwabe was the first person to establish the periodicity of sunspots, working from 1826 to 1857. R. Wolf, of Zurich, carried forward this work, using a 3-inch refractor and a power of 64, until his death in 1893. Wolf also used old records to carry back the sunspot number to 1745 with some completeness and to 1610 using such records as were available. . . . The Zurich sunspot number, R_Z, is the standard for the world. It is largely based upon the work of one observatory with a continuing tradition and practice.

It seems, however, in the present uncertain state of the world, that scientists should not be dependent upon one source alone for so important an index of the sun's activity. Starting in 1944 an American sunspot number, R_A, has been derived mainly from observations by amateurs in the Western Hemisphere, although Zurich's observations are included also. It is based, not upon the work of a few observers with a tradition, but upon the work of many amateurs without tradition, and in the beginning without much experience. Their work has thus far been blended into a whole by statistical means at the Central Propagation Laboratory of the National Bureau of Standards in Washington, D.C.

The principle is considered to be sound, but the American number has considerably exceeded the Zurich number, by what is now as much as 33 per cent. The reason for this is not clearly known. Perhaps the calibration, which was based on six months of Zurich observations in 1944 and 1945, was not suitable. It seems to the writer, however, that it is more likely that the American amateur observers, who form the principal contributors toward the determination of the American number, gradually improve their observing techniques and perhaps their equipment during the first three to five years, after which they become statistically reliable. During this entire period the individual's visual acuity is probably rising. . . .

It has been concluded recently by the Solar Division head and his technical advisers that for purposes of statistical reliability all observers should employ as nearly as possible the same instrumental means that Wolf used, and it is suggested that new observers, at least, equip themselves with instruments answering as nearly as possible the following specifications: a 3-inch refractor, or a larger one diaphragmed down to 3 inches, with a solar eyepiece in which there is one reflection off unsilvered glass, a dark glass consisting of a Willson Products, Inc. (Reading, Pennsylvania) atomic hydrogen welding goggle glass, No. 10, 12, or 14, and an eyepiece giving a power of 64. . . .

••

A Simple Spectroscope
for Solar-prominence
Observations

HAROLD LEINBACH

(*Sky and Telescope*, January 1953)

A quartz monochromator is a powerful instrument for observing various solar phenomena, especially the prominences. For those observers with mechanical ability and great patience, the construction of such an instrument is a worthwhile investment in time and money. However, there are those of us who do not have the time or the necessary practical optical experience to undertake such a task, and yet we would like to see just what these prominences look like with our own telescopes. In this case a simple instrument such as the one described below will nicely fill the bill, and at a very moderate cost. And with a simple spectroscope we may have the thrill of repeating the same experiment first performed independently by Janssen and Lockyer in 1868, which marked the first time that solar prominences were seen without the aid of a solar eclipse.

C. A. Young, in his book *The Sun* [New York, Appleton, 1881], gives a good historical and technical background of spectroscopic observations of prominences, and for those who have access to the book, the chapters on the spectroscope and on solar prominences are strongly recommended.

For our purposes, a grating spectroscope is required to obtain the necessary dispersion for the size of instrument being considered. A reflecting grating type was finally built by the writer, although a transmission grating would also have worked. It is, however, not feasible to use a single-prism instrument, because of the low dispersion in the red portion of the spectrum, where most of the solar observations will be made.

Constructing the spectroscope.   The author was fortunate in being able to borrow two small laboratory-type telescopes, a simple slit, and a good replica reflection grating from the physics department of South Dakota State College, where he was then (1949) a student. The only problem was to mount the components suitably.

The photograph in Figure 75 gives an overall view of the instrument, which is to be attached to the eye end of the main telescope. The framework consists of two pieces of strap iron riveted to the circular plate at the left. The longitudinal axes of the strap iron pass through the center of the plate. The view telescope and collimator are strapped to V-block assemblies, which are in turn bolted to the framework. . . .

After the spectroscope was attached to the main telescope, it was

Fig. 75. The spectroscope constructed by Harold Leinbach was fitted with an adapter tube for a 5-inch refractor. The grating is at the lower left. A weight of several pounds was attached to the objective end of the telescope to counterbalance this spectroscope.

found that the strap-iron framework was not strong enough, and two pieces of aluminum pipe were welded together at the 37° angle of the framework, and then bolted to the strap iron to provide rigidity.

The grating table is composed of a second plate of the same diameter as the base plate. A long bolt was soldered to the center of the upper disk, and this passes through a hole in the center of the lower plate. A compression spring was inserted between the nut and the lower plate, thus tending to hold the upper and lower plates together. The disks are held apart by three symmetrically placed bolts, which pass through nuts soldered to the bottom disk. These bolts allow for the necessary adjustments of the height of the grating table.

A piece of brass with a lip bent at right angles is bolted to the top plate and supports the grating. It is important that this plate be exactly perpendicular to the grating table, as the grating plane must be perpendicular to the plane of the optical axes for proper adjustment of the instrument.

The two telescopes used in the spectroscope have achromatic objectives of 1-inch aperture with a focal length of about 11 inches. Of course, the eyepiece of one telescope is removed so that it can be used for the collimator. The slit is the type sometimes used in elementary optical experiments, and works on the parallelogram principle. Since the slit mounting is bolted directly to the frame of this instrument, it is necessary to slide the collimator back and forth in the V-blocks in order to focus the slit. This construction was chosen for the sake of convenience only. A first-class instrument would have the slit as an integral part of the collimator, in order to do away with any possible stray light, such as might be encountered using the construction described.

Adjusting the spectroscope. An excellent description of how to adjust this type of spectroscope for prominence observations can be found in Young's book. The basic steps are:

1. The view telescope and collimator axes must be coplanar, and this plane must be perpendicular to the plane of the grating. These adjustments are made by suitably changing the heights of the V-blocks and by adjusting the leveling screws on the grating table.

2. The slit must be at the focus of the collimator. This adjustment may be made as follows: Remove the grating table and the view telescope. Focus the view telescope for infinity by viewing a distant object. Now look at the objective end of the collimator with the focused telescope, making sure that the optical axes of the collimator and telescope coincide. Now focus the slit (which entails moving the collimator back and forth in the instrument described here) until the slit appears as a sharp line. When this condition is fulfilled, the light emerging from the collimator is parallel.

3. The direction of the slit must be parallel to the lines of the grating, and these lines in turn must be perpendicular to the plane of the optical axes. If the spectrum appears to be curved as the grating is rotated, the grating is not perpendicular to the plane of the optical axes. If the spectrum has an upward or downward motion as the grating is rotated, the lines on the grating are not perpendicular to the optical axes of the system.

Using the spectroscope for prominence observations. The visible disk of the sun is known as the photosphere. Above the photosphere lies a cooler layer of gas, the so-called reversing layer, and, in turn, above this region is the chromosphere. When we view the disk of the sun with a spectroscope, we see a continuous spectrum interrupted by a multitude of dark absorption lines, the Fraunhofer lines. However, if we view the very edge of the sun, we see not only many Fraunhofer lines, but we also see that some of the Fraunhofer lines have been replaced by bright emission lines. One important emission line is the red H-alpha line of hydrogen, which has a wavelength of 6563 angstrom units.

The spectrum is really nothing more than an infinite number of images of the slit. The H-alpha line, then, is one of these images, and hence if the slit is unevenly illuminated, as it would be if we were looking at a prominence, we would expect that the spectral line would also be unevenly illuminated, and such is the case. If we now open the slit little by little, we are taking in more and more of the image of the prominence, and hence the prominence will begin to take shape in the widening H-alpha line. Unfortunately, a width is soon reached where the increasing background light obscures the image of the prominence. Thus, there is a limit to which we can open the slit. This means that if we are using a large image of the sun, certain prominences may be too big to include in the widened H-alpha line, and we will then have to build up a mental image of them while scanning the limb of the sun.

The spectroscope is effective in showing us the prominences because it tends to reduce the solar continuum by dispersion without materially decreasing the monochromatic light from the prominence. With a grating instrument, especially when the second-order H-alpha line is used, it will be necessary to place a red filter in the optical train of the telescope in order to cut out all scattered light of other colors, and particularly to cut out the overlapping third-order violet spectrum.

The author's spectroscope was used with a 5-inch f/15 refractor diaphragmed to $4\frac{1}{4}$ inches, the spectroscope being attached to the eyepiece adapter tube of the telescope. With the 2-inch image size used, it was found that prominences of the order of 50,000 miles in height could be seen in their entirety, with fair contrast with the background light. However, very large prominences could only be seen by allowing the image to drift across the slit. Since observations are best made with the slit tangential to the limb of the sun, the spectroscope must be rotated in order to view different sections of the solar limb.

In addition to the prominences in the red H-alpha line, brighter ones may be seen in the blue-green H-beta line at 4861 angstroms. The very brightest could even be seen in the helium D_3 line, at 5876 angstroms, which lies close to the well-known sodium doublet in the yellow portion of the spectrum.

This simple spectroscope is not adaptable for taking photographs of solar prominences. For that work a spectroheliograph is needed, or better still, a quartz monochromator. The monochromator is also an ideal visual instrument, because extraneous scattered light is almost non-existent, and there is no distortion of the image. Hence, contrast is high and very fine detail can be seen. On the other hand, the spectroscope can be used to view the entire visible spectrum.

The serious solar observer dreams of the day when he has his own monochromator, but until then, and for the more casual amateur, the simple spectroscope does afford a way to observe one of the most fascinating of all celestial phenomena, the solar prominences.

Several other accessories are now used on telescopes, and others are being devised. The photoelectric photometer is a photocell mounted so that the light of one star can shine on it through a small hole placed at the focus of a telescope. The electric output of the cell is amplified, measured by a meter, and converted to brightness or magnitude. Colored filters can be used in front of the photocell; the difference between "red readings" and "blue readings" measures the color of the star. This method is more accurate than photography, but requires more time if many stars are to be measured in one field.

Both photographs and photoelectric measurements can be taken through Polaroid filters that transmit light polarized in one direction only. Ordinary light is unpolarized, and observations are the same regardless of how the Polaroid filter is turned. When the light of stars or nebulae is polarized, however, the brightness as seen through a Polaroid will change as the Polaroid is turned; a measure of the amount of change indicates the amount of polarization. A simple demonstration of this effect can be made by looking at the blue sky through Polaroid glasses and turning the glasses around. In fact, Polaroid glasses can be used in this same manner behind the eyepiece of a telescope to check (roughly) whether light from a nebula is polarized. — TLP

Special-Purpose
Telescopes

As the interests of astronomers have changed (from charting the sky, to the surface detail on planets, to analysis of the light from single stars, to studies of clusters and the general spread of stars and galaxies over the sky), telescopes have changed also. Earlier chapters showed the advantages and disadvantages of mirrors and lenses, and the accessories that make possible a variety of measurements. This chapter includes discussion of telescope designs specially suited to various studies. Some of these special-purpose instruments are complex and expensive, appropriate only for professional use; others are simpler and have been constructed by amateurs.

Astronomical photography offers great advantage when a large region of the sky can be photographed all at once. Special-purpose telescopes designed to photograph a large field are called wide-angle cameras. Other specially designed telescopes, used for observing the bright sun, are called solar telescopes. These telescopes are discussed here, and for completeness, a brief discussion of radiotelescopes is also included, although this book is devoted mainly to optical telescopes.

As the following article shows, small lenses were first used for wide-angle cameras. They had short focal lengths, allowing a large region of the sky to be fitted on a photographic plate of reasonable size (8 by 10 inches or smaller). The lens aperture was small because it is difficult to construct an accurate lens with aperture more than a small fraction of the focal length, and this small aperture made these cameras "slow" (long exposures were necessary to record faint stars). Mirrors were considered useless for wide-angle photography because a paraboloid reflector gives a poor focus off the axis of the paraboloid (or away from the center of the picture; see p. 31). Then, about thirty years ago, a combination of spherical mirror with an oddly shaped lens was invented.

— T L P

....

The Schmidt Astronomical Camera

HAROLD A. LOWER

(*The Sky*, October 1938)

Visual observation, although by no means a lost art, is being displaced to an ever increasing extent by photography at all modern observatories. New telescopes and their accessories are being built primarily for use as photographic instruments. This has resulted in the production of a number of new types of astronomical instruments, one of the latest of which is the Schmidt camera.

Wide-field cameras for use as search instruments have been in use for many years, but most of them have been comparatively slow. Forty years ago E. E. Barnard made an extensive survey of the Milky Way with a wide-field camera. His beautiful photographs [such as Fig. 76] are unsurpassed, even today, but the exposures required were very long —from four to eight hours in many cases. An f/1 Schmidt camera, with the fast films which are now available, can photograph the same regions with exposures of only two minutes.

The Schmidt is remarkable not only for its speed, but for its simplicity and comparative cheapness. Instead of using four or more lenses made from several types of optical glass, the Schmidt employs a concave spherical mirror and a single thin lens. As most of the work of bending the rays of light to a focus is done by the mirror, the curve of the lens can be very shallow, and as a result chromatic aberration is so slight that for cameras of reasonable size it can be ignored.

The field of best focus of the Schmidt, instead of being flat as in the usual lens-type camera, is strongly curved, being convex toward the mirror and having a radius of curvature equal to the focal length. This disadvantage, however, is easily overcome by bending the film to fit the focal surface. Films for a Schmidt are cut circular, and are sprung

Fig. 76. Section of the Milky Way in Cygnus, showing the North America and filamentary nebulae, photographed by E. E. Barnard with a lens camera. Figure 79 shows part of the same region.

to the proper curve by a metal ring which presses the film against a metal disk having a suitable radius of curvature. When removed from the holder, the films spring flat again and can be printed in the usual manner.

All photographic instruments suffer from aberrations to a greater or less extent, and the Schmidt is no exception. However, it is free from coma and spherical aberration and is affected only slightly by chromatic aberration and astigmatism. As a result, definition is excellent over a field about 12° in diameter, and if desired, the field can be increased to as much as 20° before the definition at the edge begins to deteriorate seriously.

Several years ago Charles A. Lower and the writer constructed an 8-inch Schmidt camera with a focal ratio f/1. As this instrument was intended primarily for use in photographing meteors and for searching for clouds of obscuring matter in the Milky Way, it was designed for great speed, and to cover a field of 20°. For most purposes an f/2 covering a field of 12° would be amply fast and would be considerably easier to construct. . . .

Extreme speed may be disadvantageous, since sky fog limits the exposure to only a few minutes. When using film with a Weston rating of 24, the longest exposure which can be made with our camera is 15 minutes. Longer than that, the sky fog caused by the general luminosity of the night sky begins to blot out faint objects on the film. . . .

Quite a number of observatories are now using Schmidt cameras or have cameras under construction. These range in size from a small instrument of $3\frac{3}{4}$ inches aperture, which was used by Yerkes astronomers

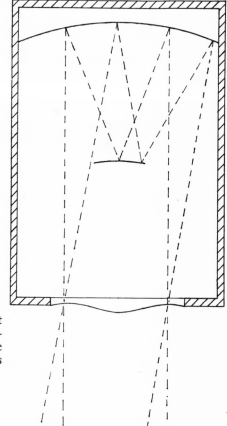

FIG. 77. Optical system of the Schmidt camera, drawn to scale except for the thickness and curvature of the lens, which are greatly exaggerated. The surface of the lens is flat to about 0.012 inch.

in the investigation of the famous red nebula near Antares, to the 18-inch f/2 Schmidt on Mount Palomar, which has been used in the search for supernovae. The Palomar camera has already found at least two super-novae and has proved so satisfactory that a 48-inch f/2.5 Schmidt is now under construction. Mount Wilson also has several Schmidts and is building more. These will be used mainly for spectrographic work.

Amateurs who may be planning to build instruments of this type will find information on the design and construction of Schmidt cameras in *Amateur Telescope Making—Advanced* [A. G. Ingalls, ed., New York, Scientific American Publishing Co., latest edition, 1953]. How-ever, as I do not want to make any enemies, I am not advising anyone to attempt a Schmidt unless he already has considerable experience in telescope making. For those who have mastered the art of mirror and lens making and are looking for more worlds to conquer, I can heartily recommend the Schmidt as an interesting and useful instrument.

■■

From the Life of
Bernhard Schmidt

A. A. WACHMANN

(*Sky and Telescope*, November 1955)

If you were to form a picture of Bernhard Voldemar Schmidt as his contemporaries saw him, and perhaps had to see him, it would be a caricature of the real Schmidt, both as an optical artist and as a man. Although he was at times attracted by other people—and there were many who thought they knew him well—basically he recoiled from them.

"Only one man alone is worth anything. Put two men together and they quarrel. A hundred of them make a rabble, and if there are a thousand or more, they'll start a war." This, in his own words, was his attitude to his fellow men.

From this attitude resulted a rather peculiar, word-sparing, and shy man, by nature even disobliging and inaccessible, who faced life alone. This explains why we have no systematic accounts of his life and why he never personally instructed others in the making of optical instru-ments, an art that he had developed to the utmost. He resisted repeated appeals to preserve in writing his professional experiences, saying: "Let the others collect that experience themselves. If I were to write it down, it would so shock the astronomers and the opticians that I'd probably never get another order to construct anything."

And thus we are left in the dark as to how he actually arrived, after one false start, at his great invention in 1929 of the coma-free reflecting system. . . .

His surviving brother gives us some reminiscences of their youthful days together at their birthplace on the Estonian island of Nargen. He was rather shy, often lost in thought, but always busy with something interesting." . . .

The persistent tale that he found the bottom of a broken bottle on the beach of his native island and ground it into a lens with sea sand is almost too good to be true. But it is likely that after the unlucky experiment with explosives that cost him his right forearm he found leisure in 1895 to follow his astronomical and optical bent, when at the age of sixteen he became a night telegraph operator for the coast guard station at Reval. Later he was a photograph retoucher, and in 1898 he started work for the Volta firm, which manufactured electrical instruments. . . .

Toward the end of 1901, at Mittweida, near Jena, Schmidt systematically began to grind small mirrors. He had to grind the mirrors in his boardinghouse room, and on top of a polished chest of drawers. His otherwise friendly landlady objected to such disrespect for a worthy

FIG. 78. Bernhard Schmidt in his workshop. (Photograph courtesy A. A. Wachmann.)

old piece of furniture and threw him out. So he went to work in unfurnished rooms and finally in a deserted bowling alley, which might be called the Bernhard Schmidt Optical Works.

It was the parabolic mirrors of up to 20-centimeters diameter produced in this workshop that made his name famous in amateur circles. . . . He wrote on May 29, 1904, to the Potsdam Astrophysical Observatory: "Permit me to ask whether you are interested in reflecting telescopes, for I would gladly provide a large mirror for the observatory at my own cost, so that I could find out what a large mirror can do photographically after it is mounted."

From this first contact with astronomers, developed a close relationship with the Potsdam Observatory, for both H. C. Vogel and K. Schwarzschild, the directors in his time, immediately recognized his genius in making fine optical surfaces. . . .

The fruitful relations with Potsdam broke off with . . . Schmidt's temporary internment as an enemy alien during World War I. This is the place to destroy the legend of Schmidt's German ancestry, which is repeated in all accounts of the man, in Germany and abroad. The name Schmidt, not exactly rare among Germans, was assumed by an ancestor of Bernhard Schmidt, named Matts, at a time when the few Germans in the Baltic countries formed a ruling class, and when it was advantageous to change an Estonian name. . . .

Schmidt's favorite instrument, his horizontal reflector, . . . consisted of a siderostat and parabolic mirrors of 11 to 31 meters focal length.

A great collection of very beautiful photographs of sun, moon, and planets testifies not only to the quality of the instrument but to the high observing skill of Schmidt, whose great persistence and knowledge of atmospheric conditions particularly aided him. . . .

On March 12, 1916, he wrote to Professor R. Schorr, then director of the Hamburg Observatory, "Allow me to send you some astronomical photographs that I have recently taken here at Mittweida." . . .

These exceptionally fine pictures completely convinced Schorr, and in October 1916, Schmidt received an order to build an identical horizontal telescope for the Hamburg Observatory. . . .

After this was finished, things did not go too well. In April 1925, Schmidt was discouraged: "Since I got back [from Hamburg] not a single order has come in. I'm ready to turn my whole stock into junk and sell it for old iron and charcoal, and then take up something new." But he was diverted from this step by Professor E. Schoenberg, of Greifswald, who purchased a horizontal reflector. . . .

Still later, one of Schmidt's letters to Schorr ends with a gleam of hope for astronomical optics. "By any chance do you have anything for me to do [at the Hamburg Observatory] in Bergedorf? Recently I have been trying out a new mirror combination, a kind of unperforated Cassegrain with complete elimination of coma and astigmatism." This is the first indication of the great problem which was from now on to occupy him.

On Schorr's invitation, toward the close of 1926 Schmidt began his activity at the Hamburg-Bergedorf Observatory as a volunteer staff member. Now he had not only the facilities of a large institution at his disposal, but the steady encouragement of Schorr, who kept him busy with optical and delicate mechanical construction work.

A glance into his workshop in the basement of the main building would reveal not only his industry but his genius at getting astounding results from apparently primitive means. Few people managed to enter there, where he worked at any hour of the day or night. If, however, he accepted you, and if you were content to watch in silence as you smoked, then you saw the true artist at work. . . .

He always knew the right moment to break off polishing to test the optical surface, whether with an artificial star or by interference fringes. Perhaps the real secret of his success lay in this, and in the ability of his practiced eye to detect the least deviation of the surface from the ideal figure. Clear reasoning and long years of experience at once told him how and by what amount these deviations were to be corrected. You would wonder at the delicacy of touch of his left hand, the only one he had. Schmidt himself said, "My hand is more sensitive than the finest gauge." . . .

In this setting, he put his great idea into practical form. Here was made the world's first Schmidt telescope, with the unheard-of focal ratio of $f/1.75$, which photographed the sky with a previously unknown sharpness [Fig. 79] that is now everywhere associated with the name of Schmidt.

It is astonishing to say the least, and also shameful, that despite loud praise for this revolutionary invention, and despite the very low delivery price of 5500 marks, not a single order was placed! Negotiations with a Russian importing agency were stalled by foreign-exchange difficulties, and another order fell through. . . .

It was a deep tragedy, an inventor's fate, that Bernhard Schmidt never lived to see the astonishing spread of his coma-free telescope after 1936, when Schorr lifted the secrecy from how its correcting plate was made.

Yet disillusionment did not prevent Schmidt from attacking further problems. For example, there is the design of a field-flattening lens to be added to the original Schmidt telescope. He anticipated increasing the focal ratio to $f/1$, and even more, that a lens system would be better

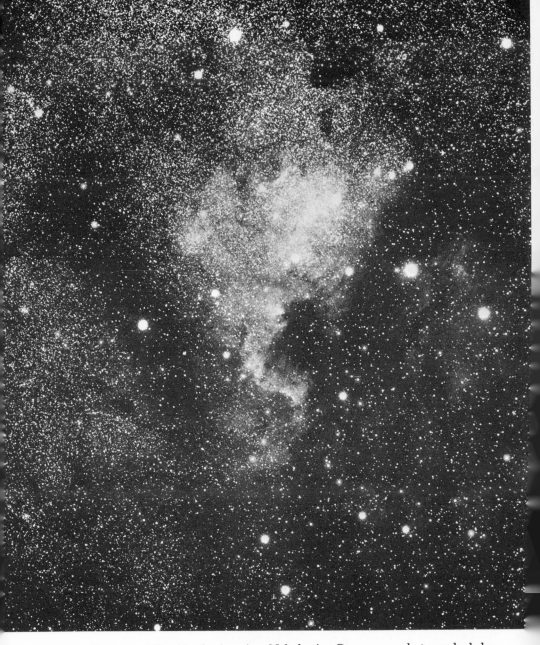

FIG. 79. The North America Nebula in Cygnus as photographed by Bernhard Schmidt on December 21, 1932, at Hamburg Observatory with the original Schmidt camera. Through an ingenious elimination of optical aberrations, a Schmidt camera combines large light grasp, sharpness of images, and wide field to an unrivaled degree. (Photograph courtesy A. A. Wachmann.)

than a correcting plate. He made detailed calculations for this, and made a first model, a typical wood-and-screw assembly of his which, despite its primitiveness, in the artist's hands took good photographs. . . .

His last project was a special reflecting system—a 60-centimeter f/2 spherical mirror from which light passed through a pair of perforated lenses, the back face of one of which was silvered to form the secondary mirror! Then death took the polishing tool from his hands, twenty years ago this December [1955].

Twenty years can change a world, but they have not dimmed the fame of a remarkable man, the greatest optical worker of our century, Bernhard Schmidt. Despite the passage of time, mirrors of high optical perfection and of the greatest astronomical significance will always remain associated with his name.

···

The New Schmidt Telescope of the Hamburg Observatory

O. HECKMANN

(*Sky and Telescope*, November 1955)

Even before World War II, it had been planned to modernize the Hamburg Observatory (located at Bergedorf, a suburb of Hamburg, Germany) by the addition of a large Schmidt-type telescope. But funds obtained at that time were completely depreciated as a result of the war, so the project had to be started afresh.

In 1947 we began design of the instrument, and in 1949 the first appropriation for the purpose appeared in the budget of the Hamburg state government. Work has progressed steadily, and the new instrument was dedicated on August 19 and 20, this year. The occasion provided an opportunity for an international gathering of more than one hundred and fifty astronomers, who heard a symposium on Schmidt telescopes and their uses. . . .

Before the war we had been thinking of an instrument with a correcting plate 80 centimeters (31.5 inches) in diameter, a mirror of 100 centimeters, and a 160-centimeter focal length. For the new project, however, we chose 80, 120, and 240 centimeters respectively, giving a focal ratio of f/3.

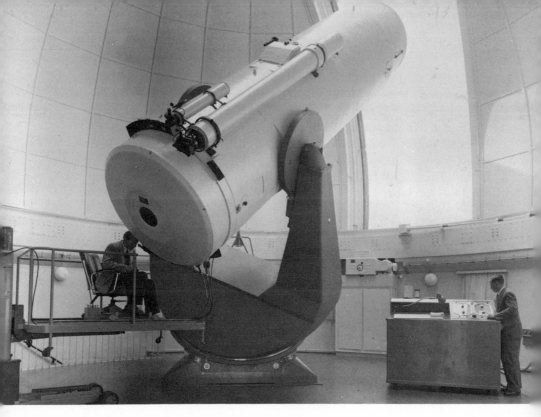

Fig. 80. The Schmidt telescope, seen here from the north, has a principal supporting unit with two oil-pad bearings. The preset and control panels are in a desk (right) that may be moved to any convenient place on the observatory floor. At the left is the hydraulic lift that carries the observer. Midway along the upper side of the telescope tube is the cover of the opening through which photographic plates are inserted. (Hamburg Observatory photograph.)

Fig. 81. This diagram shows the principle of the mounting. The latitude of the observatory is $53\frac{1}{2}°$ north. The horizontal line below the oil pads at O represents the floor of the observing chamber in Figure 80.

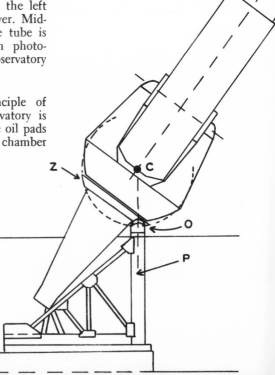

The contract for optics and tube, which form an integral unit, was given to the firm of Carl Zeiss, in Jena. The mounting was built at Hamburg in the machine shops of Heidenreich and Harbeck, under the supervision of Walter Strewinski. Cooperation between the two firms was excellent, even though Hamburg and Jena lie in two politically different parts of Germany. By the fall of 1954 the assembly of the instrument was substantially complete, and last winter and spring we could check its operation in detail.

The mirror is made of ZK7 Schott glass, which has a rather small coefficient of thermal expansion, even though it is higher than that of Pyrex glass. The back side of the mirror has been ground convex, so the mirror is bounded by two concentric spherical surfaces. This should provide more thermal homogeneity than with a mirror having a flat back and thick edges.

The correcting plate was made from UBK7 glass, which transmits ultraviolet light well. . . .

Originally we had planned to bend it into a meniscus shape, to lessen the often very undesirable reflections from the plate. This idea ran into serious difficulties during manufacture; consequently, the outer face of the correcting plate is plane, while the inner surface has the well-known profile of the Schmidt corrector. The least thickness of the correcting plate is at a distance of 0.87 of its radius from the center, thereby minimizing chromatic aberration. . . .

We tested the optics carefully in the laboratory and later on the sky. The circle of confusion, inspected visually, is about 0.5 second of arc in size; unsteady air and the diffusion of light in the photographic emulsion will naturally make the star images larger than this. With very good seeing, the smallest star images are about 0.025 millimeter in diameter. . . .

As with other Schmidt telescopes, the focal surface is located midway between the correcting plate and the mirror, and it is curved convex to the mirror. Our plates are 24 by 24 centimeters square, covering an area of the sky 5° on a side. The spherical template which is pressed against the back side of the plate is covered with a very thin rubber sheet, which takes up the tangential stresses caused by friction when the plate is bent. With plates one millimeter thick, breakage occurs only when a plate remains more than 24 hours in the plateholder. . . .

The plateholder is inserted through an opening in the tube by means of a carriage, to which different color filters can be attached as well. After it slides along a rail into the interior of the tube, the carriage is screwed firmly against three supports. The weight of the carriage, when loaded with the plateholder, is compensated by a long spiral spring at the side of the tube opposite the opening, so the plateholder carriage is inserted without effort. . . .

The two guide telescopes are fastened to the main telescope tube in such a way that no appreciable relative flexure occurs. Only one of these guide telescopes is seen in Figure 80, but the observer in the chair is looking through the eyepiece of the other. The plateholder can be focused electrically from either guide telescope. . . .

The mounting of the instrument is of the fork type, following the example of the 48-inch Palomar Schmidt—this type is particularly appropriate for conventional Schmidt telescopes. A new basic idea has been incorporated at the suggestion of Strewinski. In the diagram (Fig. 81) imagine a sphere drawn around the center of gravity (C) of all moving parts of the instrument; a portion of this sphere is marked by the dashed curve. Concentric with the polar axis, a zone (Z) of this sphere has been constructed as a bearing of steel. This bearing rests on the vertical steel pier (P) directly beneath the center of gravity, and turns on two oil-pad bearings (O) that support the entire weight of the instrument.

By this arrangement there is no weight to be supported at the lower end of the polar axis. As a consequence, it is possible to adjust the polar axis of the instrument without appreciable work against gravity. Naturally, the lower end of the polar axis must be suitably restrained in position by an adjustable ball-bearing assembly.

Thus, the telescope turns in hour angle on bearing Z, which floats on the oil film produced by the oil pads. The oil enters each pad from below through a self-adjusting biconcave "lens" of steel. The oil flows out at the edges of the lens, is collected, and is fed to the pump again.

The fork arms are made of welded sheet steel one centimeter thick. The arms have internal braces, and a special lever system substantially eliminates flexure. The crosspiece or yoke of the fork, to which the arms are bolted, is very massive in comparison to its counterpart in other instruments, and its flexure is extremely small—yet it is not unattractive in appearance. . . .

The whole instrument is electrically operated from one desk. To point the telescope at a particular heavenly object, the observer presets its position on a keyboard, to 1 second of time in right ascension and $\frac{1}{10}$ of a minute of arc in declination. Then, pressing a button turns the telescope automatically into the position desired.

The portable electrohydraulic observing platform, made by the Still Company of Hamburg, is fitted with a convenient observing chair. The observer has at hand the electric controls for moving the entire platform up, down, left, right, forward, or backward.

The platform can be removed and a heavy hydraulic support mounted on the carriage, to remove the mirror and cell from the telescope whenever the mirror needs to be aluminized again. For this purpose, the mirror is taken by elevator to a special laboratory in the east side of the observatory building. . . .

Several other large Schmidt telescopes are now in use, the best known being the one of 48-inch aperture at Mount Palomar in California. The design has also proved remarkably successful in other applications where a "fast" camera is needed—in spectrographs used on faint light sources, in television, and for other uses. The spherical mirror is easy to make, but the glass correcting plate is difficult.

Other designs of wide-angle cameras are possible, and one that is easier to make is the Maksutov camera. —T L P

....

A Cassegrainian-Maksutov Telescope Design for the Amateur

JOHN GREGORY

(*Sky and Telescope*, March 1957)

Telescope makers who take the extra effort to construct a two-element Maksutov can then enjoy many gratifying hours of fine observing. The writer has built a 5-inch instrument of this type that for convenience, ease of transporting, and observing, far outclasses the old-fashioned reflector or refractor. My own 4-inch refractor is now in moth balls.

And although you may have heard that a Maksutov is a catadioptric system requiring special design, costing upwards of a thousand dollars when commercially made, there is no question that if you are an average amateur telescope maker, you can fabricate the parts yourself. Furthermore, because of the short tube length, you will have no trouble providing an equatorial mounting. My 5-inch has an effective focal length of 100 inches, quite suitable for planetary work, yet its tube is only about a foot and a half long. . . .

D. D. Maksutov in 1944 published the basic formulas and introduced various forms of the system now named after him. The Perkin-Elmer Corporation has recently fabricated triple-element Cassegrainian-Maksutov instruments designed by James G. Baker to provide a high degree

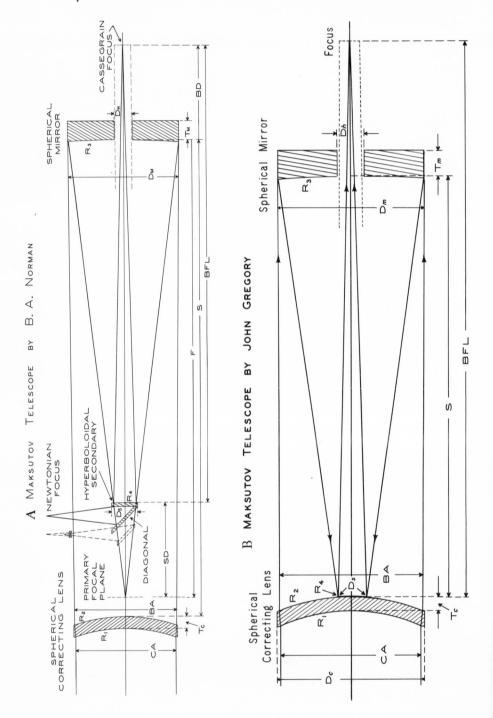

A MAKSUTOV TELESCOPE BY B. A. NORMAN

B MAKSUTOV TELESCOPE BY JOHN GREGORY

of correction for coma and astigmatism. [A triple-element design is shown in Figure 82A.]

However, for visual use and small-field photography (half a degree), the two-element design I have used makes a fine telescope with several advantages over refractors and reflectors of equal aperture. There is no secondary spider support to introduce undesirable diffraction, and there are no color fringes (secondary spectrum) that reduce image contrast. The completely closed tube does away with thermal effects, which may seriously impair resolution when an open-tubed reflector is taken from a cellar or garage into the cool night air.

Design. The Cassegrainian-Maksutov may be thought of as evolving from a Cassegrain-type reflector with a *spherical* convex secondary and a concave (spheroidal) primary of 60- to 80-per cent parabolization. Now visualize a disk or shell cut from a soap bubble of the same curvature as the secondary, with an aluminized spot in the center of the disk. This disk can be placed across the entering light beam without changing the optical characteristics of the system, as the very thin bubble shell will have no effect on the incident light.

But we would prefer the primary mirror to be spherical, for convenience and accuracy in figuring and testing. And, even if the shell were made of glass, it would be too thin to grind and polish. The shell must be made thick so it becomes self-supporting, whence it acts like a lens, introducing negative spherical aberration to the light passing through it on the way to the primary. Yet this effect is favorable, for it allows us to reduce the parabolization of the primary; in fact, we can make the primary mirror spherical.

Obviously, the thickness of the shell should then be such that its negative spherical aberration, combined with that of the secondary mirror (aluminized spot), balances the positive aberration of a spherical primary mirror. In practice, to minimize chromatic aberration of the lens, its two surfaces have slightly different radii. The formula for the axial thickness, t, that will reduce chromatic differences to an insignificant amount is

$$t = \frac{(R_2 - R_1)n^2}{n^2 - 1},$$

FIG. 82. A. Maksutov telescope by B. A. Norman (see *Sky and Telescope*, December 1957) illustrates the *triple-element* design using hyperbolic secondary mirror or flat diagonal. B. Maksutov telescope by John Gregory, with aluminized patch on the back face of the correcting lens.

where n is the index of refraction, R_1 the radius of curvature of the front surface of the corrector lens, and R_2 the radius of the back surface, which bears the secondary mirror spot.

TABLE 5. SPECIFICATIONS FOR THREE MAKSUTOV TELESCOPES*

Symbol**	Characteristic			
CA	Clear aperture of correcting lens	11.0	8.0	6.0
BA	Back aperture of correcting lens	11.25	8.18	6.14
T_C	Thickness of correcting lens	1.155	0.840	0.630
D_M	Diameter of primary mirror	12.0	8.7	6.6
T_M	Thickness of primary mirror	2.0	1.5	1.0
D_H	Diameter of hole in primary mirror	2.0	1.5	1.1
D_S	Diameter of secondary mirror	2.88	2.09	1.57
R_1	Radius of curvature of 1st lens surface	−17.094	−12.432	−9.324
R_2	Radius of curvature of 2nd lens surface	−17.747	−12.907	−9.680
R_3	Radius of curvature of primary mirror	−94.525	−68.745	−51.559
R_4	Radius of curvature of secondary mirror	−25.232	−18.350	−13.763
F	Distance from mirror to primary focus	48.226	35.073	26.305
S	Separation of lens and mirror	50.232	36.532	27.399
SD	Distance of secondary inside focus (P)	10.000	7.273	5.455
BD	Distance of Cassegrainian focus behind primary	10.000	7.273	5.455
BFL	Back focal length (P′)	48.226	35.073	26.305
	Effective focal length of primary system	46.2	33.6	25.2
	Effective f-ratio of primary system	4.2	4.2	4.2
	Effective Cassegrainian focal length	222.6	161.9	121.4
	Effective Cassegrainian f-ratio	20.24	20.24	20.24

* All dimensions are in inches.
** See Figure 82A.

Maksutov has given a very complete table of designs for the simple shell plus primary mirror, but no curves for a compound system, so I applied the principle embodied in the formula above to set up two designs. . . .

Both designs are for a Maksutov correcting lens of 6-inch clear aperture, one with an equivalent focal length (e.f.l.) of 140 inches, the other of 90 inches. At f/23, the first is intended primarily as a planetary-observing instrument, giving adequate magnification with a comfortable

TABLE 6. SPECIFICATIONS FOR TWO CASSEGRAINIAN-MAKSUTOV TELESCOPES*

Symbol**	Characteristic	$f/15$	$f/23$
D_c	Diameter of correcting lens	6.45	6.26
T_c	Thickness of correcting lens	0.520 ± 0.010	0.448 ± 0.010
D_m	Diameter of primary mirror	6.6	6.4
T_m	Thickness of primary mirror	1.1	1.1
D_s	Diameter of secondary spot	1.4	1.2
D_h	Diameter of hole in primary mirror	1.375	1.17
R_1	Radius of curvature of 1st lens surface	-6.583 ± 0.070	-8.040 ± 0.070
R_2	Radius of curvature of 2nd lens surface	-6.888 ± 0.070	-8.293 ± 0.070
R_3	Radius of curvature of primary mirror	-29.42 ± 0.50	-43.39 ± 0.50
R_4	Radius of curvature of secondary spot	-6.888 ± 0.070	-8.293 ± 0.070
CA	Clear aperture of correcting lens	6.0	6.0
BA	Back aperture of correcting lens	6.3	6.11
S	Separation of lens and mirror	12.110	18.541
BFL	Back focal length	18.70	23.05
	Effective focal length	90.0	140.0

* All dimensions are in inches.
** See Figure 82B.

$\frac{1}{2}$-inch eyepiece. The other, at $f/15$, is more versatile—a wide field may be viewed with a 2-inch ocular, yet a $\frac{1}{4}$-inch eyepiece will exhaust all definition at 360X. . . .

Either design may be scaled up or down and, to a certain extent, may be made of different speed by scaling apertures only. Between $f/15$ and $f/20$, the 90-inch design should be adapted by closing down the aperture; anything slower than $f/20$ should be scaled from the 140-inch design. With such slow systems ($f/15$ to $f/23$) the type of eyepiece chosen is not critical, and Huygens oculars can be used. I prefer the wide apparent fields of the (Abbé) orthoscopic and the Erfle eyepieces [see p. 124].

Tolerances. Because all surfaces in the Cassegrainian-Maksutov are spherical, one must not be misled into thinking that the figuring tolerances are loose. The surfaces must be well figured if the telescope is to give the high performance inherent in the design.

For instance, the secondary magnifies the primary image over six times; it is evident that any zone visible in a knife-edge test of the primary is intolerable. On the other hand, if the shell is figured well, the secondary itself presents no problem, as it is but a small part of the large back surface and will automatically be smooth.

In final assembly, spacing of the elements is very critical, the position of the final focus being proportional to the amplification factor squared. Thus, if the shell and mirror separation, s, is wrong by only 0.1 inch, the focal plane will be shifted by over 4 inches from the design position!

It is evident, therefore, that the concentricity of the shell and its thickness, T_c, have strict tolerances. The differences in edge thickness should be reduced to less than 0.001 inch—otherwise one will have a built-in objective prism giving star spectra instead of Airy star disks!

As in most lens work, figured surface by surface, the tolerances of radii are very strict. The surfaces of the corrector lens, R_1 and R_2, may vary *together* from the design by as much as 0.07 inch in radius of curvature, but both in the same direction. The variation of R_1 should equal that of R_2 within 0.004 inch. The primary mirror, however, need be made only within 0.5 inch of the specified radius of curvature, R_3.

The smoothness of all surfaces should be $\frac{1}{4}$ wave or better. If one is lucky enough to own an aluminized $\frac{1}{8}$-wave optical flat with a diameter equal to or greater than the telescope aperture, the final testing may be done by autocollimation. With the pinhole and knife edge in the focal plane, the light traverses the system twice, giving a doubly sensitive null test of the assembly.

A highly accurate paraboloidal mirror may also be used to obtain collimated light, with the pinhole placed at the focus of this mirror. The knife edge is then set in the focal plane of the catadioptric system, where it effects the null test with ordinary sensitivity. With collimated light all tolerances can be broadened, as it is possible to remove, by figuring, residuals caused by 10 times the given departures from the nominal design (with the exception of concentricity, which must still be within 0.001 inch).

If curves or thickness have fallen outside the tolerances, the final figuring involves slightly aspherizing the front surface of the corrector or the primary, but those without experience in such critical work can achieve the desired results by making each surface to strict tolerances.

The assembled telescope will perform so well that the amateur will be unable to find any fault, and will wonder why he waited so long to construct such an ideal instrument.

Materials. The glass for the corrector lens, a borosilicate crown, BSC-2 (517645), was chosen for its resistance to tarnishing, low dispersion, general availability, and cheapness, although any of the crown glasses would be quite suitable if the design were adapted appropriately. BSC-2 may be obtained from any of the domestic glass manufacturers, or Schott BK-7, imported by Fish-Schurman Corporation may be used. The disks should be fine-annealed grade A or B.

The minimum dimensions of the blank for the shell depend on the method of generating the working curves. If this can be accomplished with a diamond-wheel curve generator, only a minimum of glass is removed (the fine grinding and polishing stages require at most about 0.04 inch), and a rough blank for the $f/15$ design needs to be about $6\frac{1}{2}$ inches in diameter and $1\frac{1}{3}$ inches thick; for the $f/23$, $6\frac{1}{4}$ inches by $1\frac{1}{16}$ inches will suffice.

But if the amateur must rough out and shape the lens by handwork, starting with coarse carborundum, a substantially greater amount of glass must be available to start with. To allow for roughing out, wedge control, and radius checking, the diameter ought to be $6\frac{9}{16}$ inches and the thickness $1\frac{1}{2}$ inches for the $f/15$ design; these reduce to $6\frac{5}{16}$ inches by $1\frac{3}{16}$ inches for the $f/23$. . . .

Glass blanks may be obtained from Glass Technology Company (formerly Hayward Scientific Glass Corporation), which carries a line of pressings from 4- to 10-inch aperture. Also, the United Lens Company, Inc., has mirror blanks of Pyrex 7740 as well as numerous optical glass pressings. Fish-Schurman Corporation can supply BK-7 glass from Schott in Germany. BK-7 is close enough to BSC-2 to be substituted without a design change.

The primary mirror should be made of Pyrex or other low-expansion glass. In addition to the standard $4\frac{1}{4}$-6-8-10-inch diameter Corning series, Pyrex blanks 5 inches in diameter by 1 inch thick can now be obtained from the Glass Technology Company for about five dollars each. These would make a suitable primary for a $4\frac{1}{2}$-inch Maksutov corrector lens.

Aluminum is recommended as a tube material and is now available in seamless tubing $\frac{1}{16}$-inch thick. For the 6-inch Cassegrainian-Maksutov, if a lathe is available, consider making both mirror and lens cells as well as the tube from a single piece of aluminum pipe, thus simplifying the machining and insuring alignment of the two elements. Local warehouses can supply such pipe, usually with a wall thickness of

$\frac{1}{2}$ inch, or more in larger sizes. Aluminum seamless tubing of 8 inches outside diameter, $\frac{3}{32}$-inch wall thickness, is available from the Metal Goods Corporation.

Optical Processing. ... The concave surface, R_1, is roughed in first, with periodic checks on its radius of curvature, until the curve extends to within $\frac{1}{4}$ inch of the edge of the lens. The centering of this concave side may be roughly checked by measuring this $\frac{1}{4}$-inch annulus to see whether or not its width varies around the disk. In this work, if no iron tool is available and you are not grinding by hand, another blank, of either plate glass or Pyrex, is generated to serve as a tool. If thick enough, the reverse side can also be used as a tool for the convex surface, R_2.

While R_1 is being brought through grinding, keep a record of the thickness changes; this will help you judge how thick to leave the lens while generating R_2 in order to end up close to the nominal thickness after fine grinding. Be sure to add 0.02 to the thickness allowed, as this may be needed to eliminate any wedge effect, which will be done during fine operations on R_2. The amount of wedge may be determined with a 1-inch micrometer blocked to measure at a single diameter on the lens.

Before polishing R_1, bring R_2 through the fine-grinding stage, checking its radius of curvature on its concave tool with a depth micrometer. Then spray R_2 with Krylon or shellac to protect it while finishing R_1, which should be brought to a $\frac{1}{4}$-wave sphere by repeated use of the knife-edge test.

R_2 may now be polished, and figured by testing *through* R_1 as outlined by Franklin B. Wright in his article in *Amateur Telescope Making*, Vol. 3 [A. G. Ingalls, ed., New York, Scientific American Publishing Co., 1953]. If a smooth $\frac{1}{4}$-wave sphere is obtained, the central $1\frac{1}{4}$ inch will be well within tolerance for use as the secondary. When the lens is sent out for spot aluminizing, it would be well to include a round sheet-metal mask with a central hole of the desired spot diameter.

The reader may wish to consult Maksutov's original paper in the *Journal* of the Optical Society of America, May 1944; articles in *Amateur Telescope Making*, Vol. 3, p. 1, 163, and 574; and A. Bouwers's book *Achievements in Optics* [New York, Elsevier Book Co., 1950].

The addresses of suppliers mentioned above are Corning Glass Company, Corning, New York; Fish-Schurman Corporation, 73 Portman Road, New Rochelle, New York; Glass Technology Company, 123 Northwind Drive, Stamford, Connecticut; Metal Goods Corporation, 8800 Page Boulevard, St. Louis, Missouri; and United Lens Company, 259 Worcester Street, Southbridge, Massachusetts.

....

Maksutov-telescope Notes

ROBERT E. COX

(*Sky and Telescope*, July 1957)

Interest in the Maksutov telescope is continuing to increase. Its neat design and fine performance have aroused amateur enthusiasm everywhere. John Gregory has received inquiries from many foreign countries, especially in South and Central America. The Maksutov club of Allan M. Mackintosh, Glen Cove, New York, has already oversubscribed the first special lot of fifty corrector shells for the $11\frac{1}{4}$-inch diameter lenses.

Six f/15 Cassegrainian-Maksutov telescopes of the type designed by Gregory are under construction by members of the Amateur Telescope Makers of Boston, as are five of the f/23 design. These shells were curve-generated with a diamond wheel to a close tolerance, so that once the proper jigs are constructed only fine grinding and polishing need to be done. . . .

In John Gregory's original designs (Table 6) for Cassegrainian-Maksutovs of 6-inch aperture, the mirror sizes are 6.6 and 6.4 inches which cannot be made from standard 6-inch Pyrex blanks. Many amateurs would prefer molded blanks [which require less grinding] for mirror and lens, and these are available in 4- to 10-inch sizes from the Hayward Scientific Glass Corporation [now the Glass Technology Company, 123 Northwind Drive, Stamford, Connecticut].

The glass for the molded corrector shells will be Hayward fine annealed BSC-2 (517645), and the specifications for the 6-inch aperture are: diameter, 6.650; R_1 (first lens surface), 6.483; R_2 (second lens surface), 8.393; central thickness, 0.741; weight, 2.86 pounds.

The diameter of the molds exceeds the lens size for the f/15 lens (Table 6) by 0.2 inch. This will allow ample material for edging, but if the glass cleans up with more than 0.15 inch for mounting, it is recommended that the excess be kept. This will permit a larger mounting lip and will probably include in the unused area most or all of the turned-up or turned-down edge zone that one encounters in figuring steep shells; this will simplify considerably the working of the back surface. . . .

Gregory pointed out that the primary mirror of a Cassegrainian-Maksutov should be of Pyrex or other low-expansion glass. In addition to the Corning series and the Hayward 5-inch blanks, amateurs can now obtain mirror blanks suitable for the original Gregory designs. The glass is Hayward C-3 (508610) and for the Gregory design (Table 6) the diameter is 6.7 inches, thickness 1.25 inches, weight 3.96 pounds, and the cost [from the Glass Technology Company] is approximately eleven dollars. Other sizes are also available.

Much working time can be saved if the surfaces of a corrector blank are curve-generated with a diamond wheel before grinding begins. This also gives better control of final wedge, radii of curvature, and lens thickness. Gregory has therefore built a curve-generating machine at his home at 132 Northwind Drive, Stamford, Connecticut, and offers to perform this service for amateurs and groups aiding in the distribution of Maksutov supplies. . . .

For the serious telescope maker, further details are given in Construction of a Maksutov Telescope by Warren I. Fillmore (Sky Publishing Corp., Cambridge, Massachusetts, 1961).

Other designs of reflecting telescopes are being tried, and some are particularly convenient for amateur observers and telescope makers. One of these is similar to the Cassegrain design except that the convex secondary mirror is off to one side, out of the incoming light beam and off the optical axis of the primary mirror. It is called a brachyt reflector or an oblique reflector and is described in the following article and, more fully, in The Schiefspiegler by Anton Kutter (Sky Publishing Corp., 1958). —TLP

....

An Improved 4¼-inch Unobstructed Oblique Reflector

OSCAR R. KNAB

(*Sky and Telescope*, October 1961)

All dimensions necessary for construction of the instrument are given in Figure 83 and Table 7. The work in making this off-axis telescope is simple and straightforward, with neither castings nor special tools required.

Both the 4¼-inch primary mirror and the 2.2-inch convex secondary are spherically figured, each having a radius of curvature of 127.5 inches. In fact, I converted the polished plate-glass tool, ⅝-inch thick, into my secondary. After coarse grinding, this tool was biscuit-cut from the back to within $\frac{3}{32}$ inch or so of the front convex surface, and the cut was filled with plaster of Paris.

During all stages of grinding the primary, the curve was checked with a homemade spherometer employing a 0.0001 inch dial indicator, as described in *Sky and Telescope* for July 1958. A spherometer is a boon for quick, accurate grinding, but after the completion of fine

TABLE 7. SPECIFICATIONS OF KNAB $4\frac{1}{4}$-INCH OBLIQUE REFLECTOR*

D	Primary mirror aperture	4.25 *inches*
d	Secondary mirror aperture	2.20
r	Mirrors' radius of curvature	127.50
f	Mirrors' focal length	63.75
F	Effective focal length	111.00
e	Separation of mirrors	36.00
p'	Secondary-to-focus distance	46.45
Δ	Secondary mirror offset from incoming optical axis	3.50
Δ'	Primary mirror offset from secondary-reflected axis	8.00
ϕ_1	Tilt of primary mirror to incoming optical axis	$2°47\frac{1}{2}'$
ϕ_2	Tilt of secondary mirror to optical axis from primary	$6°25'$

* Symbolism according to Anton Kutter in *The Schiefspiegler* (*Bulletin* A of Sky Publishing Corp., Cambridge, Massachusetts, 1958).

FIG. 83. Details of construction are given by Oscar Knab's diagram of his telescope and in the frontal view below, which is to the same scale. The dashed line indicates the path of the central ray of light entering the telescope, which is reflected by the mirrors at double the angles ϕ_1 and ϕ_2. Symbols used in the drawing are identified in Table 7.

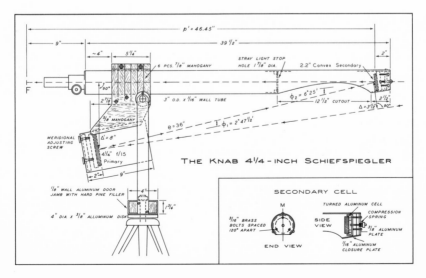

grinding the wetted primary was checked by the Foucault test. It is important to hold the radius of curvature to 1-inch tolerance if the indicated dimensions are to be used. Remember, too, that it is more difficult to achieve a good long-focus sphere than one of average focal length.

Polishing was done in the usual manner, except that another plate-glass disk was used for backing the pitch lap. Because of the very shallow curve required, this disk may be left flat if a good $\frac{1}{4}$ inch of pitch is poured on it. And after the primary was completed, the secondary, still $4\frac{1}{4}$ inches in diameter, was hot-pressed onto the same pitch lap, which quickly conformed to the shallow reverse curve.

During polishing, the convex surface was periodically tested through its flat back, using two thirds of the radius of curvature for the knife-edge position. . . . The surface could also have been checked by inter-ference fringes if it were fitted against the concave primary.

The final biscuit cut was made through the secondary's finished sur-face, which was protected from grit by two layers of masking tape. Care was needed to assure alignment of this cut with the one coming from the back. But the secondary did not suffer from the carborundum used in cutting, nor did it have a turned-down edge. It would have been difficult to achieve this result if the mirror had been ground after cutting it to size.

For the mounting, a full-sized layout should be scaled up from the drawing. The mahogany cradle (see Fig. 84) was made at a mill; I bored out the 3-inch hole in the lathe and made the $\frac{1}{8}$-inch saw cut later. The $\frac{3}{8}$-inch side pieces were left somewhat larger and were cut only after checking with the full-sized layout. A large piece of sand-paper was stretched over the curve of the primary tube, and the side pieces were lapped to it after being screwed to the cradle. Six little wood screws inside the tube secure it to the side pieces. The distance Δ' between the center of the primary mirror and the optical axis of the secondary's reflection must be precisely 8 inches. This is built into the mount, so it is very important to preserve it by fitting the side pieces and the tube together carefully.

After it is tilted into position, the secondary must be concentric with the 3-inch tube. I accomplished this by drilling the central hole in the back of the turned aluminum cell $\frac{1}{8}$-inch below center. The $\frac{1}{4}$-inch bolt that fits this hole is swivel-mounted in the cell to afford the play neces-sary for tilt adjustment. A compression spring holds the cell firmly against three pointed adjusting screws that fit into small cup-shaped recesses in the back of the cell. These screws are threaded into tapped holes in the backing plates. In both primary and secondary cells, one

FIG. 84. Oscar Knab's mahogany and jeweled-aluminum Schiefspiegler (oblique reflector) on its altazimuth mounting is particularly valuable for lunar and planetary observing because of its excellent image quality. It is less well suited for viewing dim extended objects, such as galaxies and nebulae, because its focal ratio is high.

of the adjusting screws must be in the mounting's meridional plane, as indicated by the M in the end view of the secondary cell (Fig. 83).

The curved cutout in the secondary tube was done with a wire-bladed hacksaw and then filed smooth. The slanted cutoff at the mirror end of this tube was made with the end plate of the cell fastened in place, facilitating cutting by stiffening the end. The tubes were blackened inside with two coats of blackboard slating and were machine-jeweled on the outside with steel wool wrapped around a rubber-capped wooden dowel in a drill press, and then lacquered. The mahogany received several coats of clear spar varnish.

For rough adjustment, place a tube with a $\frac{1}{8}$-inch eye hole into the eyepiece holder, and tilt the secondary by means of the three adjusting screws until the primary cell shows concentrically in the secondary mirror. This need never be repeated. To set the primary, tape a $4\frac{1}{4}$-inch cardboard disk just under the secondary tube at its outer end, to indicate the direction of the rays that will enter the primary. Direct the primary until it looks squarely at this disk, and rough adjusting is completed.

Final aligning is done on a star in good seeing with a high-power eyepiece. If out-of-focus images are elliptical, adjust the meridianal screw of the primary. If they are triangular close to focus, one of the mirrors is pinched too tightly in its cell. Residual coma of this instrument is 0.9 second of arc; and since the resolution is 1.06 seconds, the coma is invisible. Astigmatism is completely corrected by the tilt angles specified by Anton Kutter [in *Bulletin* A, Sky Publishing Corp., 1958].

This instrument is the largest that can be made with the specifications given in the table, greater aperture requiring a corrector lens and other design changes. Images are crisp, sharp, and color free, with an unusually dark background, which results from the unobstructed light path to the primary mirror. With a 1-inch Erfle eyepiece, the moon is a magnificent sight.

The finished telescope weighs less than five pounds, but it has such high magnification that it requires a very heavy, sturdy tripod. My war-surplus tripod weighs some 20 pounds. . . .

NOTE: [by R. E. Cox, 1961] It should be pointed out that readers attempting to duplicate Anton Kutter's calculations for mirror tilts, as given in his *Bulletin* A, should not use the full size of the actual secondary, as this has been enlarged to give a fully illuminated focal plane. The correct figure for the secondary semidiameter is, therefore, 0.86 inch rather than 1.1 inches.

By actual trial with a stopped-down f/12 5-inch mirror, I have verified the performance calculated for a 4-inch f/15 Schiefspiegler. But when the system was tried at a 5-inch aperture, with the secondary impinging slightly on the primary, the image deteriorated badly. Thus, only by extending the focal length could this anastigmatic form of off-axis reflector be made larger than 4¼ inches. But the final focal ratio would be so large and the consequent light level so low as to be impractical. . . .

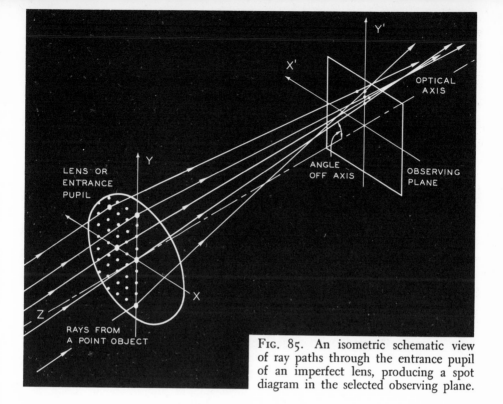

FIG. 85. An isometric schematic view of ray paths through the entrance pupil of an imperfect lens, producing a spot diagram in the selected observing plane.

Cassegrain-type Telescopes

RONALD R. WILLEY, JR.

(*Sky and Telescope*, April 1962)

Recently, the writer decided to compare the performance to be expected of a Cassegrain telescope with those of various other systems which logically represent types evolved from it. The study was made in the course of developing an automatic lens-design program for use on the IBM 7090 computer at United Aircraft Research Laboratories. Here we shall consider the Cassegrain, Dall-Kirkham, Ritchey-Chrétien, Maksutov-Cassegrain, and Schmidt-Cassegrain systems.

In the computing program[1] used, we can trace the paths of light rays through any system of lenses and mirrors that is symmetrical with respect to the optical axis. These optical elements may be spherical or aspherical. Any one of the lens or mirror surfaces can be figured mathematically to bring all of the rays to a point focus on axis. Then rays are

[1] Herzberger, M., and Hoadley, H., "The Calculation of Aspherical Correcting Surfaces," *Journal* of the Optical Society of America, 1946, **36**, 334.

traced from some off-axis object point (which might represent a star at infinity) through a rectangular array of equally spaced points in the entrance pupil of the system, and on through the subsequent refracting and reflecting surfaces until they intersect some plane at which we wish to examine the pattern formed by the rays, as in Figure 85. For example, this may be the principal focal plane.

If the lens were perfect, all the originally parallel rays would pass through a single point (neglecting diffraction effects) in the appropriate plane. Since the lens cannot be perfect but suffers from aberrations, the rays will pass through several points, forming the patterns shown by the spot diagrams in Figure 87. The larger the pattern the greater the aberrations and the less the inherent resolution of the optical system. Since the rays pass through the centers of squares of equal area in the entrance pupil, the density of points in the spot diagram directly indicates the light-intensity distribution in the image, again neglecting diffraction. Therefore, we can expect the image of a star seen through the instrument with a good eyepiece to look like the computed spot diagram if we mentally smooth the points into a continuous density distribution. Of course, where the points are widely separated, that part of the image may be too faint to be seen or photographed.

On command, the computer can find the focal planes where the image has smallest spread in the X' direction of Figure 85, in the Y' direction, and the smallest overall spread. These are respectively the sagittal-focus, tangential-focus, and circle-of-least-confusion planes.

The whole lens system and its object and image points have mirror symmetry about the tangential plane, which contains the image point and the optical axis of the system. It is, therefore, only necessary to trace rays through one half of the entrance pupil, as shown in Figure 85, in order to obtain all the information available from the computation. Each spot diagram therefore represents only half the system's aperture —the remaining half can be included by visualizing the diagram's mirror image about the horizontal line indicated in each case.

In astronomy, we are generally concerned with five primary monochromatic aberrations and two chromatic ones. *Spherical aberration* deteriorates all images, including on-axis ones. *Coma* decreases the resolution of image points, even those only slightly off axis. *Astigmatism* affects image points somewhat more off axis. *Curvature of field* requires photographic emulsions to be curved if off-axis images are to remain in focus.

The fifth monochromatic aberration is *distortion*, which is usually neglected by astronomers except when measuring star fields. As distortion can be allowed for mathematically, we shall not consider it.

The primary color aberrations are *longitudinal* and *lateral* chromatic aberration. The first occurs on axis, causing focal length to change with wavelength; it produces the colored halo commonly seen in refractors but absent in reflectors. This aberration is second in importance only to spherical aberration, since it is present even on axis in systems that contain refracting elements. It is often referred to as the secondary or residual spectrum. Lateral chromatic aberration is the sideways displacement of off-axis images as a function of wavelength, but none of the systems we shall consider suffers significantly from this effect.

Planetary observers, because of the very small fields of view that they require, are concerned almost exclusively with spherical aberration and longitudinal color. Lunar observers, studying an object half a degree in diameter, are bothered by coma and possibly by astigmatism if it is severe. Those photographing fields of stars and nebulae will be concerned with these four aberrations plus curvature of field; they must either compensate for a curved field by bending their emulsions, as in a Schmidt, or use a field-flattening lens.

Aside from any consideration of aberrations, the advantages of a compound system such as a Cassegrain come mainly from the short tube length. This reduces flexure problems, permits building a smaller observatory, provides greater portability, and decreases the effects of air currents within the tube (Fig. 86).

The *true Cassegrain* is a geometrically "pure" system, in that its parabolic primary mirror brings rays from infinity (on axis) to a perfect

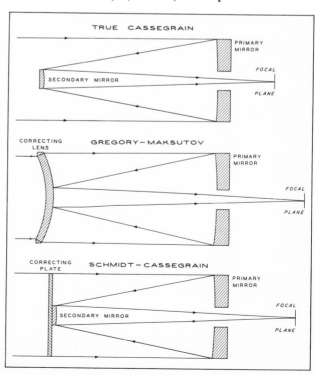

FIG. 86. Diagrams of three telescope systems discussed here. (Drawings by Robert E. Cox.)

focus, and the hyperbolic secondary transfers them to another perfect focus. This system is free from spherical aberration. Its most serious aberration is usually coma, which Robert T. Jones[2] has shown to be the same as that of a paraboloid with the same aperture and equal in focus to the effective focal length of the Cassegrain (or Gregorian) system. Aden B. Meinel[3] points out that Cassegrain astigmatism is that of an equivalent prime-focus paraboloid multiplied by the magnification of the secondary mirror. . . .

The true Cassegrain offers performance comparable with that of a prime-focus paraboloid, but the telescope's actual length is several times less. This advantage is gained at the expense of some additional astigmatism, which is usually not detrimental, and increased curvature of field. . . .

The *Dall-Kirkham* form of Cassegrain has been analyzed in some detail by P. R. Yoder, Jr., F. B. Patrick, and A. E. Gee,[4] and Jones has studied its coma. This system uses a convex spherical secondary (which is easier to make than a hyperboloid) and an elliptical primary mirror. The undercorrected primary compensates for the spherical aberration of the secondary, which effectively transfers figuring for spherical aberration from the secondary to the primary, where it actually cancels some of the correction required. . . . But the Dall-Kirkham's large coma makes its usable field of view much smaller than that of a true Cassegrain.

To avoid the adverse coma resulting from making the secondary spherical, with all the figuring on the primary, we might go the other way, using a hyperbolic primary and a more hyperbolic secondary than a true Cassegrain has. This is the *Ritchey-Chrétien* design, in which coma is essentially zero, leaving only astigmatism and curvature of field to affect resolution. At the circle of least confusion (midway between the sagittal and tangential astigmatic images) the result is less objectionable than that of an asymmetrical comatic image. The Naval Observatory's 40-inch Ritchey-Chrétien reflector at Flagstaff, Arizona, uses curved photographic plates to obtain a wider field. The 80-inch telescope at Kitt Peak is to be of this type, too.

In the past few years the *Maksutov-Cassegrain* system has been well publicized in amateur circles, particularly John Gregory's designs [p. 223]. These systems need no description here, except to say that

[2] Jones, Robert T., "Coma of Modified Gregorian and Cassegrainian Mirror Systems," *Journal* of the Optical Society of America, 1954, **44**, 630.

[3] Meinel, Aden B., *Telescopes*, 1960 (Vol. 1 of *Stars and Stellar Systems*, Kuiper, G. P., and Middlehurst, B. M., eds., Chicago, University of Chicago Press).

[4] Yoder, P. R., Jr., Patrick, F. B., and Gee, A. E., *Journal* of the Optical Society of America, 1953, **43**, 1200 and 1955, **45**, 881.

first-order spherical aberration is corrected by placing in front of the secondary mirror a meniscus shell of low power and steep curvature. In Gregory's designs the secondary is actually a small aluminized spot on the back surface of the corrector and is therefore spherical, as in the Dall-Kirkham. The primary is also spherical, with all spherical-aberration correction transferred to the correcting lens. This transfer of figuring toward the center of curvature of the primary was the guiding theme for Bernhard Schmidt's invention of catadioptric telescopes.

The advantages of this system over the simple refractor are, of course, its short length and its greatly reduced chromatic aberration. The usual spider support in a reflector is absent, and the field curvature is smaller than that of a simple Cassegrain. The closed tube has advantages, too.

Gregory-Maksutov telescopes have been designed in two sizes, f/15 and f/23. The latter seems quite satisfactory with spherical surfaces alone, but those of an f/15 cannot all be spherical. About one fringe of figuring is required on the corrector, or about one third of this amount if figured on the primary mirror. Color in Gregory's first f/15 design was small but not undetectable—for C [red] and F [blue-green] light the images were not diffraction-limited if D [yellow] light was in focus. Gregory redesigned the f/15 to reduce the color, focusing C, D, and F light all within the visual disk image. Coma is found to be somewhat worse than that of a true Cassegrain of the same size and focal length, but the f/15 is satisfactory for most work.

The last and most complex member of the Cassegain family that I have examined is the *Schmidt-Cassegrain*, which has its focus inside the system and requires a transfer optical arrangement for visual use. We might regard it as a Maksutov whose corrector shell and aluminized spot are replaced with a Schmidt plate and a separate secondary mirror. Compared with a special flat-field Schmidt design by James G. Baker,[5] we have sacrificed some flatness of field to bring the focus outside of the system, where it can be conveniently observed visually.

The Schmidt-Cassegrain has the following advantages: compactness; spherical primary mirror; possibility of secondary mirror mounted on the corrector plate to eliminate spider diffraction; less curvature of field than in the true Cassegrain; and negligible chromatic aberration.

The secondary mirror and the corrector are aspheric, with their figuring adjusted to eliminate coma. Astigmatism is undetectable. The secondary is a conic section—a convex ellipsoid that must be tested by zones, or by interference using a concave ellipsoid figured on the tool.

[5] Baker, James G. A Family of Flat-field Cameras, Equivalent in Performance to the Schmidt Camera, *Proceedings* of the American Philosophical Society, 1940, **82**, 339.

The corrector lens can be almost as large as the primary mirror, giving a larger clear aperture than an equivalent Maksutov-Cassegrain does. Since the corrector blank is nearly flat and need be only thick enough for structural support, much weight and glass are saved, and generation costs are less than with a Maksutov instrument. This element can be figured against the finished primary mirror, using the Foucault test with the appropriate zonal radii.

Schmidt-Cassegrain construction is one step more difficult than that of a Maksutov because an additional surface has to be made and figured. But the thickness and radii of curvature are not nearly as critical in Schmidt optics.

FIG. 87. Off-axis images formed by five telescopes of the same dimensions. The Airy disk diameter is 0.732 mil, the visual diffraction disk 0.300 mil. The Maksutov has coma opposite in sense to that of the other systems.

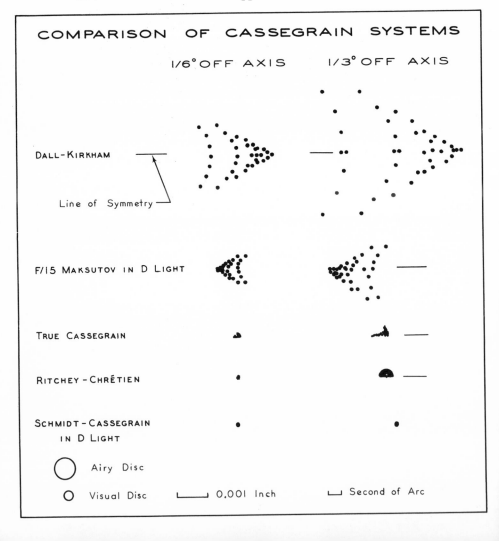

In Figure 87 various systems are compared, their physical dimensions, focal ratios, and focal lengths being essentially the same as Gregory's f/15 Maksutov. These instruments are similar in every possible structural parameter and can be placed on the same size mounting.

Since each observer has his own requirements, too specific conclusions should not be drawn here. It is well to note that off-axis resolution is relatively unimportant in planetary observations, for which the Dall-Kirkham instrument is well suited. And in photography, the smallest point that ordinary emulsions will resolve is between 0.0003 and 0.001 inch (usually nearer the latter).

Robert E. Cox points out that many observers with small-aperture instruments may find their own results far from matching the spot diagrams. In amateur telescopes, imperfect or slightly misaligned optics, tube currents, and inferior eyepieces all tend to mask the true diffraction pattern. Astronomical seeing always impairs it, so actual compound instruments are best tested in a controlled laboratory environment.

The calculations plotted in Figure 87 show the relative merits of several telescope designs under ideal conditions and illustrate a novel use of high-speed computing machines. The Schmidt design is shown to be theoretically of highest quality, although the unavoidable effects of seeing (p. 129) and imperfections in actual optics will in practice make the true Cassegrain, the Ritchey-Chrétien, and the Schmidt designs of about the same value.

Very different problems arise when a telescope is used for observing the sun, some of them noted in Chapter 7. One of the most difficult is associated with the strong glare that masks the fainter corona. Until recently the solar corona could only be observed at the time of solar eclipse; now it is regularly observed with a specially designed telescope.

— T L P

••

Harvard Coronagraph in Colorado

DONALD H. MENZEL

(*The Sky*, June 1940)

The highest astronomical observatory in the world will soon be in operation on Fremont Pass, near Climax, Colorado, 11,318 feet above sea level. Its principal instrument is to be the coronagraph developed and

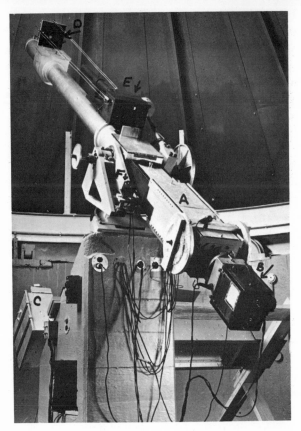

FIG. 88. Early Harvard corona-graph. The box near the far end of the tube, under the black square labeled *D*, contains the objective lens and heating coils. At the far end and all along the tube interior there are black diaphragms designed to absorb unwanted light. After the major part of the sunlight is blocked out, a photograph of the faint corona is made in the section labeled A. (The other lettered parts were added later at the High Altitude Observatory in Colorado for photoelectric detection of the corona.) (Photograph courtesy Harvard College Observatory.)

constructed during the past three years at Harvard Observatory. With this instrument, the only one of its kind in America, regular direct observations of the sun's corona will be made at the new observatory.

For best results, it is necessary to mount the coronograph at a high altitude, where frequent heavy rains wash the air clean of all suspended particles and dust, the least of which produces solar haze enough to mask the corona. The new observatory will be built on the property of the Climax Molybdenum Company, whose interest and cooperation have made this ideal location of the coronagraph possible. Located thirteen miles from the old mining town of Leadville, the site combines perfect skies with necessary electric power and water supply.

The coronagraph produces what might be called an artificial eclipse of the sun by a reflecting disk, which at the same time acts as a screen, in a manner similar to that employed in the coronaviser, developed by A. M. Skellett of the Bell Telephone Laboratories. The remaining radiation from the prominences and the corona may be sent into various pieces of auxiliary equipment, including a powerful spectrograph. Studies of motions of solar prominences, with color filters and motion picture technique, will be made.

The Harvard coronagraph is modeled after the original invention by Bernard Lyot of the Meudon Observatory of Paris, and successfully used in the Observatory of the Pic du Midi, in France. The principle on which the coronagraph operates is that the sun's corona is bright enough to be seen directly, in spite of the scattering of sunlight near the edge of the sun by the earth's atmosphere, if the air is perfectly clear and clean and if certain imperfections in ordinary telescopes are overcome. These comprise principally the scattering of light in the various parts of the telescope itself, such as diffraction at the edge of the objective, dust on the lens or in the telescope, reflections inside the tube, imperfections in the lens material itself.

Red and infrared filters eliminate a large portion of the sky light, which is predominantly blue. Hence, one may use very nearly monochromatic light in studying the corona. For the same reason, one may use simple rather than achromatic lenses, thereby eliminating reflections between the inner surfaces which occur in ordinary achromatic lenses of two or more elements. The Harvard coronagraph employs simple crown lenses, which are, furthermore, coated with the nonreflecting material developed by Massachusetts Institute of Technology for making glass "invisible."

Another investigator of solar phenomena, who has employed a coronagraph of his own design, is M. Waldmeier of Zurich Observatory. He has made many hundreds of observations and photographs of both prominences and the corona, and several thousand visual estimates of the brightness of the coronal spectral line at wavelength 5303 angstroms —in the green region of the spectrum. He has advanced three important conclusions: that the corona radiates most strongly in sunspot regions; that the passage of areas of intense coronal activity central on the sun are followed by magnetic storms on the earth; and that the coronal radiation is symmetrical about the sun's rotation axis. Waldmeier believes that the corona, rather than sunspots or prominences, is directly responsible for terrestrial magnetic disturbances, with perhaps a one-day lag, indicative of the time required for ejected coronal material to reach the earth.

Study of the sun is extremely important, economically as well as scientifically. The sun is the nearest of all the stars, and we have the opportunity to subject its surface to close scrutiny. During the past few years, many advances have been made in our interpretation of physical conditions existing on the sun. There are, nevertheless, numerous problems whose solution has not yet been achieved. Some of the unsolved solar questions will eventually have a practical aspect. The sun, of course, is the source of all energy and motive power. It is the chief agency for controlling the weather, and the source of magnetic storms that interfere with radio communication. Any information that we can obtain on the subject of solar activity may have a direct bearing on these questions of economic importance.

One of the outstanding solar problems is related to the sun's variability. The most striking variations are those concerned with sunspots. Heretofore, these have been assumed to be the most important feature of solar variation, but in all probability, they are only an incidental part of the entire problem. Like the rash that accompanies measles, sunspots are to be regarded as a symptom of some fundamental solar disease—a sort of periodic fever.

Associated with the solar variations are many additional features. There are solar prominences—great eruptions that shoot geyserlike hundreds of thousands of miles out into space and appear to be related to the form and intensity of the solar corona. If we could discover the intimate relationships that must exist between sunspots, solar prominences, and the solar corona, we should be better able to understand the physical conditions in the sun. We should then, in turn, be in position to attack more intelligently the fundamental problems of solar and terrestrial relationships.

Among the results to be expected from the new observatory is the formation of new indices of solar activity. These indices may be used to test the relationships between solar eruptions, terrestrial magnetic storms, aurorae, radio fade-outs, ozone content of the upper atmosphere, the intensity of ultraviolet radiation, plant growth, and perhaps even general weather phenomena.

Spectroscopes and spectrographs mounted on a conventional telescope were briefly described in Chapter 7, and it was noted there that clouds of gas on the sun ("prominences") emit certain specific colors of light. These "emission lines" in the spectrum can be singled out by a second slit at the correct place in the spectrum. The other colors are blocked, and the one color selected is focused in an image of a strip of the sun defined by the first slit of the spectrograph at the telescope focus. If a series of such photographs is made, strip by strip, across the sun's image, the photographs can be combined into one photograph of the whole sun, using the single color only and showing primarily the gas clouds emitting that color—clouds of hydrogen, for instance. The spectrograph is thus used as a very accurate color filter. Telescopes specially designed to observe the sun in this manner are called spectroheliographs and have been in use for fifty years or more.

In the same manner, large telescopes have been used to photograph prominences over many hours, revealing remarkable prominence motions not yet fully understood (see Vol. 3, The Origin of the Solar System). The technique is a powerful one; by adjusting the spectroheliograph to pass slightly different wavelengths (colors) of light, the motion of the prominences toward us or away from us can be detected. Similar photographs can be made in other colors, showing motions of other materials in the sun's atmosphere. With a large telescope, these techniques can also be applied to planets.

The latest form of special-purpose telescope is quite different from the ones discussed so far; it is the radiotelescope, a sensitive directional radio receiver. For eighty years radio waves have been recognized as longer than light waves—an extension of the spectrum past the red and infrared. It was not until 1930, however, that radio waves were detected from astronomical sources (by Jansky in the United States), and radiotelescopes were not in general use until 1950.

Many of the large radiotelescopes have mirrors like a reflecting (optical) telescope, but simpler forms are also suitable. The Yagi antenna is a series of short metal rods parallel to each other, properly spaced on a pole that can be pointed in the desired direction (at the sun or a star).

The results of radioastronomy are impressive: the solar corona is a strong (hot) radio emitter, and there are many "radio stars," some of them not visible in ordinary light. Hydrogen gas broadcasts radio waves of one wavelength (21 centimeters) and is found widely spread between the stars. — T L P

....

A Simple Radiotelescope

DENNIS N. DOWNES

(*Sky and Telescope*, August 1962)

Radioastronomy, although a rapidly expanding field, is usually shunned by amateurs. Some of its electronic equipment may be exceedingly complex and expensive, but not all phases of this exciting new science are beyond the means of amateurs. As a project for Harvard's freshman astronomy seminar, Reuben E. Mayo and I built a radiotelescope that can be duplicated at low cost.

In choosing our observing frequency, we considered both the difficulty in assembling the necessary equipment and the number of radio sources that could be observed. Because receivers and antennas designed for the commercial FM (frequency modulation) band between 88 and 108

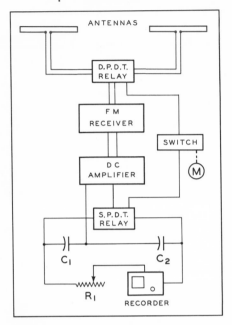

FIG. 89. A. Block diagram of the complete radiotelescope. The motor-driven microswitch at the right operates the relays in the switching circuits. B. The receiver and switching circuits for the three-meter interferometer are in the box; a recorder is at the right. The large instrument above is the DC amplifier. A speaker permits monitoring signals to identify terrestrial sources. The tracing in Figure 90 was made with a different recorder.

megacycles are readily available, this frequency range seemed a likely choice. The sun's radio spectrum runs from approximately 1 centimeter to 20 meters, so a wavelength of 3 meters (corresponding to 100 megacycles) was selected in the heart of the FM band, between television channels 6 and 7. A number of cosmic sources are also observable at this wavelength. Of course, the receiver must not be tuned to any nearby FM station.

The basic equipment consists of three common items—an FM receiver or tuner, a vacuum-tube voltmeter, and a directional antenna such as a Yagi. We used a Finco FM-4 antenna costing about $15, but there are other suitable Yagis ranging in price up to $25.

The receiver should employ a ratio detector rather than a limiter-discriminator; most low-priced receivers and tuners fulfill this requirement. Vacuum-tube voltmeters can be purchased in kit form for about $25. The meter reads the level of AM (amplitude modulated) signals at one plate of the ratio-detector tube. This is possible because FM receivers amplify both AM and FM in their first few stages and reject the AM just prior to final amplification. . . .

In order to perform a wider range of experiments, we made several additions to our radiotelescope. One of these was a second antenna, converting it to an interferometer, which is capable of higher resolving power without undue expense.

In many applications, a recorder is far more convenient than a meter, so we decided to incorporate one. This meant connecting a direct-current amplifier to the ratio detector to boost the signal strength enough to drive our Esterline-Angus chart recorder. We used a surplus General Radio model 715 AM, but any workable combination of DC amplifier and recorder would serve.

We also built a switching circuit that makes our receiver a Dicke-type radiometer (*Sky and Telescope*, November 1959). As the block diagram of the complete radiotelescope (Fig. 89A) shows, the antennas are connected to a double-pole double-throw (D.P.D.T.) relay that switches them in and out of phase. A second relay (single-pole double-throw, S.P.D.T.) operated in synchronism, feeds the output of the amplifier first to capacitor C_1, then to C_2. The difference in charge between the two capacitors is recorded. Thus, any signal that remains constant over an entire switching cycle will contribute equally to each capacitor and will not appear on the record.

Our two Yagis are mounted 60 meters apart in an east-west direction on the roof of Harvard Observatory. They can be pointed to any altitude along the meridian, and in addition, one antenna can be aimed by hand at any part of the sky.

A good time to make a radio observation is during the transit of a source. The antenna is pointed at the correct altitude on the meridian, and the output of the radiometer is recorded as the earth's rotation carries the antenna beam across the source. An alternate procedure is to sweep the beam over the source by moving the antenna. We have used both methods.

For solar-interferometer observations, the receiver is operated at local noon, when the sun is crossing the meridian. Other sources require a little more planning to predict their times of transit. Positions for a number of radio sources may be taken from Harvard Observatory's radio-noise maps (available for $2.00), from the Skalnate Pleso *Atlas Catalogue* (available from Sky Publishing Corp., Cambridge, Massachusetts), or from any one of a number of radioastronomy texts. Table 8 gives right ascensions and declinations for a few of the more powerful sources, with designations used by the International Astronomical Union. Once the position of an object is known, its time of transit can be determined [see p. 12].

TABLE 8. INTENSE RADIO SOURCES

Name	R.A.	Dec.	IAU
Taurus A	5^h31^m	$+22°.0$	05N2A
Virgo A	12 28	$+12$ .7	12N1A
Centaurus A	13 22	-42 .8	13S4A
Cygnus A	19 58	$+40$ .6	19N4A
Cassiopeia A	23 21	$+58$ .5	23N5A

We allow the equipment to warm up for about half an hour to stabilize it. Meanwhile, if we are planning an interferometer observation, we set both antennas to the desired declination by means of simple scales attached to their mountings. When the time of transit approaches, the recorder is started. The pen moves back and forth across the paper as the receiver responds to interference from electric buses, automobile ignition systems, airline radio signals, and other "conveniences" of surrounding civilization. However, if the celestial source is powerful enough, its signal can be seen rising above the noise. But it soon falls, as the source passes between the "fingers" of the interferometer beam, then rises during the approach to the next maximum in the antenna pattern.

The chart in Figure 90 (reading from right to left) shows the other type of observation, made with only one antenna. It was manually aimed at the rising sun, then swept back and forth across the area of the sky that included the strong "radio star," Cygnus A, held steady for 30 seconds, and then swept across another strong radio source, Cas-

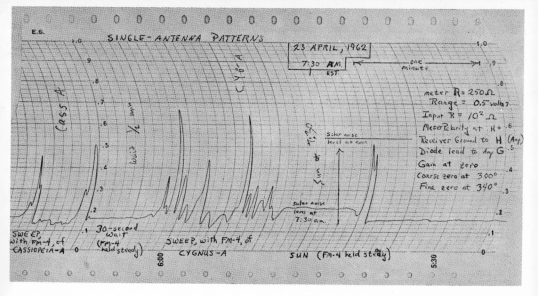

Fig. 90. A chart recorder tracing (running right to left) of three radio sources on the morning of April 23, 1962. First, solar noise was sampled for comparison with the average noon level that has been added to the record. To the left, Cygnus A and Cassiopeia A produced the tall spikes as the antenna was swept over their positions.

siopeia A. The large peaks in the record occurred when the antenna pointed directly at a source; lesser peaks indicate near misses.

We hope to improve the instrument by replacing the mechanical relays with electronic switches and by calibrating the equipment in terms of known radio sources such as Cygnus A and Cassiopeia A. A number of observational programs are also contemplated: measurement of angular diameters of sources from their interference patterns, study of refraction effects as sources rise and set, and observations of solar flares. All of these projects are within the reach of amateurs who provide themselves with suitable equipment.

....

A Radiotelescope for Amateurs

JOSEPH K. ALEXANDER AND LARRY W. BROWN

(*Sky and Telescope*, April 1965)

In recent years, radioastronomy has significantly advanced our knowledge of the heavens. Amateur radioastronomers can participate in some areas of this growing field with only limited equipment and technical

Fig. 91. With this quadruple array of Yagi antennas, Joseph K. Alexander and Larry W. Brown have observed decameter radio emission from the Milky Way, Jupiter, and the sun. The antennas are spaced 1 wavelength (34.7 feet) apart in the east-west direction and ¾ wavelength north-south. Each element forming the Yagis is about ½ wavelength long and is separated from the others by ⅕ wavelength.

capabilities. Here we describe a simple radiotelescope of the solid-array type; any radio amateur can build one like it.

Working at decameter wavelengths with the quadruple array pictured here (Fig. 91), we can detect the cosmic radio noise that comes predominantly from the Milky Way and reaches maximum intensity toward the galactic center in Sagittarius. Other observations can be made of the sun and Jupiter. Solar flares may produce radio noise that can be monitored with our equipment. Jupiter also has bursts at decameter wavelengths.

The array shown in Figure 91 is stationary, "sighting" along the local meridian, as a transit telescope does. It does not follow an object in hour angle, but waits for it to pass through the reception beam, as a result of the earth's rotation. The antenna array can be adjusted in the north-south direction to any selected declination.

Our antenna is an arrangement of four three-element Yagi antennas oriented east-west. It has a beam-width to half-power points of 25° east-west and 40° north-south. This elliptical area is about 2 per cent of the area of the entire celestial sphere.

The antennas are hooked up to a Ryle-Vonberg radiometer, which compares the received antenna power with that of a standard noise source. A superheterodyne receiver is used as a null detector. An electronic switch alternately samples the signals from the antenna and from the noise source (a vacuum-tube diode) and applies them to the radio receiver at an audio rate. Hence, the audio output of the receiver is a square wave, with amplitude proportional to the difference in power from the antenna and from the source.

This square wave is synchronously demodulated to produce a direct-current error signal, which is used to control the power output from the noise source. The servo loop so formed minimizes the error signal by equating the output power of the noise source to that of the antenna. Thus, the power needed from the standard source to null the antenna is a measure of the cosmic noise being received.

By measuring the anode current of the noise tube (which is directly related to the power output), we obtain a record of the cosmic noise. The system is calibrated by substituting a second standard source in place of the array. The whole setup is shown in the block diagram, Figure 92.

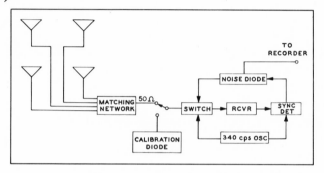

Fig. 92. A schematic diagram of the authors' radiotelescope.

Although this system has certain advantages in accuracy, sensitivity, and resolving power, comparable results can be obtained from a simpler system, consisting of one or more antennas and a standard communications receiver. . . . Care must be taken to insulate and shield all such connections. The *Radio Amateur's Handbook* (American Radio Relay League) gives much useful information on construction practices.

Our observations in September and October 1963 were made at a frequency of 28.49 megacycles per second, which is in the 10-meter amateur radio band. This frequency was chosen as the band is infrequently used during sunspot minimum, and commercial antennas are available at low cost. We found negligible interference much of the time, especially in the early morning hours. For our observations the band width of the receiver system was 100 kilocycles per second, and a postdetection integration time of 20 seconds was used. Continuous observations were obtained with an Esterline-Angus clock-operated recorder, having a paper speed of 3 inches an hour.

Figure 93 shows four profiles of the cosmic noise background (in a band around the sky) when the antennas were set at declination +5°. The profile's shape remains practically unchanged each sidereal day, but varies in intensity with changing absorption by the earth's ionosphere.

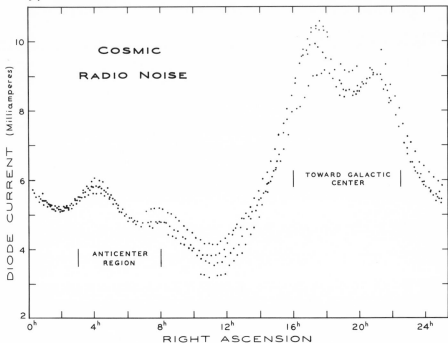

FIG. 93. With the antenna pointed constantly at declination $+5°$ while the sky rotated, the authors obtained this profile of radio emission. When the galactic center passed nearest the antenna beam a strong peak was recorded, a weaker one when the anticenter region was being observed. Several days' records are plotted here, differing in shape and amplitude because of variations in ionospheric absorption. Dips at right ascension 6^h30^m and 19^h30^m are instrumental effects.

Heavy ionospheric absorption is expected at decameter wavelengths, and its observation presents an interesting subject for amateurs. The ratio of the intensity of cosmic radio noise from day to day gives a direct measure of this absorption. The effect was quite pronounced in September 1963, due to a particularly active region on the sun which affected the earth's ionosphere.

Effects of a solar flare are illustrated in the record obtained on September 16 (shown in Fig. 94). According to the High Altitude Observatory *Preliminary Report of Solar Activity*, a solar flare of importance 2 was observed in hydrogen-alpha light, beginning at 14:35 Universal Time and reaching maximum at 15:09. We recorded an intense burst of continuous radio emission which began at 14:40 and continued until about 16:35. The level of cosmic background noise after the flare was clearly lower than the noise level the following day at the same time. This indicates an increase in ionospheric absorption caused by radiation produced in the flare.

Another example of a flare-associated radio burst was observed on October 22. The optical flare was of importance 2+, and lasted from 13:32 to 15:02 UT. A decameter radio burst began at 13:56. . . .

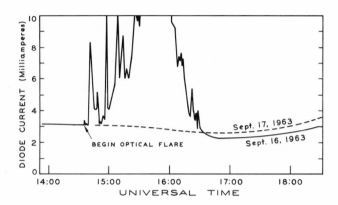

FIG. 94. Decameter radio emission associated with a class-2 solar flare, September 16, 1963. Following the flare, increased ionospheric absorption was observed.

Since Jupiter was near opposition during September and October 1963, it was possible to observe radio-noise storms from that planet without changing the equipment. The high intensity and irregular pattern of Jupiter's radio bursts were particularly evident.

Although the observations described here can be made with simple equipment, the experimenter should be aware of manmade interference, which often has the same general appearance as solar and Jovian radio bursts.

Details on the construction of amateur radiotelescopes are given in "A Simple Radiotelescope," by Dennis N. Downes [see p. 247], and in *Radio Astronomy*, by Frank W. Hyde (New York, Norton, 1963). Two general surveys of radioastronomy are *Radio Astronomy*, by J. H. Piddington (New York, Harper, 1961), and *Radio Astronomy*, by J. L. Steinberg and J. Lequeux (New York, McGraw-Hill, 1963).

Famous

Observatories

and Telescopes

Any telescope that is used for astronomical measurements soon becomes known for the observations made with it. In the present state of astronomical knowledge a telescope with a large aperture is often required in order to study faint stars or nebulae or galaxies, and such a telescope may be called a "special-purpose" instrument. Many of today's best-known telescopes are large ones, the 200-inch Hale reflector on Palomar Mountain, California, being the largest built to date. Others of lesser size are well known among astronomers and are featured widely in other volumes of this series.

There are two hundred and seventy observatories listed in the American Ephemeris and Nautical Almanac, and it is impossible to do justice to a significant fraction of the most active ones in this chapter. The editors have selected articles showing the wide variety of locations, telescopes, and observations made. Aside from economic and social considerations, location is of technical importance; the majority of the large observatories are in the Northern Hemisphere, where the southern polar cap of the sky cannot be viewed. An important part of the Milky Way and the Magellanic Clouds (two nearby galaxies outside our own) can be studied only from observatories in South America, South Africa, Australia, and New Zealand. The new Commonwealth Observatory in Australia is described below; discussions of older observatories in Argentina and South Africa must unfortunately be omitted.

An observatory's location is also important for reasons of weather and other local conditions. It is natural that the site of a large telescope costing several million dollars should be chosen for clear skies, good seeing (p. 129), and the absence of nearby lights and of dust and smoke. The dry climate of the southwestern United States makes for more observing hours per year there than in other areas. Many observatories have been built on mountain tops, at altitudes of 6000 feet or more, where they have a clear horizon and there is less air and water vapor between telescope and stars. Strong winds are to be avoided; they often bring clouds, and they cause poor seeing.

An observatory far from civilization requires astronomers to live in isolation or to travel long distances to work, but it avoids the sky glow of city lights and the smog now common over large centers of population. Both of these urban effects make it difficult or impossible to find faint objects with a telescope, and the unwanted light fogs photographs and introduces artificial spectrum lines when a spectrograph is used.

Most observatories are associated with—or part of—universities, even though they are located many miles away from the campus. For instance Yerkes Observatory is ninety miles from the University of Chicago, Lick Observatory is fifty miles from the University of California (Berkeley), Palomar one hundred and seventy miles from the California Institute of Technology, and McDonald Observatory four hundred miles from the University of Texas.

Most of the observatories described here welcome visitors during some hours of the day and set aside an evening once a week or once a month when visitors can look through a telescope. Demonstrations, photographs, and other exhibits are additional attractions.

As a reminder of the progress in telescope making, the following article describes a famous old observatory in India.   — T L P

··

Jai Singh and His Observatory at New Delhi

K. M. TALGERI

(*Sky and Telescope*, December 1958)

For over two thousand years astronomy has been cultivated in India. The traditional Hindu system of astronomy, *Surya Siddhanta*, is of unknown origin, but it was influenced by the Greco-Babylonian school of astronomy, which became known in India after the conquests of Alexander the Great. During the Dark Ages, the countries of the Near East and India became the custodians of classical science.

More than a century after the invention of the telescope, astronomers in many countries of the world, practically isolated from their European contemporaries, used naked-eye methods of observing the sun and stars to obtain time and position. Among the greatest of such astronomers was the Maharaja Jai Singh, who in 1724 built the famous Jantar Mantar at New Delhi, which the American novelist Lillian Smith has called one of the most fascinating places on earth.

Famous as an astronomer and mathematician, Jai Singh II was ruler of the state of Jaipur, and in 1728 founded its capital city of the same name, about one hundred and fifty miles southwest of New Delhi. As an erudite scholar he had mastered the Surya Siddhanta, and he studied Ptolemy's monumental work the *Almagest*. He also read the thirteenth-century translation, by the Persian astronomer Nasir Ul Din, of Euclid's *Elements* . . . .

Jai Singh was much dissatisfied with the Indian calendars of his day, and resolved to provide a better basis for them from new observations. This led him to construct five astronomical observatories, at New Delhi, Jaipur, Banaras, Ujjain, and Mathura. Guided by Moslem rather than European example, his instruments were gigantic masonry structures for naked-eye sightings of celestial bodies. . . .

The New Delhi observatory is known as the Jantar Mantar, from the Sanskrit word *yantra*, instrument. It consists of a number of structures, the Samrath Yantra, the Rama Yantra, the Jai Prakash Yantra, and the Misra Yantra. The second and third of these are in pairs.

In the center of the observatory area is the Samrath Yantra, an enormous equatorial sundial whose gnomon (shown in Fig. 95) casts its shadow on an arc of masonry which is marked in hours, minutes, and seconds. . . .

The Rama Yantra (see Fig. 96) consists of two circular buildings, each with a central pillar from which shafts radiate horizontally to the outer wall. The azimuth of a celestial body is determined by its direction when sighted across the top of the pillar, and to measure altitude an observer stands either in the wall or in the slots between the shafts, sighting to the object across the top edge of the pillar.

Altitude graduations are marked on the inside of the wall, starting with 0° at the top, for an object on the horizon (as seen by an observer at the top of the wall), and reaching 45° where the wall and shafts join. For altitudes of 45° to 90°, the scale is marked on the shafts themselves,

FIG. 95. A view northward up the steps of the huge gnomon of the Samrath Yantra. Figure 97 was taken from a point high on these steps. At the left is the Niyat Chakra Yantra. (Photograph courtesy K. M. Talgeri.)

FIG. 96. The horizontal shafts of the Rama Yantra, radiating from the central pillar, bear markings of the altitude scale. An observer can walk between the shafts and sight to an object from the markings at eye level. (Photograph courtesy K. M. Talgeri.)

increasing to 90° (for an object in the zenith) at the base of the pillar.

Inasmuch as the observing slots and shafts are partly obstructed by the masonry itself, two such instruments had to be built, the openings in one corresponding to the masonry supports in the other.

For a similar reason, the third instrument is also in two parts. It is the Jai Prakash Yantra (shown in Fig. 97), also known as the Bowl of Berossus, after the Babylonian astronomer of about 280 B.C. To afford access for the observer, the solid parts of one building correspond to the vacant spaces of the other. Each hemispherical cavity is plastered and polished, with lines to represent the meridian, equator, and circles of altitude and azimuth. The rim, which denotes the horizon, is divided in

FIG. 97. Looking south down the steps of the Samrath Yantra into the Jai Prakash Yantra. In the distance are the two circular buildings of the Rama Yantra, each with a central pillar of wall height. (Photograph courtesy K. M. Talgeri.)

degrees and minutes. Exactly north-south and east-west over the bowl are stretched cross wires that carry at their intersection a piece of perforated metal. The position of the sun in the sky can be found by locating its pinhole image on the bowl.

The Misra Yantra is the most complex of the New Delhi instruments, consisting of four parts. Of these the most interesting is the Niyat Chakra Yantra, for observing the sun. As seen in Figure 95, there are four semicircular arcs, whose common center is halfway up the stairway of the gnomon. When the shadow of a rod that may be mounted at this center falls in turn on one of the arcs, the moment is local apparent noon at one of four observatories in widely separated lands. The arc farthest right, for example, is supposed to show Greenwich noon.

Observations with these massive instruments began in the year 1729, and it was intended to compile tables of the positions of the planets, but these were never published. According to the German historian Ernst Zinner, Jai Singh said that from seven years of observation the lunar tables of [the European astronomer Phillippe de] La Hire were in error by as much as half a degree, and that the eclipse predictions from them were up to six minutes off.

The maharaja's second observatory, at Ujjain, probably dates from the years 1728–34. Apparently, this location was chosen because it had been used as the zero meridian of longitude by medieval astronomers in India. No observations seem to have been made at that observatory, however, nor at the one Jai Singh erected at Banaras in 1737. The Jaipur observatory, built in 1734, is well known and still standing. The fifth of the series, at Mathura, was never finished and was demolished later in the eighteenth century.

Today the Jantar Mantar at New Delhi remains an impressive monument to the astronomical interests of Maharaja Jai Singh II.

The positions of moon, planets, and stars in the sky are observed today with much higher precision than was possible with Jai Singh's Rama Yantra sighting devices. Many observatories have been involved in such measurements, but there are far fewer now than there were thirty years ago. The Royal Greenwich Observatory near London, and the U.S. Naval Observatory in Washington, D.C., are among the most active.

One of the special problems of positional astronomy is the measurement of parallaxes, from which distances to the stars are calculated. The results, which are fundamental to much of astronomy, require microscope measurements of high-precision photographs. An observatory devoted to this work and, like many other observatories, to the teaching of astronomy in a small university is described below as it was twenty-five years ago. Other instruments have since been added. —TLP

....

The Van Vleck Observatory of Wesleyan University

FREDERICK SLOCUM

(The Sky, January 1939)

The Van Vleck Observatory is the third observatory to be built on the Wesleyan campus in Middletown, Connecticut. The first was erected about 1838 to house a 6-inch Lerebours refractor, bought by President Willbur Fisk in Paris in 1836. In 1868, through the efforts of Professor John M. Van Vleck, Wesleyan secured a 12-inch refractor from the Alvan Clark company of Cambridgeport, Massachusetts, and the second observatory was built during that same year. This observatory was taken down in 1915 as the third observatory was nearing completion.

The Van Vleck Observatory is a memorial to two brothers, John Monroe Van Vleck, professor of mathematics and astronomy at Wesleyan for over fifty years, and Joseph Van Vleck, a businessman of Montclair, New Jersey, whose financial assistance made the observatory possible.

This observatory is located on the top of a hill, 200 feet above sea level, on the edge of the Wesleyan campus. It is constructed of Portland brownstone.

The main part of the building is 40 by 80 feet, one story high, and contains a classroom, library, time room, two computing rooms, director's office, and a bedroom. In a wing extending to the west is a transit room, containing two 3-inch transits. At the end of a second wing, extending to the east, is the tower and dome for the chief instrument, a visual refracting telescope of 20 inches aperture and 27.6 feet focal length, to which is attached a 10-foot spectrohelioscope. For convenience in observing, the tower is equipped with an elevator 33 feet in diameter, with a vertical range of 10 feet. The basement contains two rooms for photographic work, a spectroscopic laboratory, and a workshop. . . .

Since 1925 the chief research problem has been the determination of stellar parallaxes from photographs made with the 20-inch telescope. Since this is a visual refractor, a "minus blue" filter is used in connection with Eastman Special 1-G green-sensitive plates. . . .

Other research problems include observations of the asteroid Eros for a new determination of the solar parallax, observation of eclipses, solar

FIG. 98. In addition to the New Delhi Observatory, Jai Singh built similar installations at four other sites. The inset shows the area covered by the detailed map.

FIG. 99. With the 20-inch visual refracting telescope, Frederick Slocum instructed college students, followed the proper motions of faint stars, and derived the parallaxes of variables, novae, binaries, and planetary nebulae. (Photograph courtesy Van Vleck Observatory.)

prominences, and flocculi with the spectrohelioscope, and occultation of stars by the moon.

From the distances and motions of stars, measured in New England, we turn to other kinds of observing, in Arizona. Observations of the planet Mars and the discovery of Pluto are discussed in Vols. 1 and 2 of this series. (See also Mars, by E. C. Slipher, Sky Publishing Corp., Cambridge, Massachusetts, 1962.) —TLP

....

The Lowell Observatory

ROGER LOWELL PUTNAM

(The Telescope, July–August 1937)

The founding of the Lowell Observatory presents an unusual combination of a long pondering over an idea and a sudden inspiration. Percival Lowell, the founder, had had since boyhood a latent—one might say, a smoldering—interest in astronomy. It was concealed under a layer of other interests—real ones, not whimsies—which outwardly absorbed his talents until he was almost forty. The astronomical fire must have been burning all this while, for, from time to time, the pressure became so great as to cause a rift in the overlying layers and an occasional bursting forth. Finally they were worn so thin that the fires of science and astronomy broke out completely, never to be confined again.

As a boy, he had had a telescope on the roof of his father's house in Brookline, Massachusetts, and his library contained many books on astronomy, given to him by members of his family, particularly by his mother, during his boyhood and young manhood. Long before he went to college he frequently came over to the Harvard Observatory to talk with Professor Winlock. . . . For many years thereafter, no astronomical sign again appeared. . . . It was in the late autumn of 1893 that the final eruption took place. . . . To the world, Lowell became, in studying the markings on Mars, the successor of the keen observer Schiaparelli, whose eyesight was beginning to fail. He must build an observatory, and probably in Arizona. This decision sounds logical enough, but would Lowell have ever heard of Schiaparelli, much less known about his eyesight's failing, if he had not long been studying in this field? As for building a new observatory in Arizona, there were two reasons. The astronomical profession had on the whole taken Schiaparelli's work [on the "canals" of Mars] with several grains of salt. No existing observatory would have taken kindly to a confessed amateur's entering the field independently and working under its name on such problems. More important was his realization that such work required the very best possible "seeing," and there was no observatory located in the ideal position to have a thin and steady atmosphere. A high, dry, plateau, he pointed out, was essential. Time was pressing, because a close opposition of Mars was to occur in October of 1894. In March, he sent an observer to the Southwest to test the "seeing" in different places. By April, Flagstaff, Arizona, had been selected, and before June 1, regular observing was under way with a borrowed 18-inch refractor. The mounting was built in the East, under his direction, and a dome was erected on the mesa a mile west of the town of Flagstaff, at an elevation of 7250 feet, Professor W. H. Pickering contributing much help and advice.

This observatory was a temporary affair, built solely to observe that particular opposition of Mars. The original investigations had convinced Lowell that Flagstaff offered the best seeing in the United States, but what of the rest of the world? In the winter of 1896–7, the telescope was moved to Mexico for a trial, and a year later Lowell went to North Africa, to investigate conditions there, but he found them very disappointing.

While possible sites were being studied and world atmospheric conditions examined, Alvan Clark was commissioned to supply the best 24-inch refractor his skill and experience could provide. He produced for the Lowell Observatory his last big glass, and he said, too, that it was his best. The mesa west of Flagstaff was confirmed as the permanent site. The community offered the necessary land. A dome was built, and the new 24-inch installed there permanently upon its return from Mexico. The founding of the observatory is typical of the tone he set for its future work: careful thought, inspiration, willingness to undertake new problems, thorough analysis, and, once a decision was reached, the utmost dispatch in execution.

The first two years' work was almost wholly on Mars. There was the same painstaking thoroughness in the investigation that characterized all he undertook. Schiaparelli's markings were all visible, and many more. In the clear atmosphere of Flagstaff, with the efficient new telescope, much more could be seen than from the shores of the Mediterranean. For their future interpretation, it is perhaps unfortunate that the Italian name *canali* for the straight lines on the planet should have been carried over bodily into the English *canals*, but straight lines they were, and apparently connecting one visible place with another. They darkened as the polar caps melted and faded away in the autumn. Where lines crossed, there were often dots, blacker and larger than the lines.

This is not the place to enter into a long description of these findings and their implications. The purpose is to show only that when any investigation was once started, Lowell carried it through with minute attention to detail and with characteristic energy. He was observing practically every night during this first opposition, and much of each day was spent in study of results. Over nine hundred drawings were made at this one opposition. . . .

Because Mars was the immediate cause of the founding of Lowell Observatory, and because the first active work had been in observing this planet, the site was nicknamed Mars Hill. Like most nicknames, the appellation is not entirely accurate. While the Mars work was going on, many other projects were being carried forward. The whole solar system became the object of Lowell's great and absorbing interest. It was at Lowell that Mercury was first systematically and scientifically observed in the daytime; through the thin atmosphere overhead could be seen many features that were invisible when the planet was close to the horizon. The ring system of Saturn was studied carefully, and new divisions not discernible elsewhere were recorded. Slipher began his spectroscopic work on planetary bodies and, in the midst of other problems, determined the rotation period of Uranus by this means. . . .

In studying comets, Lowell became convinced that there must be at least one planet beyond Neptune, a conviction he never relinquished, although he did not attack the problem mathematically until some years later. . . .

Lowell's final work was the prediction of the position and orbit of a ninth planet from the residual perturbations of Uranus' orbit. The drama of the finding of Pluto has been too recently told to need repetition. The calculations were published shortly before his death in 1916, but not until fourteen years later was the planet itself finally located.

Instrumental equipment was forthcoming when the need appeared. The original 24-inch refractor, carrying also an excellent Clark 12-inch lent by George Agassiz, occupies the dome visible from the Santa Fe Railroad. West of this, sheltered by the pines, is the dome of the 42-inch reflector. The library and administration building lies between the two; on an elevation to the rear is the smaller dome, housing the 13-inch Lawrence Lowell search telescope, the one through which Pluto was actually found. . . .

Much more could be said about the many discoveries and researches of the past two decades, but these few examples are sufficient to show that the character of the Lowell Observatory has been consistently maintained from its foundation. There has always been present the capacity for taking infinite pains, which has been defined as "genius,"

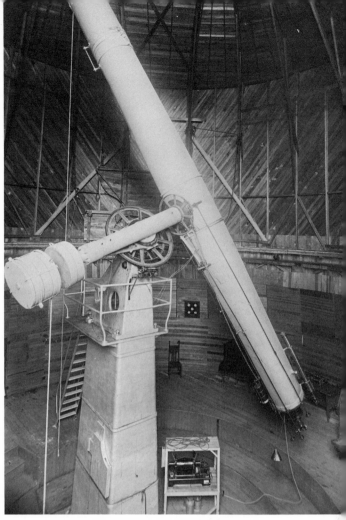

FIG. 100. A. The 24-inch Clark refractor. B. Administration, library, and laboratory building. (Lowell Observatory photographs.)

and always present, too, has been the inspiration to new interpretations and new attacks. Animated as it always will be by these traditions, and with the means that will some day be at its disposal, the observatory will gather an even greater harvest.

There are many observatories with similar breadth in observational programs and long records of accomplishment. One of these in France and one in the Soviet Union are described below.   —T L P

··

Meudon Observatory

GERMAIN EPSTEIN

(*The Sky,* January 1939)

When I arrived in the quaint town of Meudon, near Paris, on Thursday, July 21, the sun was shining with all its splendor yet with a mien which seemed to defy us to solve definitely the mystery of its innermost actuating forces. I had read in textbooks that the Meudon Solar Observatory was one of the most important in the world. . . . At the threshold of the observatory an official guard who expected me led me to Monsieur D' Azambuja and his wife, both eminent and active astronomers.

The Meudon Observatory was founded in 1876 on the site and in the remaining buildings of the castle of Meudon, the greater part of which burned down in 1795 and 1871. The Meudon Observatory has perhaps the unique distinction of having been obliged, at the very beginning, to adapt itself to buildings whose original uses were far from astronomical purposes. Since then new domes and buildings have been added. . . .

Meudon's spectroheliograph is still perhaps the most powerful, if not at least the most complete and manageable of this style of instruments. From 1908 to 1909 its users were able to recognize and separate images corresponding to the successive components of the H and K spectral lines of the ionized calcium and of the hydrogen H-alpha line. A series of photographs of the upper layers of these two elements are still taken daily. This spectroheliograph, which faces south and extends 52 feet, is used with either three prisms or a grating and allows four different combinations. . . .

Among the fascinating pictures taken with the spectroheliograph was a series of photographs showing the queer evolution of a sun prominence from August 23 to September 4, 1929. The apparent thin leaflike shape as well as the arch formations of this prominence were quite a revelation. . . .

The battery of the observatory's telescopes is composed of the following instruments:

Large refracting equatorial telescope, called Grande Lunette. Composed of two paired telescopes, one photographic of 33-inch opening, the other visual of 25-inch opening, both of 54-foot focal length and mounted together in a square tube. The telescope is housed in the castle proper under a dome of 61-foot inside diameter. It was with this instrument that the world-renowned astronomer E. M. Antoniadi made his frequent observations of Mars, gathered in a celebrated volume entitled *La planète Mars.*

Newtonian telescope. With 40-inch mirror and 10-foot focal length, constructed by Gautier, equipped for photography and visual observations. Provided with astronomical eyepiece having two separable prisms for viewing double stars.

Two smaller refracting telescopes, of 8-inch and 10-inch opening respectively. . . .

B. Lyot, an active Meudon astronomer, conceived a scheme whereby one may dispense with natural eclipses when wishing to observe the sun's corona. . . . His instrument is called a *coronagraph.*

FIG. 101. The "table equatoriale" with its unique accessories is the most striking instrument at Meudon Observatory. The plans of the new instrument were ready in 1925, but the Lyot coronagraph was not put into operation until 1931. (Meudon Observatory photograph.)

The Poulkovo Observatory (1839–1941)

OTTO STRUVE

(*Sky and Telescope*, February 1942)

The October 1941 issue of *The Observatory* contains the following brief notice: ". . . news has been received of the destruction of the historic Pulkovo Observatory in the fighting near Leningrad. The observatory celebrated its centenary in 1939, and its loss will be felt with grief and horror by all astronomers." History will record the name of Adolf Hitler along with that of Khalif Omar, whose General Amru in A.D. 641 finished by fire the destruction of the great library in Alexandria, and that of the patricide Abdallatif, who, in 1449, murdered his illustrious father, Ulugh-Beg, and thus brought to an end the work of the great observatory at Samarkand.

B. A. Gould once called the Poulkovo Observatory "the astronomical capital of the world," and in 1903 Simon Newcomb wrote, "The instruments which Struve designed sixty years ago still do as fine work as any in the world. . . . The air is remarkably clear."[1] . . .

In 1919 the White Russian forces under General Udenich besieged Poulkovo for several days and shells burst among its buildings. But no serious damage was done. . . .

To recall the beginning of the Poulkovo Observatory, let us turn back to the year 1808. One day in summer a boy of fifteen was walking through the fields near his native town of Altona, then a part of Denmark. The world was in turmoil. A powerful and reckless dictator had conquered nearly all of Europe, and only two countries—England and Russia—were blocking his progress toward world domination. Napoleon was determined to conquer Russia and even then was preparing an army for the drive against Moscow. Although Denmark was neutral, the boy, a Danish subject on Danish soil, was about to learn that dictators may disregard the rights of citizens in neutral countries. He was accosted by French recruiting officers who demanded that he join the French army and, when he refused, abducted him. He was taken to Hamburg, where his captors locked him in a room of a two-story building overlooking the

---

[1] *Reminiscences of an Astronomer*, Boston and New York, Houghton, Mifflin, 1903, p. 312. [The Struve mentioned here is F. G. W. Struve, great-grandfather of the author of this article.]

Fig. 102. A general view of historic Poulkovo Observatory. The revolving turret of the 15-inch refractor appears in the center.

River Elbe. Young F. G. W. Struve had no desire to compromise. When all was quiet at night he opened a window and jumped into the water below. He was strong and a good swimmer, and he struck out in the direction of a ship in the harbor. The ship was Russian, ready to set sail for Riga. Struve was taken aboard and sailed to Russia, determined to make a home for himself in a new land.

He worked his way through the University of Dorpat, and a few years later he became the director of the observatory there. . . .

The capital of Russia, St. Petersburg, had only a small and inadequately equipped observatory. One of its instruments was a telescope permanently fixed on a wall toward that point in the sky where the star Vega crosses the meridian. Evidently, the purpose of the instrument had been to determine the parallax of Vega—a task which had not been completed. This point is of interest in connection with his later success in determining the first reliable parallax of a fixed star, and the name of this star was Vega.

In 1834 Struve was presented to the Czar Nikolai and obtained from him permission to draw up plans for a new large observatory. The cornerstone was laid in 1835, and the opening of the new institution took place on August 19, 1839. The principal instruments were a 15-inch refractor by Fraunhofer, a large transit instrument, and an equally powerful meridian circle. The refractor—then the largest in the world—was used for double-star observations, first by the son of the founder, Otto Struve, and later by his grandson, Herman Struve, and many others. . . .

Most of the early work of the observatory was devoted to the observation of accurate star positions. These were used by F. G. W. Struve for the determination of the constant of aberration, for which he gave in 1843 the value 20″.4451—remarkably close to the modern value of 20″.47. . . .

In a recent volume of the *Annals* of the observatory, one of the principal tasks of Poulkovo is described as "the observation of a fundamental catalogue of several hundred stars at intervals of about twenty years, for the purpose of constructing a reference system and deriving accurate proper motions." . . .

In 1878 the observatory installed a new 30-inch refractor with a lens by Alvan Clark. . . . The new refractor, the largest in existence until the completion of the 36-inch Lick telescope, was used for double stars, satellites in the solar system, planets, and radial velocities.

After the retirement of Otto Struve, who succeeded his father in the directorship, this post was occupied by Oscar Backlund, then by Belopolsky. Under his administration the observatory passed through the years of a revolution and civil war. He was followed for a short time by A. A. Ivanoff, then by A. Drosd. The rapid succession of directors seems to have done considerable harm. The period between 1920 and 1932 was relatively unproductive, as is evidenced by the meager results of the observatory's publications.

In 1932 the Soviet government appointed as director the former Kharkov University professor B. P. Gerasimovich. One of the three best known modern astronomers of Russia, he was a man of great ability and exceptional energy. . . . In 1937 he disappeared in one of the great "purges" and his fate is not known. With him disappeared several other astronomers of Poulkovo. . . .

The great majority of Russian astronomers have at one time or another been connected with Poulkovo. . . .

The library contained the original manuscripts of Kepler, which have never been completely evaluated historically. . . .

The observatory had from the beginning received the attention of Czar Nikolai I. The Poulkovo hill had been an imperial estate, and the peasant serfs in the village were owned by the government. The serfs were liberated in 1861, but even after that date former government serfs and soldiers, retired after twenty-five years of mandatory service, were employed for turning the domes and opening the shutters. Most of these men were deeply attached to the observatory and to the astronomers. The story is told of one, Dimitri, who, on a November evening in 1866, excitedly burst into the room of the director and asked, "What will become of us? The stars are all falling out of the heavens! The government will close the observatory and we shall lose our jobs!" . . . [He was referring to an intense meteor shower.]

Astronomers from all countries came to see Poulkovo, and because of transportation difficulties, were usually entertained in the director's residence. To Poulkovo came the Italian Schiaparelli, the American

Newcomb, the Royal Astronomer, Airy, and countless others. There came the fierce Prince Shamil of unconquered Georgia, who carried his dagger with him wherever he went. On another occasion the observatory had a visit from the Emir of Bukhara. . . .

Indeed, Poulkovo's "loss will be felt with grief and horror by all astronomers."

In the early part of this century, astronomy in the United States developed rapidly along new lines, prompted by improved photography and the spectrograph. (The full story is told by Otto Struve in Astronomy of the 20th Century, New York, Macmillan, 1962.) In 1900 the Harvard College Observatory in Cambridge, Massachusetts, was one of the most active, and George Ellery Hale had just founded the Yerkes Observatory near Chicago, where the largest refractor ever built had been installed. —TLP

ı■■■ı

Yerkes Observatory
(1897–1941)

W. W. MORGAN

(*The Sky*, June 1941)

The history of the Yerkes Observatory falls rather naturally into three periods: the first, under the directorship of its founder, George E. Hale; the second, the period of 20 years from 1904; and the third, from around 1925 to the present time. For a number of years before the dedication of the observatory in 1897, Hale, still in his twenties, made elaborate and far seeing plans for the establishment of an observatory which he hoped to make suitable for all types of astronomical work. For a man of any age this would have been a remarkable feat; for such a young man it is almost unique. . . .

A successful beginning was made in the various large-scale projects which Hale had outlined. These included, among other tasks, the construction of a large spectroheliograph, a three-prism spectrograph with a constant-temperature case, adaptation of the 40-inch telescope for direct photography, and the construction by Ritchey of a 24-inch and a 60-inch reflector. These projects (with the exception of the mounting of the 60-inch) were all completed by 1904, and in addition, a number of important investigations by Hale, Frost, and Adams, among others, had been concluded. Hale had also taken a step which was to produce

FIG. 103. The dome of the 40-inch refractor appears on the right in this photograph of Yerkes Observatory.

FIG. 104. The Yerkes 40-inch refractor, the largest telescope of its type in the world. (Yerkes Observatory photograph.)

results of fundamental importance in modern astronomy. He arranged for Frank Schlesinger to undertake the work of systematic investigation of stellar parallaxes with the 40-inch telescope. In the years 1904 and 1905, Schlesinger laid the foundations of modern high-precision parallax determinations, and this work must be considered as one of the most important single developments in the history of modern astronomy. Among other work of great importance was that of Frost and Adams on the radial velocities of early-type stars and the investigation by Hale, Ellerman, and Parkhurst of the spectra of the carbon stars. . . .

In 1904 Hale, Adams, and Ellerman made an expedition to California and set up a solar telescope on Mount Wilson. This observing station developed into the Mount Wilson Observatory of today. Its establishment was of the greatest importance for the future of astronomy, but the loss of such a group of distinguished astronomers was a serious blow to the Yerkes Observatory. . . .

The visual and photographic investigations of Barnard and the double-star work of Burnham, which had been begun considerably earlier at the Lick Observatory, were continued; similar investigations were made later by Van Biesbroeck and Ross.

Among astronomers who spent varying periods of time at the Yerkes Observatory at the start of their careers [and who were, in 1941, in the following positions] are W. H. Wright, director of the Lick Observatory; S. A. Mitchell, director of the Leander McCormick Observatory; Walter S. Adams, director of Mount Wilson Observatory; Frank Schlesinger, director of the Yale Observatory; Frederick Slocum, director of the Van Vleck Observatory; Philip Fox, former director of the Dearborn Observatory and the Adler Planetarium; O. J. Lee, director of the Dearborn Observatory; J. S. Paraskevopoulos, head of the Harvard Observatory station at Bloemfontein; and E. P. Hubble, A. van Maanen, Alfred H. Joy, and Ferdinand Ellerman, all of Mount Wilson Observatory. . . .

Otto Struve the younger was born [in Kharkov, Russia] in 1897. After adventures as hair-raising as any in fiction, first in the World War, and later in the Russian Revolution, Struve came to the United States and the Yerkes Observatory in 1921. He received the Ph.D. degree from the University of Chicago in 1923. . . . His early work at Yerkes was concerned principally with studies on various aspects of spectroscopic binaries. . . . In 1929 he had pursued his investigations of stellar spectra to a point where he could state, "Analysis of the physical properties of the interstellar calcium leads us to believe that the whole galactic system is immersed in a gaseous substratum consisting of atoms of various elements." . . .

On the retirement of Frost in 1932, Struve was made director of the

FIG. 105. Otto Struve when he was director of Yerkes and McDonald Observatories. (Photograph courtesy California Academy of Sciences.)

Yerkes Observatory. The need for a large reflector for carrying on spectrographic work had become acute, and plans were discussed immediately for enlarging the scope of the observatory and obtaining a new telescope.

As a result of a cooperative project between the University of Texas and the University of Chicago, the McDonald Observatory came into being [see p. 277]. . . .

Later work by Struve included investigations of diffuse nebulae and of double-star systems. . . .

The above is a very incomplete summary of a few of the investigations of one of the most active men ever to work in astronomy. . . . The impetus he has given to general astronomical activity, in the United States in particular, must be considered of importance comparable to his own scientific investigations. When he was made director of Yerkes, he also became managing editor of the *Astrophysical Journal*, one of the most important astronomical publications in the world. . . .

Struve has attracted to the Yerkes Observatory young men of exceptionally great ability. Kuiper . . . discovered a large number of new white dwarfs. . . . In the field of theoretical astronomy, Chandrasekhar worked on stellar interiors and galactic dynamics. Also of the first importance has been the appearance during the past fifteen years of the Milky Way atlases of Barnard and of Ross. Yerkes Observatory has taken a part in the general surge that has animated astronomical research everywhere, and which shows as yet, at least in the United States, no sign of diminution.

The Birth of the
McDonald Observatory

OTTO STRUVE

(*Sky and Telescope*, December 1962)

In 1932 the universities of Chicago and Texas signed a thirty-year contract for the joint operation of a new observatory in the western part of North America. Each university reserved the right to withdraw from the agreement upon one year's notice, but both institutions were expected to continue the arrangement until 1962, when a new contract might be negotiated. This has now been done, in a manner that should be beneficial to both universities. . . .

In 1932, Yerkes Observatory had three major instruments: the 40-inch refractor presented by Charles Yerkes, on which we used the old Bruce spectrograph for photographing stellar spectra; the 24-inch Ritchey reflector; and the old 12-inch refractor that G. E. Hale had used at his private Kenwood Observatory before 1900.

During the 1920s it had become apparent to Georges Van Biesbroeck and me that these instruments were inadequate. We spent many cloudy night hours trying to think how we could secure a moderately large reflector—preferably in some other location that had more clear nights than Williams Bay, Wisconsin. We were thinking of a small observing station equipped with a 60-inch telescope, and . . . noted a good location in the high plains of the Texas panhandle, near Amarillo. . . .

Six years earlier, a wealthy resident of the little town of Paris, Texas, had died, leaving the bulk of his estate to the state university at Austin "to erect and equip, or to aid in erecting and equipping, an astronomical observatory for the promotion and study of the science of astronomy." W. J. McDonald had been a bachelor with no close relatives, but distant relations contested the will on the grounds that he was of unsound mind when he executed it.

This was known to many astronomers who, like Frost, were asked by the university's lawyers to make depositions to the effect that a donation to astronomy did not necessarily imply insanity. The case was finally adjusted out of court, the university receiving about $800,000.

The president of the University of Texas, H. Y. Benedict, had been trained as an astronomer, receiving his Ph.D. degree in that science at the University of Virginia. . . .

I happened to mention this bequest one day in the early spring of 1932 to President Robert M. Hutchins of the University of Chicago. He took an immediate interest in the matter and telephoned Benedict. Within ten minutes the two university presidents had agreed upon a broad plan of cooperation, whereby Texas would pay for the telescope and retain ownership of it, while Chicago would pay all salaries and most of the operating expenses. Part of the McDonald fund was to be saved for possible future use by the University of Texas, but the interest earned on this reserve would help with the cost of operation. . . .

The thirty-year duration of the Texas-Chicago contract was suggested by President Hutchins as the length of time I was expected to serve before retirement. But my own reason for favoring it was that in thirty years Texas would probably be able to run its own astronomy department, with a greater share of observing time, and Chicago would quite likely be interested in other aspects of astronomy.

Hutchins asked me to go to Austin to arrange the details. . . . With the support of President Benedict, it was decided that the choice of the site would be unrestricted. In fact, if it should be shown that the weather conditions outside Texas were better than inside, the observatory could be placed beyond the state boundary.

We borrowed one of the 4-inch telescopes that had been used in the site survey for the 200-inch reflector. During the summer of 1932, C. T. Elvey and T. G. Mehlin, Jr., were sent on an expedition by truck through Texas, New Mexico, and Arizona to examine star images. . . . Their results contained no clear evidence of better conditions in New Mexico than in western Texas, so several possible sites were selected in the Davis Mountains. In December I went to Fort Davis, Texas, and together with Elvey, made tests on many nights atop two mountains—the fairly steep 7500-foot Black Mountain, and what was then called the U-up-and-Down Mountain (after the brand of a neighboring ranch), about 7000 feet high. . . . We finally chose U-up-and-Down, because it was five miles nearer the town of Fort Davis, and because the chances of finding water nearby seemed better. This double hill was later named Mount Locke, after Mrs. Locke, owner of the ranch on which it stood. She gave the site as an outright gift to the University of Texas.

All my plans for McDonald Observatory were based on the conviction that no time-consuming experiments should be undertaken and that a telescope of standard design, similar to others already in existence, be constructed and placed in the hands of the astronomers as soon as possible. . . .

I wrote to all the better-known telescope builders and asked them to submit proposals. The list was soon reduced to two—the Warner and

Swasey Company in Cleveland, Ohio, and J. W. Fecker in Pittsburgh, Pennsylvania. . . . On a boat trip from Boston to Plymouth, Massachusetts, during the 1932 Harvard general assembly of the International Astronomical Union, E. P. Burrell, director of engineering at Warner and Swasey, informed me that his company had decided to start an optical shop, with C. A. R. Lundin in charge. The latter had made fine telescope lenses of moderate size, but he had not previously been engaged in grinding and polishing large parabolic mirrors. Lundin had been associated with the firm of Alvan Clark [see p. 49] at Cambridgeport, Massachusetts, where his father had taken part in making the Poulkovo 30-inch, Lick 36-inch, and Yerkes 40-inch objectives.

However, the decision to award the contract to Warner and Swasey was mainly due to their willingness to make a two-pier mounting resembling those of the Victoria and Perkins telescopes, but providing for a coudé arrangement. . . .

After the contract with Warner and Swasey was signed, a Pyrex glass disk was poured at the Corning Glass works on December 31, 1933. The grinding and polishing started on October 19, 1934, and lasted four years—longer by far than had been expected.

During the last year, 1937–8, Warner and Swasey engaged the services of J. S. Plaskett, director emeritus of the Dominion Astrophysical Observatory. He made the final tests, which indicated an excellent figure, but this work was done in the shop and not at the telescope. The fact is that the secondary mirrors were tested quite superficially. The 82-inch

Fig. 106. The McDonald reflector at the time of its dedication in May 1939. (McDonald Observatory photograph.)

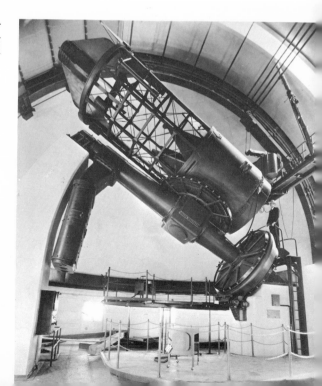

mirror has an excellent shape, but its original supporting mechanism frequently allowed it to become astigmatic. . . . A new supporting mechanism was built after I left the observatory in 1950, and my successor, G. P. Kuiper, has told me that the performance of the mirror is now excellent.

The dedication of McDonald Observatory took place on May 5, 1939, and was followed by a symposium on "Galactic and Extragalactic Structure."

Some observing with various small instruments had been carried on at Mount Locke between 1933 and 1938, but after the dedication all our efforts were directed to making full use of the 82-inch reflector—the world's second in size at that time—surpassed only by the Mount Wilson 100-inch.

Today astronomers may ask whether the scientific work of McDonald Observatory has justified the large amount of money and energy spent in its construction. The answer is undoubtedly yes. The most important single discovery made with the 82-inch was W. A. Hiltner's finding of interstellar polarization. But several other results, though less spectacular, have been equally satisfying.

Among them were A. Unsöld's analysis of the atmosphere of Tau Scorpii, P. Swings' and my work on the properties of peculiar stars, Van Biesbroeck's search for very faint stars sharing the proper motions of bright ones, Elvey's and later Hiltner's photoelectric studies, and my investigation of more than a hundred spectroscopic binaries. Kuiper has made important observations of intrinsically faint stars and of planets and satellites.

B. Strömgren there perfected with the 82-inch his method for photoelectric classification of stellar spectra; D. Popper and C. K. Seyfert determined the radial velocities of many faint B-type stars; and G. R. and E. M. Burbidge measured the rotations of a large number of distant galaxies. A cooperative arrangement with Indiana University enabled F. K. Edmondson to ascertain the radial velocities of many faint A and K stars.

I believe that the two universities have every right to be pleased with the outcome of their thirty-year alliance!

Otto Struve, author of many articles reprinted in this series, made many contributions to astronomy and deserves great credit for establishing the McDonald Observatory. After his death, in 1963, it was decided to name the 82-inch the Struve Telescope. A dedication conference was held at the McDonald Observatory in May 1966. By this time there were five larger telescopes in the world, at the Palomar, Lick, Mount Wilson, Crimean (U.S.S.R.), and Kitt Peak Observatories. —T L P

....

The Lick 120-inch Reflector

(*Sky and Telescope*, March 1955)

Famous among the telescopes of the world are the two 36-inch instruments of Lick Observatory of the University of California. One of these is a refractor, built by Warner and Swasey in 1888, with optics by Alvan Clark. For a decade it was the largest refracting telescope in the world, and is still exceeded only by the Yerkes 40-inch refractor. It is in regular use on a variety of programs that may be effectively carried out in a restricted color range, with long focal length and excellent observing conditions.

The other is the Crossley reflector, the mirror of which was made in London in 1879 by A. A. Common and presented to Lick Observatory in 1895. This versatile instrument operates regularly for direct photography, spectroscopy, and photoelectric photometry of the fainter stars and brighter nebulae.

At Lick, where the emphasis is on observational astronomy, these instruments are in constant use. But the need has long been felt for a larger telescope that can gather many times more light than a 36-inch aperture. Both W. W. Campbell, director from 1901 to 1930, and R. G. Aitken, his successor from 1930 to 1935, were anxious to obtain funds for a large reflector. In the later 1930s, director W. H. Wright and his staff proposed a large instrument as part of an extensive building program envisaged by President R. G. Sproul of the University of California. J. H. Moore, director from 1942 to 1945, was a strong backer of the project, but little progress was possible during World War II.

Near the close of the war, Moore retired, and C. D. Shane, professor of astrophysics in the Berkeley department of astronomy, left his wartime position as director of personnel at Los Alamos Scientific Laboratory to assume the leadership at Mount Hamilton. For the new telescope project, an advisory committee was set up, consisting of three astronomers from Mount Wilson and Palomar Observatories, including director W. S. Adams, and three Lick astronomers.

Plans were drawn for an instrument somewhere in size between the 100-inch and the 200-inch, its cost not to exceed a million dollars. In this size range, it was felt that much costly experimental engineering could be avoided, and standard practice and components utilized. Experienced Mount Wilson observers greatly influenced the committee's recommendation that a 120-inch f/5 reflector would be the most effective instrument for Lick Observatory. . . .

On March 13, 1946, Governor Earl Warren signed an appropriation bill that included $900,000 for Lick's new instrument. This was afterwards increased several times, to $1,800,000. Additional appropriations by the regents of the university and the state of California bring the total budget for the telescope and instrumentation to approximately $2,500,000.

W. W. Baustian, an engineer from California Institute of Technology, was engaged as engineer in charge of design and construction of the building and instrument. The optical work was placed in the hands of D. O. Hendrix of the Mount Wilson optical shop, well known for his work on the 48-inch Palomar Schmidt telescope. All optical processing of the 120-inch disk and secondary mirrors is being carried on at Lick Observatory, in an optical shop located in the basement of the building for the large reflector.

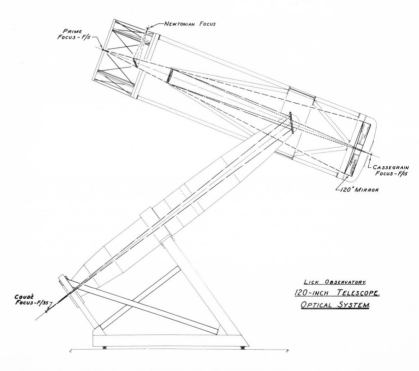

FIG. 107. The 120-inch reflector design provides for four focal points, as shown by this sketch of its optical arrangements.

Procuring a solid Pyrex disk 120 inches in diameter was the next major problem. Up to 1948 it was still not known just how well the ribbed 200-inch mirror would actually perform; therefore, a 120-inch ribbed disk previously cast to test the 200-inch mirror was not considered at first. . . . About 1949 the 200-inch came into operation, and showed that problems of the ribbed mirror had been overcome by a suitable supporting system. Therefore, the Lick astronomers decided to purchase the 120-inch ribbed blank from Caltech, for the modest sum of $50,000. . . .

The 120-inch mirror is a conventional paraboloidal reflector, with a focal length of 50 feet. The plate scale at the prime focus will be 13.5 seconds of arc per millimeter, nearly 3 times the scale of the Crossley reflector.

It is this large plate scale, together with a light-gathering power $1\frac{1}{2}$ times that of the 100-inch telescope, that has the Lick astronomers anxiously awaiting the day when they can observe the fainter stars, galactic nebulae, and galaxies with the 120-inch. N. U. Mayall will work on the brighter resolved parts of the nearer galaxies, observing their globular clusters, emission patches, brighter stars, and variable stars with a prime-focus spectrograph. He will study the rotations of elliptical galaxies and early-type spirals by measuring the inclinations of their spectral lines when the slit is placed lengthwise on such an object. Hitherto, the scale of the Crossley has been rather small for such observations, and the f/19 refractor too slow.

Shane has for many years been engaged in counts of galaxies with the 20-inch astrographic telescope (see *Sky and Telescope*, August 1954). With the new reflector he hopes by direct photography to get sample counts of faint galaxies, probably to the 22nd magnitude.

Photoelectric astronomers G. E. Kron and O. J. Eggen expect to use highly sensitive cells at the prime focus, where the maximum amount of light will be insured by only one reflection—that of the primary mirror. In the southeast part of the observatory building there is a room in which the photoelectric recording apparatus will be permanently installed. The observer in the prime-focus cage will always have an assistant in that room, with telephonic communication.

In the photoelectric work there will probably be heavy emphasis on the infrared, and six-color studies will be carried out on galactic clusters. Photoelectric observations will be made of individual stars and star clusters in the nearer galaxies, M31 and M33. The great light-gathering power may permit photoelectric work on bright individual objects out as far as the Virgo cluster. The magnitude limit for a 1P21 photocell on the 120-inch will be of the order of 21.5.

For the coudé focus, a versatile spectrograph for high and medium dispersion will be constructed according to optical designs by George Herbig. He and W. P. Bidelman will use this instrument principally in extensive detailed studies of stellar spectra of all types. . . .

Throughout the whole 120-inch project there has been close cooperation with Mount Wilson and Palomar astronomers. Their experience was invaluable in design and construction problems. This cooperation will also extend to observing programs, which will be closely coordinated to avoid duplication and to insure that the different instruments in California will be used to best advantage in the solution of astronomical problems.

Large telescopes became an American specialty during the first half of this century. Besides the ones described here, there were the 100-inch and 60-inch reflectors at Mount Wilson in California, a 60-inch reflector in Ohio, another in Massachusetts, and two large ones in Canada. It was to be expected that others would be built overseas.   — T L P

FIG. 108. Lick Observatory as photographed from the water tank toward Kepler Peak on January 28, 1952. The completed dome dominates the scene. To the left is the housing of the 20-inch astrographic refractor, and on the summit beyond is the main observatory building, with domes for the 36-inch and 12-inch refractors.

FIG. 109. Rough grinding of the Lick Observatory 120-inch disk took 80 hours. Here a cast-iron doughnut-shaped tool with outer and inner diameters of 24 and 16 inches is used. A 2-horsepower motor spins the 400-pound tool at 80 revolutions per minute, while the Draper arm moves the tool across the mirror 12 to 20 times a minute. It is possible to adjust the Draper-arm speed and the pivot location by remote control without stopping the machine.

FIG. 110. In late 1954 the 120-inch telescope and mounting were complete. Note that the declination axis is one quarter of the way up the tube. The 12-sector aluminum cover, operated by a worm-and-chain drive from a motor in the lower ring girder, is closed over the mirror cell. On the north and south sides of the telescope framework are parallel vertical tubes; in one of these the position of a sliding 200-pound counterweight can be set to balance the telescope for differing weights of observers at the prime focus and for changes of instruments.

FIG. 111. The upper end of the telescope tube, with the prime-focus unit in position. The entire length of the instrument is 50 feet, from the bottom of the mirror ring girder shown in Figure 110 to the upper end of the prime-focus unit. The total weight of the tube assembly, including the mirror, is almost 40 tons. (Figures 107–111 courtesy Lick Observatory.)

¹■■■¹

Crimean Astrophysical
Observatory

A. B. SEVERNY

(*Sky and Telescope*, October 1955)

An observatory belonging to an amateur astronomer served as the basis for the southern branch of the Poulkovo Observatory, set up in 1908 near Simeis in the southern Crimea at a height of 1200 feet. The first astronomer in charge of the station was A. P. Gansky, a well-known investigator of the sun. During World War II the observatory was heavily damaged by the forces of occupation, and its 40-inch reflecting telescope was destroyed.

After the war it was decided not only to restore the observatory at Simeis but to find another site, where the seeing conditions would be better for spectrographic work. Today a new observatory has been built near the village of Partizanskoye, 2100 feet above sea level, in the central part of the Crimean peninsula.

The new station has a 50-inch reflecting telescope with two spectrographs, a 20-inch Maksutov telescope with a coudé focus, equipped for photoelectric registration of stellar spectra and colors, and a double 16-inch astrograph with an objective prism. In 1954 a solar tower telescope was set up, which uses a coelostat [flat] mirror 27½ inches in diameter [to reflect light into a fixed telescope with] a 16-inch concave primary mirror. The tower telescope has a spectrograph and a photometer for recording the solar spectrum photoelectrically, and it can be used to take motion pictures of the sun in the light of a single spectrum line, as is done at the McMath-Hulbert Observatory in the United States. There is also a coronagraph of the Lyot type, with several narrow-band filters, including one for the infrared helium line at 10,830 angstroms.

At the rebuilt Simeis station there is a 25-inch coma-free telescope, a nebular spectrograph, a 12-inch horizontal solar telescope with a Hale spectrohelioscope, and two cameras with which minor planets are regularly being photographed. There are several radiotelescopes working at meter wavelengths. Sixteen astronomers and several radio engineers work here.

At both observatories the work in stellar spectroscopy includes spectral classification of faint stars and the areas of stellar associations, and nebulae are being studied with narrow-band filters and the nebular

FIG. 112. A. These three domes at the Crimean Astrophysical Observatory, from left to right, house the 50-inch reflecting telescope, the 16-inch photographic refractor, and the 20-inch Maksutov-type telescope B. The solar tower telescope at the new Crimean station in southern Russia.

spectrograph. Motion pictures are regularly taken of the sun in hydro-gen-alpha light, and spectroheliograms are obtained in light from the H and K lines of ionized calcium. Solar radio emission is being regularly observed on a wavelength of 1.5 meters, and observations of the mag-netic fields of sunspots have begun.

In 1951 an electronic image converter was used to obtain photographs of the galactic center in infrared. A statistical study of novae by Kopylov has led him to conclude that these stars are not genetically related to the other types of explosive variables (novalike stars, recurrent novae, super-novae) nor to other types of hot stars.

Shajn and Hase have discovered a large number of new hydrogen emission nebulae. Many of these consist of nearly parallel filaments. To explain these very elongated nebulae, the hypothesis has been ad-vanced that there is an interstellar magnetic field which controls the distribution and perhaps the motion of diffuse matter in our galaxy.

Crimean investigations of large emission nebulae stress their internal motions and, in particular, the outward motions. The conclusions appear probable that nebulae in their emission stage have short lifetimes, of the order of 1 to 10 million years, and that they have a strong tendency to disintegrate. Observations of the brightnesses of the most conspicuous emission nebulae in M33, M101, and other galaxies have led to an estimation of the masses of these nebulae as some thousands or tens of thousands of solar masses.

The writer and his associates have paid particular attention to solar studies. One investigation was the detailed examination of the spectra of fifty flares. One flare seems to appear, on the average, for every seven hours of the lifetime of a sunspot group. Photoelectric observations of the sun's spectrum have indicated the presence of deuterium on the sun, and Dubov has determined the solar lithium abundance. . . .

Since this article was written, Soviet astronomers have built a 102-inch reflector at the Crimean Astrophysical Observatory. It is reported that they are building an even larger telescope, probably larger than the Palomar 200-inch.   —T L P

The Australian Commonwealth Observatory

OLIN J. EGGEN

(*Sky and Telescope*, June 1956)

Australia's Commonwealth Observatory stands on Mount Stromlo, about 2600 feet above sea level in the Australian southern highlands, some ten miles from the capital city of Canberra. The observatory is the best equipped in the Southern Hemisphere, and considering the light-gathering power and diversity of its instruments, it is one of the world's major astronomical institutions.

The astronomical history of Australia is, in a sense, older than its political history, for when Lieut. James Cook took the bark *Endeavour* out of Plymouth harbor in 1768, his "secret instructions" were twofold: to observe the transit of Venus at Tahiti and to look for "Terra Australis Incognita," the suspected great southern continent. Among the astronomical instruments on board was a clock that had just been returned from the American colonies, where it was used by two veterans of the previous transit of Venus, Charles Mason and Jeremiah Dixon, in surveying the Mason-Dixon line. When the *Endeavour* sailed into Botany Bay in 1770, that clock was used in the first astronomical observations, the determination of the longitude of what is now Sydney.

Eighteen years later the first permanent settlers came to the country. Capt. William Bligh, of *Bounty* fame and one of the early governors of the new colony, tells us: "Among the buildings that were undertaken shortly after arrival must be mentioned an observatory, which was built to receive the instruments sent out for the purpose of observing the comet that was expected about the end of that year [1788]."

Although the comet was not seen and the observatory soon fell into disuse, Australian astronomy had begun. During the next hundred years observatories were established in the states of New South Wales, Victoria, South Australia, and Queensland; the Perth Observatory in Western Australia was established in 1896. All of these were mainly concerned with time service and similar "government astronomy," but the names of many nineteenth-century astronomers in Australia are still familiar today. R. T. A. Innes, H. C. Russell, and James Dunlop did

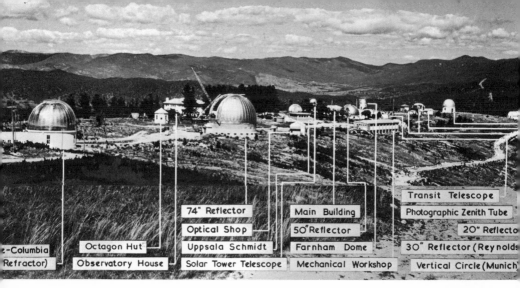

74" Reflector
Optical Shop
Uppsala Schmidt
Solar Tower Telescope
Main Building
50" Reflector
Farnham Dome
Mechanical Workshop
Transit Telescope
Photographic Zenith Tube
20" Reflector
30" Reflector (Reynolds)
Vertical Circle (Munich)
-Columbia Refractor)
Octagon Hut
Observatory House

FIG. 113. The Commonwealth Observatory on Mount Stromlo in Australia as seen from the 9-inch Oddie refractor. Here, instruments of many sizes and types carry on studies of the southern skies, which are inaccessible to the large telescopes of the Northern Hemisphere. (Photograph courtesy Australian News and Information Bureau.)

pioneer work in double stars; K. L. C. Rümker was noted for meridian astronomy; John Tebutt became famous for his comet discoveries. . . .

In 1905, soon after the establishment of the federal government of Australia, W. G. Duffield conceived the idea that eventually led to establishment of the Commonwealth Observatory. He was a young Australian science graduate, attending the Oxford meeting of the International Union for Solar Research, when he was impressed with the fact that Australia could plug the longitude gap in the existing chain of solar observatories. Although he approached the government with supporting resolutions from the IUSR, the Royal Society, and the British and Australian Associations for the Advancement of Science, it was nearly twenty years before Duffield's proposal was put into effect.

An Australian solar-physics committee was formed in 1909 with Duffield as secretary, and the next year this committee accepted the first telescopes for the projected observatory: two Grubb refractors, a 6-inch from the estate of Lord Farnham, and a 9-inch from James Oddie of Ballarat. The Oddie telescope was mounted on Mount Stromlo in 1911, and for two years the government astronomer of Victoria, P. Baracchi, carried out astronomical and meteorological observations there. . . .

In April 1922 the government definitely committed itself to building the observatory, and . . . director Duffield opened the new Commonwealth Solar Observatory on January 1, 1924, but it was not until late in 1926 that the staff moved to Mount Stromlo. . . . Shortly after his appointment, Duffield had accepted the gift of a 30-inch reflector from J. H. Reynolds, but because of the pressure of other work, the dome was not completed and the telescope erected until 1930. In recent years the Reynolds reflector has been used by S. C. B. Gascoigne for photoelectric measurements of variable stars and clusters in the Magellanic Clouds. Also, over two hundred and fifty plates of bright southern galaxies have been taken with this telescope by G. de Vaucouleurs.

On December 4, 1939, a new director, R. v. d. R. Woolley, arrived at Mount Stromlo. He was formerly chief assistant at both the Greenwich Observatory and the Cambridge University Observatory. . . . Unfortunately, all plans were forestalled by the war, and from 1940 to 1944 the observatory was literally transformed into an optical munitions factory.

When scientific work was resumed late in 1944 the word "Solar" was dropped from the title, the director became the Commonwealth Astronomer, and the way was clear for an expansion program, which is still continuing.

The first step in this new growth was the acquisition in 1944 of the historic "Great Melbourne" reflector, which has been transferred from the discontinued observatory at Melbourne, Australia. The original (1868) mirror of speculum metal has been replaced by a 50-inch spherical glass mirror of shorter focal length, and a 30-foot dome has been erected. Set up as a Gregorian, but not quite finished, the instrument is already being used for photoelectric work.

Next, in 1947 the Commonwealth government approved the purchase of a 74-inch reflector with dome and observing platform from Grubb Parsons and Company, Ltd. This instrument, which was completed in 1955, is the seventh in the world of 72 inches aperture or larger to go into operation, and only one other, the 74-inch at Pretoria, South Africa, is in the Southern Hemisphere. These two reflectors are almost identical. The new telescope has a focal length of 30 feet, and its moving parts weigh some 40 tons. . . .

As part of its expansion program, the observatory has invited overseas institutions to erect instruments at Mount Stromlo. The 26-inch Yale-Columbia refractor, famous for its work of measuring trigonometric stellar parallaxes, is now housed in a dome provided by the Commonwealth Observatory. . . . The first program plates with this instrument in its new location were taken on January 1, 1956, by G. de Vaucouleurs and Dirk Brouwer, [then] director of Yale University Observatory. Another dome has been provided for the 20-inch Schmidt telescope of the Uppsala Observatory, Sweden; it is expected to arrive sometime this year. . . .

Fig. 114. The 74-inch reflector at the Commonwealth Observatory has a mounting of the cross-axis type, which allows long exposures near the meridian and provides access to the south celestial pole. (Photograph courtesy Australian News and Information Bureau.)

Woolley left in December 1955 to take up his duties as the eleventh Astronomer Royal. [He was succeeded by Bart J. Bok, a Dutchman who spent much of his life in the United States, at the Harvard College Observatory.] Before his departure, Woolley pointed out the desirability of having the observatory associated with the new and rapidly growing national university rather than with the department of the interior, to which it has been attached for administrative purposes since its start.

Regardless of the final organizational arrangements, the wide variety of effective instruments at one site will make Mount Stromlo an unusually versatile center of astronomical research, in solar work, stellar spectroscopy and photometry, galactic and extragalactic studies, and in precise positional work. Australian astronomers will continue to use the advantages of the Commonwealth Observatory's instruments and Southern Hemisphere location for the promotion of further astronomical knowledge.

Government-operated observatories have a long tradition; essentially they were founded for the practical requirements of ocean navigation over two hundred years ago. In the last fifty years navigation for sea and air has become relatively less important, and national observatories have shifted their activities to the use of large telescopes—in the United States as well as in Australia. —TLP

The Flagstaff Station of the U.S. Naval Observatory

JOHN S. HALL AND ARTHUR A. HOAG

(*Sky and Telescope*, November 1956)

The major light-gathering instrument of the U.S. Naval Observatory is its 40-inch Ritchey-Chrétien telescope, which had been in operation at Washington since 1934. But as the nation's capital grew, increasing city lights and smoke reduced the effectiveness of this instrument. Through the efforts of the senior author and Capt. F. A. Graf, superintendent of the observatory from 1951 to 1956, money was appropriated in 1954 for the transfer of the telescope to a more suitable location.

After a study of meteorological factors and consideration of records from existing observatories, a site-test survey was carried out in the vicinity of Flagstaff, Arizona. A two-man team visited this area in 1951 and made visual observational checks. The results of these tests and other factors, such as accessibility, finally led to the choice of a hilltop about five miles west of Flagstaff.

This new observatory site is 7600 feet above sea level. It is easy to reach, being only one mile south of U.S. Route 66, on a new graded road. The excellence of the atmospheric conditions here is well shown by the photograph (Fig. 115) of the moon rising over Mount Elden, nine miles away. Staff members at the new station are not scientifically isolated, for Lowell Observatory and the Atmospheric Research Observatory of Arizona State College are close at hand.

The telescope shelter at the Flagstaff station is drastically different from the conventional dome that housed the reflector when it was in Washington. The roof of the new building rolls off on tracks to the north, thus permitting rapid setting of the telescope from one part of

Fɪɢ. 115. Trees on the horizon silhouetted against the rising moon, photographed with the 40-inch telescope of the U.S. Naval Observatory, Flagstaff, Arizona. (Photograph courtesy U.S. Naval Observatory, Flagstaff.)

the sky to another. The observer enjoys a majestic view of the heavens that more than compensates for the greater warmth of a dome.

In this type of building, buffeting of the telescope by the wind is a disadvantage that has been overcome by wind screens—movable panels on the interior walls of the observatory. These can be raised hydraulically by as much as nine feet. In addition, winds from the north are blocked by the movable roof. . . .

The 40-inch itself is the last instrument built by the late George W. Ritchey, and is the largest telescope of the Ritchey-Chrétien design. He had previously constructed a 20-inch pilot model. The mounting of the 40-inch is of the fork type, closely resembling that of the 60-inch reflector at Mount Wilson Observatory, an instrument also built by Ritchey. A cylindrical float, located just below the base of the fork and concentric with the polar axle, rides in a mercury-filled trough, and effectively relieves the polar-axle bearings of the telescope load.

The optical design of the telescope, conceived by Henri Chrétien, is akin to the Cassegrainian form. However, it does not have the latter's paraboloidal primary mirror and hyperboloidal secondary; instead, the cross sections of the two mirrors' surfaces are modified conic sections. The f/4 primary mirror has a central hole 9 inches in diameter. Behind this is the focal surface, which, though curved, is free from spherical aberration and coma. In contrast to the restricted field of a conventional Cassegrainian, the Ritchey-Chrétien design gives good images on curved plates over a field 1.5 degrees in diameter.

The relatively large, 16-inch-diameter, secondary mirror is only 96 inches distant from the primary, so the tube is extremely short. . . . The effective focal length of the telescope is 272 inches, corresponding to a focal ratio of f/6.8, and the scale is about 30 seconds of arc per millimeter at the focal surface. . . .

The most significant modernization of the 40-inch telescope is the control console, built for us by the Lombard Governor Corporation, Ashland, Massachusetts. This allows a chairborne observer to operate the instrument and building, greatly increasing the ease and rapidity of handling the telescope. Two large dials on the left side of the console panel give the right ascension and declination toward which the telescope is pointing. (The right ascension is displayed directly, by means of a differential that automatically subtracts the hour angle of the telescope from the sidereal time.) Three smaller dials indicate the mean time, local sidereal time, and hour angle. The panel also indicates the focal setting of the telescope, and the air mass through which the instrument is looking. There are driving-rate indicators, and a timer for photographic exposures. . . .

The brains of the console are the two vibrating-wire frequency stand-

FIG. 116. This outer skeleton tube of the 40-inch reflector is square, and it contains counterpoises to neutralize flexure. The octagonal framework carries the secondary mirror, which is focused by an electric motor. The primary mirror, at the lower end of the tube, is covered in this picture; extending upward from its center is a cylindrical light baffle. (Official U.S. Navy photograph.)

FIG. 117. An observer seated at the console at the right has full control of the instrument and building. The large dials display right ascension and declination. Among the others is a counter that indicates the focal setting of the secondary mirror. (Official U.S. Navy photograph.)

ards in the service building, and their power amplifiers. These standards, developed by Henry E. Warren, president of the Lombard Governor Corporation and inventor of the Telechron clock, control the diurnal drive of the telescope and the console clocks. Similar frequency standards are in use at Palomar and Lick Observatories. Their chief advantage is that the driving rate of the telescope is easily varied by remote control in order to compensate for refraction effects, to widen spectra by trailing, or for other purposes. . . .

A further improvement to the telescope is the addition of a skylight baffle of the "stovepipe" variety. This shields the focal surface from light not coming through the optics of the telescope.

The observing programs of the 40-inch telescope include both photography and photoelectric photometry. . . . Three photoelectric photometers are available. One is a conventional DC photometer. A second is an AC colorimeter which allows star magnitudes and colors to be measured simultaneously. The third is an AC polarimeter for measuring the polarization of starlight; it is equipped with a programer that guides this photometer automatically through a fairly complicated observing cycle. We are now assembling additional apparatus that will automatically punch the data directly onto IBM cards as the observations are made. This will permit all data handling to be done by high-speed computing machines, and a larger part of our time may then be spent in obtaining new observations.

A plane-grating spectrograph completes the battery of attachments currently used with the 40-inch telescope. . . . With this equipment we photograph spectra at a dispersion of 200 angstroms per millimeter in the first order in infrared light (7000 to 9000 angstroms), and at a dispersion of 100 angstroms per millimeter for blue light in the second order. In a reasonable exposure time we can obtain usable spectra in the blue for stars as faint as magnitude 14.

At the Flagstaff station, observing conditions are recorded by a Polaris monitor—a small telescope fitted with a photoelectric receiver which is driven to follow Polaris continuously. Its operation is automatic; the receiver is programed to observe Polaris, a comparison source within the instrument, and a blank patch of sky near Polaris, all in a continually repeated cycle. These observations are reported to a recorder in the service building. Here is displayed a continuous record of the transparency and brightness of the sky in the direction of the pole, as well as the scintillation of Polaris at two different frequencies. The monitor is turned on after dark and is stopped before dawn by a control timer. It needs no attention except to change the recorder chart once a month and to replenish the ink supply occasionally!

The clear, cool, dry climate at Flagstaff leaves little for the astronomer to desire. However, summer thunderstorms make July and August less satisfactory than other months for observing. The day-to-night temperature range is large—as is to be expected at high elevations—but on still nights this is moderated by good air drainage at our site. It is not uncommon for us to have nighttime temperatures 15 degrees above those recorded in the town of Flagstaff, which lies some 600 feet lower. Clear nights are three times as frequent and are much more transparent than those in Washington. But most impressive of all is the darkness of the sky at the Flagstaff station—only one fifteenth as bright as in Washington on a clear moonless night. Seeing at the new site is consistently better than at the old one, and preliminary comparisons show it to be as good as at nearby Lowell Observatory, which has long enjoyed a reputation for excellent seeing. In these very favorable surroundings, the modernized Ritchey-Chrétien reflector should better serve both the U.S. Naval Observatory and astronomy in general.

A new 60-inch reflector of Ritchey-Chrétien design has recently been added to the U.S. Naval Observatory's station at Flagstaff, Arizona, for use in measuring accurate positions of faint stars. In the meantime, a new national observatory on Kitt Peak, near Tucson, Arizona, was organized by a group of U.S. universities and financed by the National Science Foundation. It is equipped with an 84-inch telescope and several special-purpose instruments (see Sky and Telescope, January 1962). Still another major observatory came into operation in 1960: the Karl Schwarzschild Observatory (see Sky and Telescope, May 1964) near Jena in East Germany, equipped with the largest Schmidt telescope in the world, 52.8 inches in aperture. In northern Italy, at Asiago, a 60-inch telescope has been in operation since 1956 and in France there are several other major observatories.   —T L P

France's Haute Provence Observatory

JEAN DUFAY AND CHARLES FEHRENBACH

(Sky and Telescope, July 1961)

In 1936, responding to a wish of French astronomers, Mme. Irène Joliot-Curie, first under-secretary of state for scientific research, decided to establish a well-equipped astrophysical observatory in a favorable climate. The Haute Provence Observatory has since become one of the principal institutions operating directly under the National Center of Scientific Research, which is part of the French ministry of national education.

The site was quickly chosen, thanks to long reconnoitering previously organized by André Danjon, with the collaboration of André Couder and Jean Dufay. Five years of testing with a temporarily mounted 32-inch telescope at Forcalquier verified that the Basses-Alpes region of southeastern France was perfectly suited for large instruments.

After further detailed site testing, the observatory was constructed at St. Michel, on a rocky plateau 2000 feet high, less than six miles from Forcalquier and about sixty miles north of Marseilles. This region of Haute Provence, on the last foothills of the Alps, possesses a typically Mediterranean climate, with very few rainy days. An average year has two hundred and fifty nights when observing is possible, over one hundred of which are clear throughout. . . .

Undertaken in the beginning of 1938, construction work proceeded very rapidly until the war. Little was done, of course, from 1940 to 1945; yet the first telescope, a 47-inch, began operation in 1943.

The observatory at present possesses four standard reflectors, with apertures of 24 inches (Cassegrainian), 32 inches (Newtonian and Casse-grainian), 47 inches (Newtonian), and 76 inches (Newtonian, Cassegrainian, and coudé). It also has an f/2 Schmidt camera with a correcting plate 12 inches in diameter.

For special work, there are two objective-prism spectrographs of the Fehrenbach type, with apertures of 6 and 16 inches; a Lyot coronagraph; and spectrographs and photometers for observing the air glow of the night sky. The optical parts of the principal instruments, including the three largest reflectors, were figured by Couder at the Paris Observatory's optical laboratory. We have a large interferometer for the study of galactic and extragalactic radio sources. . . .

The Haute Provence Observatory is at the disposal of all French astrophysicists, who may reside on the grounds while using the facilities for specific projects. Accommodations include a dining room and a

Fig. 118. A general view of the Haute Provence Observatory, showing (from left to right) an antenna of the radio interferometer, the dome of the 75-inch telescope, workshop, laboratories, the dome of the 47-inch, and living quarters. (Photograph courtesy Haute Provence Observatory.)

thirty-room guest house, the Maison Jean Perrin. Observing is the only activity at St. Michel; guest scientists plan their programs and analyze data at their home observatories.

There are, therefore, no astronomers now in permanent residence at the observatory, although coauthor Fehrenbach has been going there for eight consecutive years. . . . Administration of the observatory was originally undertaken by coauthor Dufay, director of Lyons Observatory. In 1943 he was joined by Fehrenbach, who is also director of Marseilles Observatory.

A directing committee, presided over by André Danjon, meets regularly to plan the observing schedule and assign telescope time. Foreign

Fig. 119. Inside the dome of the 75-inch reflector. An observer stands at the Newtonian focus near the tube's upper end. His observing platform rides up and down the heavy column (far right), the base of which can be moved completely around the edge of the dome. The Newtonian secondary mirror can be turned to reflect light to any one of four positions spaced around the tube, so the plateholder can be conveniently placed. With other secondary mirrors, the telescope may also be used as a Cassegrainian or as a coudé, with focus in the south end of the polar axis, beneath the control console. (Photograph courtesy Haute Provence Observatory.)

astronomers are authorized to work at the observatory under the same conditions as our countrymen.

The largest telescope of Haute Provence Observatory was put in operation in July 1958. Its primary mirror, used with an aperture of 75 inches, was cast in France in 1939, from low-expansion glass, but it could not be ground until after the war. It is relatively thin, weighing only 3000 pounds; its cell has three fixed supports on the back and two on the side, aligning the optical axis. Thirty balanced supports compensate for flexure. The figure of this mirror is excellent, no aberration exceeding $\frac{1}{14}$ wave. Quartz was used for the various secondary mirrors.

The telescope is pointed, with a precision of 1 minute of arc, by remote control from a console where the right ascension and declination of the observed object can be read directly. The Newtonian focus (focal length 31.5 feet, f/5) is easily accessible by means of a movable observing platform, no matter where the telescope is pointing in the sky. This platform rides up and down a tall column, which in turn stands on a movable ring-shaped portion of the floor.

Observing at the Cassegrainian focus (equivalent focal length 93.5 feet, f/15) is facilitated by a rising floor 31.2 feet in diameter and having 11.8 feet of vertical travel. At the coudé focus (187 feet, f/30) the light is conducted into a large laboratory where a constant temperature is maintained. Finally, the possibility of using the instrument's prime focus has been left open. . . .

Particular precautions are taken to reduce temperature fluctuations in the dome's interior and to avoid air turbulence. The dome covering consists of two sheets of aluminum mounted on steel ribs and separated from each other by an insulating air space filled with crumpled aluminum foil.

It is desirable that the rays of light entering the dome and telescope travel within a laminar flow of air so that no turbulence will exist along the light path. The observing slit can be partially closed with movable shades, leaving an opening only 8 feet square above the upper end of the telescope. The tube is doublecovered. Exterior air that enters it is drawn through the inner casing of porous nylon and blown out into the dome by six fans placed on the metallic outer casing of the tube not far from the primary mirror. Eight larger fans are mounted in the dome opposite the slit. The slight vacuum they create in the building causes a smooth inward flow in front of the telescope.

This system, due to Couder, has been found in careful tests to be very effective. Almost perfect images can be obtained if external atmospheric turbulence is also rather small. Currently, observations at the coudé focus are being made of stellar images whose diameters are between 0.3 and 0.8 second of arc.

A large spectrograph of Fehrenbach design . . . is installed at the coudé focus, on a pier rigidly connected to the telescope supports. . . . It's 8-inch collimating mirror is 14.8 feet in focal length. Two Bausch and Lomb gratings, 6 by 8 inches, are instantly interchangeable from a control panel at the top of the spectrograph, and send the light into any one of five cameras. The largest of these has a 31-inch mirror of 7.38-foot focus and a photographic plate 14 inches long. . . . The dispersion is about 4 angstroms per millimeter, and it can record spectra of eighth-magnitude stars in a 6-hour exposure. . . .

The other cameras furnish dispersions in the neighborhood of 10, 20, 40, and 50 angstroms per millimeter. The two fastest cameras are f/1.1 and are particularly suited to the observation of nebulae.

More than a thousand plates have been made since the spectrograph was installed in July 1959, and definition is excellent. . . .

Two novel Haute Provence telescopes are 6- and 16-inch refractors with objective prisms for the determination of radial velocities of stars. Their design was conceived by Fehrenbach and developed by Danjon. . . .

Other instruments at the observatory are of the conventional type. We hope to keep pace with new developments in instrumentation, so that French astrophysicists will have at St. Michel every facility to meet their observing requirements.

The wide variety of telescopes and accessories at a large modern observatory is well illustrated in the last few articles. At the Mount Wilson and Palomar Observatories in California, large telescopes have dominated the scene ever since George Ellery Hale moved on from the Yerkes Observatory (p. 273) in 1904. From 40 inches aperture to 60 and then 100 inches took about ten years. Then, in another twenty years, the Hale Telescope, still the largest in the world, was built. — TLP

··

The 200-inch Telescope

ROBERT R. COLES

(*Sky and Telescope*, September 1948)

In tribute to the great American astronomer George Ellery Hale, whose vision and foresight made its construction possible, the 200-inch reflector has been named the Hale Telescope. While we are awaiting the first observations from Palomar Mountain, it is interesting to speculate on the meaning of the great task that was culminated in its dedication. Why does man build such telescopes? How can these giant reflectors serve the hundreds of millions of persons who are not directly concerned with the science of astronomy?

The answer to the first question is to be found in the inherent curiosity of man. He is curious about the infinitely great and the infinitesimally small. He is desirous of learning just where he fits into the picture of creation and of becoming better aware of the interdependence of all nature. This is enough to inspire him to devise means of probing the outer limits of cosmic space on the one hand and the inner depths of the atom on the other.

But curiosity alone is not enough. Another trait with which man is endowed is imagination. Every scientist possesses this in large degree, and certainly George Ellery Hale had more of it than most men. He dreamed of the new 200-inch eye and visualized its tremendous possibilities when men of lesser stature were saying that it could not be done.

The Hale reflector will not in any way be a competitor of the telescopes now in operation throughout the world. With its ability to gather four times as much light, to penetrate twice the distance into the depths of the universe, and to double the theoretical resolving power of the 100-inch telescope, this new instrument will be busy for years just extending the programs its predecessors started. . . .

Fig. 120. George Ellery Hale, founder of the Mount Wilson and Palomar Observatories.

Fig. 121. A sketch by Russell S. Porter of the 200-inch Hale Telescope on Palomar Mountain.

THE · TWO · HVNDRED · INCH ~

One of the disadvantages of the yoke mounting used on the 100-inch telescope at Mount Wilson is that the telescope cannot point to within 25° of the north celestial pole. . . . The horseshoe mounting of the 200-inch permits it to reach this region, allowing direct comparison of magnitudes observed there with those of stars and galaxies in other parts of the sky. This is especially important where observations of some of the galaxies near the north pole of the sky, such at M81 and M82, are concerned.

At present, the primary mirror and Cassegrainian mirror are installed and in operation, but the auxiliary mirrors of the coudé system are in the process of installation. Altogether there are seven mirrors in the giant telescope:

1. The 200-inch mirror, a paraboloid having a focus of $55\frac{1}{2}$ feet, or 666 inches.

2. The Cassegrain convex, 41 inches in diameter, hyperboloidal with an eccentricity of about 1.52, providing a focal length of $266\frac{2}{3}$ feet, or 3200 inches.

3. Two coudé hyperboloids, 36 and 32 inches in diameter, each of eccentricity 1.25 and producing a focal length of 500 feet, or 6000 inches.

4. A coudé diagonal plane mirror, 36 by 53 inches, to reflect the light along the polar axis to the coudé spectrograph in a constant-temperature room directly south of the telescope.

5. Two auxiliary plane mirrors, 28 and 20 inches in diameter, for use with the coudé diagonal when objects north of 50° declination are observed.

All of these mirrors are made of Pyrex glass, and all except the two small flats are of the ribbed-back construction with internal supports. In a talk before the American Astronomical Society and the Astronomical Society of the Pacific, John A. Anderson of California Institute of Technology . . . mentioned that the coudé flat, on account of its shape and relatively large size, was in many respects more difficult to make than any of the other mirrors in the telescope.

Another speaker at the June [1948] gathering was Bruce Rule, also of Caltech, who pointed out that the . . . telescope must not deform in any position more than $\frac{1}{16}$ inch, in order that the optics remain collimated and the mirror surfaces in their proper optical shape. . . .

The oil-bearing system of support for the polar axis, as well as many other mechanisms of this mainly automatic telescope, had to be designed to function correctly for a wide range of temperature, humidity, and position. . . . The focal length of $55\frac{1}{2}$ feet may change relative to the tube by about $\frac{1}{4}$ inch because of differential expansion between the glass and the steel tube. . . . The change in length of one of the south tube

I-beams is measured with respect to an Invar bar having substantially a zero expansion coefficient. This change in tube length is transmitted to the prime-focus cage to the nearest $\frac{1}{100}$ millimeter, allowing the observer to compensate for changes during long exposures.

The matter of temperature control in the observatory itself has been carefully studied. . . . A copper model 36 inches in diameter was used in a variety of tests with direct loading, uniform hydraulic loading, and wind-tunnel loading. . . . The outcome of these tests, together with the space requirements, resulted in the construction of a hemispherical dome 137 feet in diameter on top of a 27-foot-high cylindrical section. . . .

Rule went on to describe the unique manner in which the internal steel ribs extending from balcony level to the main arches of the dome provide a continuation of the air-venting space from the lower double walls of the stationary building. This construction permits the removal of absorbed heat from the external steel shell during the day, yet insulates the closed interior from temperature changes departing from the average night temperature. Air dampers in the lower walls provide for venting air either from inside or outside the building. Heat dissipation from lights, machinery, and people affects the time required to stabilize the optical components after opening the shutter at night, as well as badly affecting the internal dome "seeing." For this reason, all lighting equipment is ventilated to the dome air stack, as are the visitors' gallery and the large machinery on the lower floor. Insulated darkrooms and laboratories are separately electrically heated and air-conditioned, and the exhaust fumes are transported underground away from the building.

FIG. 122. The dome of the Hale reflector, with the slit partly open.

What, if any, value will this great telescope have for Mr. John Q. Public? From the narrow monetary point of view it is doubtful if anyone will be wealthier because of the new reflector. But if man were to operate only those projects which benefit him financially, he would develop little culture. Fortunately, the discoveries and achievements of specialists in science, art, literature, and music become accessible to everyone who is interested. In a very real sense this new Hale Telescope is the property of all people. The pictures that it procures will be available to all who care to study them. Progress with the 200-inch will be interpreted and reported to the public through all our modern newscasting services.

New discoveries will come slowly from Palomar Mountain. Research of the type done at our observatories today is mainly by the study of carefully exposed photographic plates. Further care is required in the reduction of data and in its interpretation in the light of other observations. It may well be that this instrument, as did the 100-inch before it, will open up more problems which may seem to require even a larger telescope to solve.

Many new discoveries have been made during the first eighteen years' use of the Hale Telescope, some of them to be covered in articles about stars, nebulae, and galaxies in later volumes of this series. One of the most recent and most exciting to astronomers is the discovery of quasi-stellar objects ("quasars"), first detected by radiotelescopes, then studied with the Hale 200-inch and found to be probably the most distant objects we can see. This, and other significant studies with large telescopes, combined with increased interest in space exploration (see Vol. 1, Wanderers in the Sky), led to a review of the United States' need for larger telescopes. —TLP

....

Updating a Blueprint for
American Astronomy

(*Sky and Telescope*, October 1965)

"It is impossible to gaze into a crystal ball and gauge the needs of astronomy for as much as ten years ahead. Such long-range planning is extremely useful, but it needs to be done every two to three years. I hope very much that the National Academy of Sciences will take the necessary steps to bring the Whitford report up to date in the very near future, and to fill in its obvious gaps."

TABLE 9. RECOMMENDATIONS OF THE ORIGINAL WHITFORD REPORT, GROUND-BASED ASTRONOMY—A TEN-YEAR PROGRAM, WASHINGTON, D.C., 1964.

Optical Astronomy

1. *Three* large telescopes of the 150-to-200-inch class. The Kitt Peak 150-inch is considered as the first of this group. $60.0 million
2. An engineering study for construction of the largest feasible optical reflector. $ 1.0 million
3. *Four* intermediate-size telescopes of the 60-to-84-inch class. $ 4.0 million
4. *Eight* small modern telescopes of 36-to-48-inch aperture. $ 3.2 million

Total cost of the optical facilities and engineering study is $68.2 million with no operating expense included.

Included in these costs are funds for the initial instrumentation, such as spectrographs, photometer, and spectrum scanner, with which to start operations. Included also is the cost of site development, land acquisition, and building for the case of items 1 and 3 above.

Radioastronomy

1. A very large high-resolution pencil-beam array with low sidelobes to be constructed as a national facility.
   Cost of basic dishes. $30.0 million
   Cost of land development with buildings. $ 4.0 million
   Cost of electronics and other auxiliaries. $ 6.0 million
   Total cost $40.0 million

2. A high-resolution array consisting of about eight antennas to be constructed at the Owens Valley Observatory. $10.0 million
3. Two fully steerable 300-foot paraboloids. $16.0 million
4. Engineering study for the largest possible steerable parabolic antenna. $ 1.0 million
5. Support for existing radioastronomy departments for new small instruments and special, unique problems. $30.0 million

The total support for new radio instruments is then with no annual support to maintain new facilities included. $97.0 million

Auxiliary Instruments and Automation

1. New auxiliary instruments for both optical and radio. $10.0 million
2. Data-processing instruments and automation of telescopes. $10.0 million

The combined cost of recommended auxiliary instruments and data-processing and automation equipment thus totals $20.0 million.

Annual Operating Support

1. Annual operating support of new optical facilities at a rate of 4 per cent of the value of the facilities completed at any given time. $ 5.3 million
2. Annual operating support of new radio facilities at a rate of 10 per cent of the value of the facilities completed at any given time. $33.6 million

Total operating support $38.9 million

The total cost of the entire ten-year program is thus $224.1 million.

These were the words of Leo Goldberg, of Harvard and Smithsonian observatories, who was the speaker at the American Astronomical Society's banquet [in August 1965]. The Whitford report to which he referred was issued in November 1964 by the National Academy of Sciences under the title *Ground-Based Astronomy—A Ten-year Program*. It was a very thorough investigation by eight leading astronomers, whose task was "to study the probable need for major new astronomical facilities in the United States during the next five to ten years and to recommend guiding principles and estimates of cost in order that federal funds may be employed with maximum efficiency to promote advancement of astronomy in all its branches."

Some highlights from the panel's 105-page report include a recommendation that the government spend 224.1 million dollars in the next decade for the construction and operation of new optical and radio telescopes, together with auxiliary equipment.

The Whitford report has been transmitted to all the government agencies that support astronomy (especially the National Science Foundation, National Aeronautics and Space Administration, and Office of Naval Research). On the initiative of Donald F. Hornig, director of the Office of Science and Technology at the White House, NSF has established a committee under the chairmanship of Geoffrey Keller for a government-wide assessment of the recommendations of the Whitford report. Hopefully, the outcome of this and other studies will be reflected in the budget planning of federal agencies for the next fiscal year, 1967.

"The most important thing we astronomers can do to bring these badly needed facilities into being," Goldberg said, "is to provide high-quality proposals and to prove that the 1964 recommendations will continue to be valid through the next ten years."

While praising the Whitford report, the Harvard astronomer pointed out that such important areas as solar, planetary, and radar astronomy received little emphasis in it. Even though NASA and the Department of Defense have taken a special interest in these fields, it would be advantageous to have the requirements of solar-system astronomy assessed with the rest of the science.

Also needing fuller discussion is the relationship between ground-based and space astronomy. The Whitford report includes some mention of important observations that can be made only from above the atmosphere, and it compares the relative costs of a 36-inch telescope on the ground and in space. But the very difficult question of priorities remains unanswered. At any particular time, would it be better to spend 50 million dollars on a new space telescope or on new ground facilities? Such decisions have many political and nonscientific overtones, but they must be faced sometime. At present, the primary responsibilities for furnishing ground and space facilities lie in different government agencies. Much better coordination of effort will be needed for thoroughly effective exploration of the universe in years to come.

Goldberg noted the difficulties in estimating the rate of growth in the numbers of astronomers and of the instruments they will need. The Whitford report predicted that American universities would have 793 graduate students in astronomy in 1966, but it is already clear that the actual number will be substantially smaller, although the migration of scientists from other disciplines into astronomy offsets this deficit. Probably the predictions of astronomical manpower available during the coming decade are substantially correct.

However, the forecasts of future equipment requirements may have been less accurate. The panel members seem to have reasoned that since the number of astronomers would double in ten years, it would suffice to double the number of telescopes in the same time. This may err on the conservative side by not providing sufficient observing opportunities for the many young astronomers at the graduate level and just beyond. The Whitford panel recommended the building of four more 60- to 84-inch telescopes by 1973. Goldberg believes that perhaps twice as many will be required to satisfy the pressing need for observing time.

Rather than have these large instruments erected at many new sites, it would be much better to have them concentrated at a few well-located centers, though serving astronomers from all over the country. Kitt Peak National Observatory was established in Arizona eight years ago for just this purpose. Kitt Peak now has only one 84-inch reflector, although the number of potential users has more than doubled. . . .

There should be no insoluble administrative problems in greatly enlarging that observatory. Meanwhile, a careful study should be made to determine the number and kinds of additional telescopes that could be erected there.

Astronomy is competing with other sciences for federal support and may find itself at a disadvantage unless astronomers can arrive at some agreement on where their new facilities should be put.

"My own vote," Goldberg said, "would be to give first priority to expanding our existing observational centers in the West and Southwest." . . .

Each large telescope is a remarkable achievement as a special-purpose instrument for work on faint stars and galaxies, but no one instrument can be considered the be-all and end-all for astronomical observation. Thousands of smaller telescopes are in use every night, and more are being built every day. Much larger structures are in use as radiotelescopes —one "bowl" in Arequipa, Puerto Rico, being 1000 feet in diameter. Other modern developments involve telescopes in orbit around the earth (see Vol. 1, Wanderers in the Sky).

The purpose of this book has been to review the nature and astronomical use of optical telescopes, both large and small, and to point out the immense importance of these instruments in man's continuing exploration of the universe.   —T L P

APPENDIX I
The Origin of
Sky and Telescope

In March 1931 publication of a small quarterly magazine, *The Telescope*, began at Perkins Observatory of Ohio Wesleyan University in Delaware, Ohio, with the director of the observatory, Harlan T. Stetson, as editor. By July 1933 the magazine had become a larger, bimonthly periodical. After Stetson moved to the Massachusetts Institute of Technology, the Bond Astronomical Club, a society of Cambridge amateur astronomers, and Harvard College Observatory assumed sponsorship of the magazine. Loring B. Andrews became editor, and in 1937 Donald H. Menzel succeeded him. *The Telescope* carried stories of important astronomical discoveries, reviews of current astronomical work, and articles on the history of the science.

In the meantime, the first issue of the small *Monthly Bulletin of the Hayden Planetarium* (New York City) appeared, in November 1935, edited by Hans Christian Adamson. In addition to a review of the current show at the planetarium, it contained other astronomical notes and articles. The interest and encouragement of its readers led, in October 1936, to the enlargement of its size and scope. Its name was changed to *The Sky*, and while retaining its planetarium ties, it became the official organ of the Amateur Astronomers' Association in New York City, replacing the magazine *Amateur Astronomer*, which had been published from April 1929 to the spring of 1936.

The Sky grew in reputation and circulation. Various regular monthly departments, in addition to those describing the current Hayden Planetarium show and the activities of junior and amateur astronomers, were developed. Articles were contributed by members of the planetarium staff and by many other professional astronomers. In February 1938 Clyde Fisher, curator-in-chief of the planetarium, became editor.

On November 1, 1939, *The Sky* passed from the sponsorship of the planetarium. The Sky Publishing Corporation was formed, owned by Charles A. Federer, Jr., who for four years had been a planetarium lecturer, and his wife, Helen Spence Federer. They edited and published *The Sky* through its fifth volume, ending with the October 1941 issue.

Then, encouraged by Harlow Shapley, director of the Harvard College Observatory, Sky Publishing Corporation moved to Cambridge, Massachusetts, and combined *The Telescope* and *The Sky*, into *Sky and Telescope*, born with the November 1941 issue. The Federers continued as editors. The ties with Harvard have been strong. Until the middle 1950s the magazine's offices were in the observatory—now they are located less than a mile away.

During its twenty-five years, *Sky and Telescope* has been a distinguished and increasingly well-received publication, with two overlapping purposes. It has served as a forum where amateur astronomers can exchange views and experiences, and where they are furnished with observing data. It has brought to an ever-widening circle of scientists and educated laymen detailed and reliable information on new astronomical developments, and through its pages, has introduced them to the important figures of modern astronomy.

···

APPENDIX II
Astronomy through the Ages: A Brief Chronology

ca. 5000 B.C.:   Earliest recorded Babylonian observations of eclipses, planets, and stars.

ca. 2500 B.C.:   Egyptian pyramids constructed, oriented north-south by the stars.

ca. 2000 B.C.:   Babylonian story of creation: *Enuma Elish*.
Stonehenge built in southern England with stones lined up by the stars.

ca. 1000 B.C.:   Beginnings of Chinese and Hindu astronomical observations.

700–400 B.C.:   Greek story of creation: Hesiod's *Theogony*.
Hebrew story of creation: *Genesis*.
Greek philosophers Thales, Pythagoras, and Meton note regularity of celestial motions.

400–300 B.C.:   Greek philosophers Plato, Eudoxus, and Calippus develop the concept of celestial motions on spheres.
Aristotle develops the idea of four elements and the concept that heavy things fall, light ones rise.

300–100 B.C.:   Aristarchus proposes that the earth moves.
Eratosthenes measures the size of the earth.
Hipparchus makes accurate observations of star positions.

ca. A.D. 150:   Ptolemy's *Almagest* summarizes the geocentric theory; the planets' motion is explained by epicycles and other motions in circles.

ca. 1400:   Ulugh-Beg in Samarkand reobserves star positions.

1530:   Copernicus, in Poland, postulates that the earth and planets move around the sun because this involves fewer circular motions. This revolutionary idea later rouses strong opposition.

ca. 1600:   Tycho Brahe measures the motions of the planets accurately; Kepler uses these measurements to show that the orbits of planets are ellipses rather than combinations of circles.

Galileo uses the first telescope to observe the moons of Jupiter and the crescent shape of Venus, supplying strong support for the Copernican idea. Galileo also establishes that falling weights would all be accelerated in the same way if there were no air to hold the lighter ones back.

1680:   Newton combines Kepler's and Galileo's findings, together with observations of moon and comets, into the fundamental laws of mechanics and gravitation. He also studies light, its colors, and spectrum. By this time, accurate pendulum clocks are in use.

1690:   Halley notes the periodic reports of a large comet every seventy years and concludes they refer to one object moving in a long, thin ellipse around the sun.

1755:   Kant postulates that the sun and planets were formed by the coagulation of a cloud of gas like the spiral nebulae.

1780:   William Herschel builds large telescopes, discovers the planet Uranus, and explains the Milky Way as a flat disk of stars around the sun.

1700–1800:   Mathematical astronomy flourishes, involving many Europeans—Cassini, Bradley, d'Alembert, Laplace, Lagrange, and others—who apply Newton's mechanics to celestial motions with remarkable precision.

1849:   The first astronomical photograph (of the moon) obtained at Harvard. By 1910 photography is well established for accurate observations with telescopes ranging up to 40 inches in aperture, photographing stars 100,000 times fainter than those visible to the naked eye.

1800–1900:   Navigation has become a precise and important practical application of astronomy. The accurate observations of star positions show that annual parallax is due to the earth's orbital motion around the sun, confirming the Copernican idea and providing a method of measuring distances to the stars. Other small motions show that the stars are moving.

1850–1900: The laboratory study of light together with physical theory shows that spectrum analysis can be used to determine temperature and chemical composition of a light source.

1843: Doppler explains the effect of motion on the spectrum of a light source.

1877: Schiaparelli observes "canals" on Mars.

1900: Chamberlin and Moulton speculate that the planets were formed after another star passed close to the sun.

1904–20: Einstein establishes the theory of relativity.
Large reflecting telescopes are built at the Mount Wilson Observatory in California.

1917–30: Russell and Eddington establish the theory of stellar structure.

1920–30: Shapley and Oort establish the size, shape, and rotation of the Milky Way Galaxy.

1930: Discovery of Pluto.

1910–40: Slipher and Hubble find that other galaxies are moving away from ours. De Sitter, Eddington, Lemaitre, and others explain this recession by application of relativity theory.

1930–60: Bethe, Gamow, and others in the U.S. apply the results of nuclear physics to explaining the source of stellar energy. This is followed by the work of many astrophysicists on evolution of the stars from large interstellar gas clouds.
Von Weizsäcker, Kuiper, Urey, and others develop a theory of the origin of the solar system from a large gas cloud.

1947–60: Instruments are shot above the atmosphere in the U.S. for astronomical observations.
Large radiotelescopes are built in the U.S., Australia, and England.

1957: Sputnik I, the first artificial satellite of the earth, is launched by Soviet scientists.

1959: First space probe to hit the moon is launched by Soviet scientists.

1961: First manned space flight around the earth by Soviet astronaut Yuri Gagarin.

1963–64: Radiotelescopes locate quasi-stellar sources ("quasars"), found to have large optical red shifts.

1964–65: First photographs of the lunar surface obtained by U.S. space probes Ranger 7 and Ranger 8.

1965: Photographs of Mars, taken at about 11,000 miles' distance by Mariner 4, show a cratered surface.

1966: First soft landing on the moon (by the Russian Luna 9). Photographs of the surface taken from a few feet show no dust.

APPENDIX III

Notes on the Contributors

ALEXANDER, JOSEPH K. (1940–), physicist in the Radio Astronomy Section of NASA, at Goddard Space Flight Center, Greenbelt, Maryland; his specialty is low-frequency radioastronomy. ("A Radiotelescope for Amateurs," with Larry W. Brown)

ASHBROOK, JOSEPH (1918–), astronomer specializing in variable stars; on the Yale faculty from 1946 to 1953, when he joined the editorial staff of Sky and Telescope. ("Determining the Field of an Eyepiece")

BAILEY, EDWIN F. (1907–), assistant to the director of the Fels Planetarium of the Franklin Institute, Philadelphia; formerly an industrial optician; member and former president of Rittenhouse Astronomical Society, Philadelphia. ("Herschel as a Telescope Maker")

BAKER, JAMES G. (1914–), astronomer and optician; research associate at Lick Observatory since 1948 and at Harvard College Observatory since 1949. (Notes on "Limiting Visual Magnitudes for Small Telescopes")

BARTON, WILLIAM H., JR. (1893–1944), civil engineer, teacher of astronomy, and a regular contributor to The Sky and Sky and Telescope; curator and lecturer at the Hayden Planetarium, New York City, from 1935 until 1942, when he became its chairman; coauthor of A Guide to the Constellations. ("Exploring the Moon")

BATES, RALPH S. (1906–), professor of history at Bridgewater State College in Massachusetts; past president of Bond Astronomical Club and of the South Shore Astronomical Society, both in Massachusetts; author of Scientific Societies in the United States. ("Alvan Clark and Sons")

BATTEN, ALAN H. (1933–), English astronomer; since 1961 on the staff of the Dominion Astrophysical Observatory in British Columbia; his chief interest is spectroscopic observations of close double stars; he is skilled in the nonastronomical but very British art of change-ringing. ("Why Observe Stellar Eclipses?")

BROWN, EARLE B. (1909–), optical engineer with Perkin-Elmer Corporation in Connecticut; a former member of the Amateur Astronomers' Association of New York; edited the department "Gleanings for Amateur Telescope Makers" in *Sky and Telescope* from 1953 to 1956; author of *Optical Instruments, Basic Optics for the Sportsman*. ("Notes on Basic Optics," "Refractor versus Reflector," "Principles of the Cassegrainian," "A Grinding Machine," "Make Your Own Spectroscope")

BROWN, LARRY W. (1938–), a graduate student in astronomy at University of Maryland, and also a staff member of NASA at Goddard Space Flight Center, Greenbelt, Maryland. ("A Radiotelescope for Amateurs," with Joseph K. Alexander)

CAVE, THOMAS R., JR. (1923–), precision optician; owner of Cave Optical Company, Long Beach, California; for thirty years an observer of Mars, Saturn, Venus, and the moon; past president of Western Amateur Astronomers and of the Los Angeles Astronomical Society; member of the Mars Committee for the Western Hemisphere. ("Observations of Mars")

COLES, ROBERT R. (1907–), educator; associated with the Hayden Planetarium, New York City, as a lecturer and curator from 1939 to 1951 and as its chairman from 1951 to 1953. ("The 200-inch Telescope")

COOKE, RICHARD H. (1885–1959), a member of the architectural firm involved in the planning and construction of the Hayden Planetarium building in New York; business manager of the Hayden Planetarium from 1935 until his retirement in 1949. ("A Visit to Peiping's Ancient Observatory")

COX, ROBERT E. (1917–), optical engineer at McDonnell Aircraft Company and Lecturer at McDonnell Planetarium, both in St. Louis, Missouri; former director of the planetarium at Stamford, Connecticut; active in teaching optics, elementary astronomy, and telescope making; since 1957 has edited "Gleanings for Amateur Telescope Makers" in *Sky and Telescope*. He gave valuable advice and assistance to the editors on this volume. ("The Custer $12\frac{1}{2}$-inch Springfield Reflector," "Balancing the Tube of a Reflecting Telescope," "Balancing a German Equatorial Mounting," "Eyepieces of Interest to Amateurs," "Maksutov-telescope Notes")

DOWNES, DENNIS N. (1943–), graduate student in astronomy at Harvard; has worked at Harvard's Radio Astronomy Station at Fort Davis, Texas; former member of Thames Amateur Astronomical Society, Connecticut. ("A Simple Radiotelescope")

DUFAY, JEAN (1896–), French astronomer; professor at the University of Lyons; director of the Lyons Observatory (since 1933) and of the Haute Provence Observatory (since 1936); member of the French Academy, and well known for his work on spectra. ("France's Haute Provence Observatory," with Charles Fehrenbach)

EGGEN, OLIN J. (1919–), astrophysicist; Director of the Mount Stromlo Observatory, Canberra, Australia; was at the Royal Greenwich Observatory, Herstmonceux Castle, Sussex, England, from 1953 to 1962. ("The Australian Commonwealth Observatory")

EPSTEIN, GERMAIN, an active member of the Amateur Astronomers' Association in the 1930s; from 1905 to 1941 with Sussfield, Lorsch and Company, New York, makers of optical specialties. ("Meudon Observatory")

ERPENSTEIN, O. M. (1901–), German-born instructor in mechanical engineering at Heald Engineering College, San Francisco; member of the East Bay Astronomical Society and the American Association of Variable Star Observers; author of *Uncle Habakuk*. ("Mountings of Today and Yesterday")

FEHRENBACH, CHARLES (1914–), French astronomer; professor at University of Marseilles; director of the Marseilles Observatory since 1948; active in stellar and nebular spectroscopy; founder of the French station in South Africa for the study of the Magellanic Clouds. ("France's Haute Provence Observatory," with Jean Dufay)

FLEISCHER, ROBERT (1918–), astronomer; on the faculty of Rensselaer Polytechnic Institute, Troy, New York, from 1946 to 1963; now with the National Science Foundation in Washington, D.C. ("Story of the Telescope")

GINGERICH, OWEN (1930–), astrophysicist; lecturer at Harvard, also working on computations of model stellar atmospheres at the Smithsonian Astrophysical Observatory; former director of the observatory at American University of Beirut. ("A Telescope Drive with Right-ascension Circle")

GREGORY, JOHN (1927–), optical engineer; has designed photographic equipment for the AGENA, MERCURY, and MARINER spacecraft as well as for the POLARIS and NIMBUS programs; member Fairfield County Astronomical Society (Connecticut) and assistant chairman of the Stamford (Connecticut) Museum, for which he designed a 22-inch Maksutov telescope. ("A Cassegrainian-Maksutov Telescope Design for the Amateur")

HALL, JOHN S. (1908–), astronomer; director of the Astrometry and Astrophysics Division, U.S. Naval Observatory in Washington, D.C., from 1948 to 1958; director of the Lowell Observatory, Flagstaff, Arizona, since 1958. ("The Flagstaff Station of the U.S. Naval Observatory," with Arthur A. Hoag)

HECKMANN, O. (1901–), German astronomer; noted for his work in stellar dynamics and cosmology; appointed to the faculty at Göttingen in 1925; in 1941 became director of the Hamburg Observatory; in 1962 joined the European Southern Observatory; is now planning a large telescope to be established in Chile. ("The New Schmidt Telescope of the Hamburg Observatory")

HERSCHEL, SIR JOHN (1792–1871), astronomer; son of the famous Sir William Herschel; surveyed the southern skies as systematically as his father had studied the northern heavens; his discovery that sodium hyposulphite dissolves silver salts provided the standard fixing agent, "hypo," in photography. ("The Old Telescope")

HOAG, ARTHUR A. (1921–), formerly astronomer at the U.S. Naval Observatory, now at the Kitt Peak National Observatory in Arizona. ("The Flagstaff Station of the U.S. Naval Observatory," with John S. Hall)

JULIAN, M. J. (1893–), account executive in a New York advertising agency, the Fred Gardner Corporation; former president, Better Vision Institute, New York; author of *Why We See Like Human Beings*. ("What Is Light?")

KEENE, GEORGE T. (1929–), since 1952 with Eastman Kodak Company in Rochester, New York, where he is now a group leader in the research and development section; former president of the astronomy section of the Rochester Academy of Sciences; author of *Stargazing with Telescope and Camera*. ("Color in Astrophotography")

KELLY, FRANK J. (1896–), director of Satellite Station 8604 of the Smithsonian Astrophysical Observatory Teams; member of the American Association of Variable Star Observers and of the St. Petersburg (Florida) Astronomy Club. ("Limiting Visual Magnitudes for Small Telescopes")

KNAB, OSCAR (1908–), architect; interested in planetary and lunar observing, and telescope making; member of the St. Joseph Valley Astronomical Society, South Bend, Indiana. ("An Improved 4½-inch Unobstructed Oblique Reflector")

LA PELLE, R. R. (1905–), supervisor of the Space Environment Simulation Laboratory of the Boeing Company, Seattle, Washington; former president of the Seattle Astronomical Society and the Astronomical League. ("Testing Your Telescope by Observations")

LEINBACH, HAROLD (1929–), geophysicist and astronomer; now at the State University of Iowa as a specialist in solar-terrestrial relations, after spending ten years in research at the University of Alaska; member of the American Association of Variable Star Observers. ("A Simple Spectroscope for Solar-prominence Observations")

LOCKWOOD, MARIAN (1889–), educator; with the American Museum of Natural History and at Hayden Planetarium from 1929 to 1946; associate editor of *The Sky* from 1936 to 1940; science editor of the *Book of Knowledge* and editor-in-chief of *Encyclopedia Yearbook*, 1946–62; co-author of *Astronomy*, *The Story of Astronomy*, and *The Earth Among the Stars*. ("The Constellations")

LOWER, HAROLD A., an active amateur astronomer in San Diego, California, until his death about 1950; one of the first in the U.S. to make and use a fast Schmidt camera (in 1935). ("The Schmidt Astronomical Camera")

McKELLAR, ANDREW (1910–60), Canadian astrophysicist; at the Dominion Astrophysical Observatory, Victoria, B.C., from 1935 until his death. ("Aluminizing the 72-inch Mirror at Victoria")

MENZEL, DONALD H. (1901–), astrophysicist; until early 1966 director of the Harvard College Observatory; author of *Stars and Planets*, *Story of the Starry Universe*, *Our Sun*, *Flying Saucers*, and *The Universe in Action*. ("Harvard Coronagraph in Colorado")

MILLER, ROBERT. No biographical information available. ("How to Make a Position Micrometer")

MORGAN, W. W. (1906–), astronomer; since 1926 at the Yerkes Observatory of the University of Chicago, Williams Bay, Wisconsin; since 1960 director of the Yerkes Observatory; an authority on stellar spectroscopy. ("Yerkes Observatory")

OSYPOWSKI, THOMAS (1941–), student at St. Francis Seminary in Milwaukee, Wisconsin; member of the Milwaukee Astronomical Society and the Association of Lunar and Planetary Observers. ("High-resolution Photography," with Thomas Pope)

PFLEUMER, HANS (1880–), Austrian-born rubber engineer whose hobby is astronomical photography; member of the Association of Lunar and Planetary Observers; author of *Sky Observers Guide*. ("A Simple German Mounting," "Astrophotography for the Amateur")

PHELPS, WILLIAM LYON (1865–1943), educator and literary critic; taught English literature at Yale from 1901 to 1935; his course in modern fiction and drama was the first of its kind given in an American university; author of *Essays on Russian Novelists, Reading the Bible, What I Like in Prose*. ("The Stars and William Lyon Phelps")

POPE, THOMAS (1937–), photographic observer at the New Mexico State University Observatory in Las Cruces; a former portrait and industrial photographer and member of the Milwaukee Astronomical Society. ("High-resolution Photography," with Thomas Osypowski)

PUTNAM, ROGER LOWELL (1893–), manufacturer of packaging machinery in Springfield, Massachusetts, and at one time mayor of that city; sole trustee of the Lowell Observatory in Arizona. ("The Lowell Observatory")

ROSEBRUGH, DAVID W. (1899–), retired electrical engineer; life member and past president of the American Association of Variable Star Observers; recipient of the eleventh Merit Award of that organization and of the New York Amateur Astronomers' Medal. ("Visual Observing Programs for Amateurs," "Observing the Sun")

RYAN, LOUISE (1912–), newspaper bureau chief (*Southtown Economist*, Chicago); former public relations director of the Chicago Planetarium Society. ("Telescope Making at the Adler Planetarium")

SEVERNY, A. B., director of the Crimean Astrophysical Observatory of the Academy of Sciences of the U.S.S.R., Pochtovoe, Crimea, U.S.S.R. ("Crimean Astrophysical Observatory")

SLOCUM, FREDERICK (1873–1944), astronomer; at Wesleyan University, Middletown, Connecticut, and director of its Van Vleck Observatory from 1914 to 1918 and from 1920 until his death; an expert in nautical science, stellar parallaxes, and eclipses. ("The Van Vleck Observatory of Wesleyan University")

STRONG, JOHN (1905–), professor of experimental physics at Johns Hopkins University; a former member of the Cal Tech faculty ("Aluminizing Telescope Mirrors")

STRUVE, OTTO (1897–1963), astrophysicist; last of a family which produced four generations of renowned astronomers; director of the Yerkes Observatory from 1932 to 1949, of the McDonald Observatory from 1938 to 1949; at Lauschner Observatory of the University of California at Berkeley from 1949 to 1959; director of the National Radio Astronomy Observatory, Green Bank, West Virginia from 1959 to 1962; author of many research papers and books, his last being *Astronomy of the 20th Century*. ("The Poulkovo Observatory," "The Birth of the McDonald Observatory")

SWEGER, PAUL R. (1906–), mechanical engineer whose career as an amateur astronomer began with an interest in optics; member of the Rockford (Illinois) Amateur Astronomers. ("Alarm-clock Telescope Drive")

TALGERI, K. M. (1913–), journalist; now communications specialist in the Union Ministry of Health, Goverment of India, New Delhi; interested in the history of Hindu astronomy. ("Jai Singh and His Observatory at New Delhi")

THOMPSON, ALLYN J. (1901–1955), assistant superintendent at Grand Central Post Office, New York City; art student at Pratt Institute, and in his youth a semiprofessional baseball player; an amateur telescope maker; author of *Making Your Own Telescope*. ("The Paraboloid," "The Diagonal," "Some Aids to Collimating a Newtonian," "Magnification, Eyepieces, Field of View")

VAUGHN, FRANK (1923–), optician; with the Tinsley Laboratories, Berkeley, California; former member of the Association of Lunar and Planetary Observers. ("Astronomical Seeing")

WACHMANN, A. A. (1902–), German astronomer; on the staff of the Bamberg Observatory since 1927; since 1956 the chief observer at the Hamburg Observatory; known for observations of variable stars and measures of the brightnesses and proper motions of stars. ("From the Life of Bernhard Schmidt")

WARKOCZEWSKI, S. J. (1906–), motion picture technician; an amateur astronomer skilled in color photography; member of the Astronomy Club of Kansas City, Missouri. ("An Experience with the Dall Null Test")

WILLEY, RONALD R., JR. (1936–), optical physicist and designer; with Geo Space Corporation, Melbourne, Florida; former member of Central Connecticut Amateur Astronomers. ("Cassegrain-type Telescopes")

WITHERELL, PERCY W. (1877–), graduate of MIT and past president of the Bond Astronomical Club at Harvard College Observatory; for many years treasurer of the American Association of Variable Star Observers. ("Saturn and Its Rings," "Variable Stars")

WOOD, H. E. (1881–1946), English astronomer; after 1906 at the Union Observatory, Johannesburg, South Africa; its director (the "Union Astronomer") from 1928; known for his photographs of the southern sky, his star charts, and his observations of comets, asteroids, and variable stars. ("The Observation of the Minor Planets")

WORLEY, CHARLES E. (1935–), astronomer; engaged in the study of multiple stars and stellar parallaxes at the U.S. Naval Observatory; recorded more than ten thousand meteors for the American Meteor Society. ("The Construction of a Filar Micrometer")

YEAGLEY, HENRY L. (1899–), professor of natural philosophy and chairman of the department of physics and astronomy at Dickinson College, Carlisle, Pennsylvania. ("Practical Advice and Aid in Telescope Making")

Glossary

aberration Defects in images formed by a lens or concave mirror. Two common types are *chromatic* (colored) and *spherical* aberration. See p. 26; Figure 7. (The term is also used for shifts in star positions caused by the earth's orbital velocity.)

altitude The angle from the horizon up to a star.

angle Angular distance measured in degrees, minutes, and seconds of arc. All the way around the sky is 360°; 1° = 60′ (minutes of arc), 1′ = 60″ (seconds of arc).

aperture The diameter of a lens or mirror, usually given in inches.

apogee The point farthest from the earth on an orbit around the earth.

apparent motion The change in direction of an astronomical body, including the effect of the observer's motion.

asteroid One of many very small planets in orbit about the sun, most of them between the orbits of Mars and Jupiter.

astronomical unit The distance from sun to earth (about 93 million miles), used as a unit of distance in the solar system.

astrophysics Study of physical conditions in planets, stars, nebulae, galaxies, and regions between them.

atmosphere The layer of gas around the earth or another planet. Layers of the sun near the surface we see are also called an atmosphere.

aurora Green and red glow of gas high in the earth's atmosphere due to bombardment by ions from outside the atmosphere.

axis The line around which something rotates; as, the earth's "axis of rotation." A telescope mounting usually allows a north-south swing around the *declination axis* and an east-west swing around the *polar axis*. Another meaning is the center line of the lens or mirror in a telescope. The centers of eyepieces and plateholders are usually "on axis." See p. 92.

azimuth The angle measured around the horizon from the north point to a point under a star to be located.

binary stars Pairs of stars close together in space, moving around one another due to gravitational attraction. See p. 174.

calorie A unit of energy; the amount of heat energy necessary to warm up one gram of water 1° C; equal to 4.185×10^7 ergs. (Food analysts use the word for a larger unit, 1000 of these "small calories.")

Cassegrainian A type of reflector telescope design. See Figure 9.

celestial sphere The "sphere of sky" with moon, stars, and planets "attached," half of which appears to arch over us on a clear, dark night. Maps of the sky are maps of this sphere. The position of a star on the celestial sphere indicates a direction in space.

chord   A straight line between two points on a circle.

cluster   A group of stars close together in space.

collimator   A lens or concave mirror that forms a parallel beam of light from a small light source at its focus. See Figure 74.

coma   A defect of paraboloid mirrors which causes off-axis star images to have fuzzy shapes, like little comets. See p. 27.

comet   A small body, probably formed of ice and dust, moving in a long ellipse around the sun, forming a tail when near the sun.

contour   A line drawn on a map or photograph to connect adjacent points that are at the same height above sea level, or have the same brightness, or have some other common characteristic.

coordinates   Numbers that describe the position of an object. In the sky, altitude and azimuth or right ascension and declination are used. See Figure 2.

corona   A faint haze and streamers around the sun; the corona is directly visible only during a total solar eclipse. The inner part can be photographed with a coronagraph on a very clear day.

coudé focus   The place where a large telescope with extra mirrors forms an image that remains fixed when the telescope is moved.

craters, lunar   Saucer-shaped depressions on the moon's surface; some of them are 100 miles across.

crown glass   Optical glass commonly used for lenses with high refractive index. Flint glass, also used, has smaller refractive index. See p. 24.

declination   Angle north or south of the celestial equator, used as a coordinate in the sky. See Figure 2.

density   Mass per unit volume, usually expressed in grams per cubic centimeter. (The density of water is about 1 gm/cm^3.)

diaphragm   A hole, generally a circular one, in thin metal, used to limit the size of a beam of light or the aperture of a lens.

diffraction   The bending of light around an obstruction of any size, such as the edge of the moon or the edges of small particles.

dipole antenna   A radio antenna formed of a single straight wire with a lead wire from the center to the radio receiver.

drive   The mechanism that turns a telescope around the polar axis to follow a star by canceling the earth's rotation. See p. 91.

dyne   A very small unit of force, about 0.001 the weight of a gram; the force necessary to speed up one gram by 1 cm/sec in 1 sec.

eccentricity   A measure of the elongated shape of an ellipse, irrespective of its size. The eccentricity of a circle is zero, that of a parabola (an ellipse infinitely long compared to its width) is 1.

ecliptic The path of the sun among the stars; also the plane of the earth's orbit.

ellipse An oval-shaped closed curve, precisely defined by the equation in rectangular coordinates $x^2/a^2 + y^2/b^2 = 1$.

emission line A sharp excess of one color (one wavelength of light or radio waves) in a spectrum; generally characteristic of low-density gas.

emulsion The light-sensitive coating on photographic film or plates.

ephemeris A list of predicted positions in the sky for planets, satellites, or other moving objects.

equator A circle on the earth halfway between the poles. The celestial equator is similarly located in the sky (see Fig. 2) and is the base line for equatorial coordinates.

equatorial mounting Mechanism on a telescope pier that allows a telescope to swing around a polar axis, following lines in the sky parallel to the celestial equator. See p. 12.

equinox Either of two dates of the year (about March 21 and September 21) when the sun is above the horizon just twelve hours. The *vernal* equinox is a point in the sky (or direction in space) where the center of the sun crosses the celestial equator on March 21, and is used as an origin of coordinates in the sky.

erg A unit of energy; the work done in pushing one gram so that it speeds up from rest to 1.414 cm/sec.

escape velocity The velocity of a body that will carry it to an infinite distance from the earth (or another planet, or the sun) despite gravitational attraction. Near the surface of the earth the escape velocity is about 7 miles per second; farther away it is smaller.

eyepiece A small lens at the eye end of a telescope or microscope that magnifies the image. See Figures 45, 47.

field The region of the sky visible in a telescope, or photographed with good definition. See p. 210.

flare see **solar flare.**

flint glass see **crown glass.**

focal length The distance from the center of a lens or mirror to the point where the light of a star or other object is brought to a focus. The focal ratio of a camera or telescope is the aperture divided by the focal length. See Figure 10.

focus The point at which a lens or concave mirror causes the parallel rays from a star to converge. See Figure 3.

Foucault knife-edge test A method of locating the focus and testing the optical quality of a telescope. See Figures 19, 22.

frequency Number of periodic changes (cycles) per second. The *period* is the reciprocal of the frequency. Radio waves have frequencies of thousands of cycles per second (kilocycles per second) to many millions (megacycles per second, or Mc/sec), and wavelengths of c/f, where c is the velocity of light and radio waves, 3×10^{10} cm/sec, and f is the frequency.

galaxy A vast disk-shaped assemblage of stars, gas, and dust. The sun is located in the Milky Way Galaxy.

gibbous Oval shaped, as is the moon when more than half full but less than full.

gnomon A pillar or prong which casts a shadow in sunlight from which the time of day can be measured.

grating A set of parallel wires or scratches on glass. Where the spacing is small these form a spectrum of the light passing through, because of diffraction and interference. Coarse gratings are also used for testing mirrors. See p. 69.

guiding Keeping images of stars or other objects in the same place on the photographic film or plate during a long exposure for which a telescope is used.

horizon A line around the sky exactly 90° from the zenith (point directly overhead).

hyperbola The open-ended curve followed by a high-speed particle deflected by gravitational attraction as it passes the earth (or sun, or any other large mass) at a speed greater than the escape velocity. A hyperboloid is a surface (sometimes used on mirrors) shaped so that its cross section is a hyperbola.

image The "picture" of an object formed by a lens or concave mirror. It is formed at the focus of a telescope used on celestial objects. See Figure 3.

incandescence Emission of light by material at high temperature.

inclination The angle between two planes. A planet's orbit lies in a plane with some inclination to the ecliptic.

infrared "Color" of invisible light with longer wavelength than red light and shorter wavelength than radio waves.

intensity Energy received per second, usually in the form of light or radio waves (also sound waves, and particles such as cosmic rays). The intensity of an *absorption line* measures the gap in energy near one wavelength or frequency in a spectrum.

interferometer Two separate detectors of radio waves or light waves which show the effects of interference of the waves coming from different directions. See p. 249.

ionosphere The upper regions of the earth's atmosphere consisting mostly of ions—atoms with one or more electrons removed.

kinetic energy Energy of motion, $\frac{1}{2}mv^2$; equal to the work done in pushing a mass, m, until it moves at speed v.

limb The edge of an image of the moon or the sun or a planet. Because the moon wobbles, the *limb of the moon* as seen from the earth is not always the same circle on the moon's surface.

lines Gaps (colors missing) in the spectrum of sunlight are called *Fraunhofer lines*; gaps in the spectra of light from other stars are called *absorption lines*. The stronger ones (H lines and K lines, for example) are known by letters. All of them can be designated by wavelength. Nebulae and some stars have *emission lines*, brighter patches in their spectra. See **spectrum.**

magnifying power The increase in angular size of an object viewed in a telescope as compared to a direct view. Eyepieces that magnify a telescope image fifty times are said to have "power 50" or "50X magnification." See p. 22.

magnitude An indication of the brightness of a celestial object. The brightest stars are of first magnitude, and the faintest stars visible to the naked eye are of sixth magnitude (6 mag.). With telescopes the scale has been extended to over 20 mag. Every 5 magnitudes correspond to a factor of 100 in faintness. See p. 142.

Maksutov A type of telescope design named after its Russian inventor. See Figure 82.

maria Large dark areas, roughly circular in shape, on the moon's surface.

megacycle per second (Mc/s) One million cycles per second, a unit of radio *frequency.*

meniscus The shape of a spherical shell of glass of uniform thickness. See Figure 82.

meridian A circle in the sky from the south point on the horizon through the observer's zenith to the north celestial pole.

meteor A "shooting star"; caused by a small chunk of material moving through the earth's atmosphere at such high speed that it becomes white hot.

metric system Distance units: millimeter (0.001 meter), centimeter (0.01 meter), meter (about 1 yard), kilometer (1,000 meters); mass units: gram, and kilogram (about 2 pounds).

micrometer An instrument used on a telescope for measuring small angles between stars. See Figures 60–63.

nebula A vast cloud of gas between stars.

nova A star that suddenly increases its light output 10,000 times or more within a few days and then fades slowly.

objective The major image-forming lens or mirror in a telescope.

occultation The eclipse of a star or planet by the moon.

oscillator An electronic circuit in which the electric current vibrates at some constant frequency; sometimes used to produce radio waves.

parabola   The open-ended curve followed by a particle or comet that, starting almost at rest, falls from a very large distance toward the sun (or some other large mass); an extremely elongated ellipse of eccentricity 1.

paraboloid   The surface formed by rotating a parabola about its axis; generally used for telescope mirrors.

parallax   The very small change in direction of a star due to motion of the earth around the sun. It can be measured only for the nearer stars, on photographs taken about six months apart, and is used to obtain the distance (1/parallax = distance in parsecs; 3.26/parallax = distance in light-years).

perigee   The point closest to the earth on an orbit around the earth.

period   The time for one complete circuit of an orbit, or one complete rotation of a rotating body, or the complete cycle of any recurrent change.

phenomenon   An event or occurrence that can be observed.

photometer   An instrument designed to measure the brightness of light falling on it. It is described as visual, photographic, or photoelectric, depending on the detector used.

photosphere   The surface of the sun that we can see or photograph in visible light. There are gases above, and the sun is gaseous below, but the gas is opaque to visible light below the photosphere.

polarized light   Light which consists of waves that vibrate across the beam of light in one direction. Ordinary light is generally unpolarized, and the vibrations are in all directions. The polarization may be partial or complete (100 per cent).

pole   A point on the earth where its axis of rotation cuts the surface. The *celestial poles* in the sky are the directions of the two ends of the earth's axis and are located at the centers of the stars' circular motions during any night. See Figure 1.

power   Energy output per second; often measured in watts. See also **magnifying power**.

prism   A wedge-shaped object; the prism of glass or quartz in a spectrograph or spectroscope serves to separate white light into its component colors. See **spectrum**.

prominence   A flamelike cloud of luminous gas; usually photographed in light of one emission line of that gas, near the edge of the sun.

proper motion   The very small change in direction of a star due to its velocity across the line of sight as seen from near the sun. It is expressed as a fraction of a second of arc per year and can be measured on photographs of the star taken many years apart.

quadrant   One quarter of a circle, or 90°. Also, an instrument used by early astronomers for measuring angles in the sky, and formed of a quarter circle with angle units (degrees) marked on it. See Figure 12.

quantum The energy packet associated with light of frequency f (or wavelength λ). The smallest amount of energy that can be interchanged with light of this color is $E = hf = hc/\lambda$; where c is the velocity of light, and h is Planck's constant.

radar A radio transmitter and receiver designed to measure the distance to an object by the travel time of a radio pulse sent out, reflected by the object, and returned as an echo.

radial velocity The motion of a star or other light source along the line of sight, detected by *Doppler shift* of lines in the spectrum; red shift indicates recession (positive radial velocity).

radioastronomy The study of astronomical bodies by use of radiotelescopes.

refractive index A measure of the bending of a light ray as it passes from air into glass. Also called the *index of refraction*, it is different for different kinds of glass. See p. 24; Figure 6.

refractor A telescope in which a large lens (rather than a concave mirror) forms images of sun, stars, moon, or planets. See Figure 46.

refrangibility The different tendencies of the various colors of light to be deflected on passing through a glass prism.

resolving power The ability of a telescope to distinguish two stars very close together in the sky; the ability of a spectrograph to distinguish two lines very close in a spectrum.

resonance Occurs in an electronic circuit when a radio wave of the proper frequency causes it to oscillate at the same (tuned) frequency.

right ascension A coordinate in the sky like longitude on the earth. It is the angle measured eastward from the vernal equinox around the celestial equator. See Figure 2.

Schmidt A type of telescope or camera named after its German inventor. See Figure 77.

second A unit of time ($\frac{1}{3600}$ of an hour), abbreviated "sec" or "s." A second of arc ($1''$) is a (different) unit of angle ($\frac{1}{3600}$ of a degree). In 1 sec the earth rotates $15''$ eastward and a star seems to move $15''$ toward the west.

sidereal time Time measured by the stars rather than by the sun. When the vernal equinox is on the meridian the sidereal time is o. A sidereal day is about 4 minutes shorter than a normal solar day, and sidereal clocks are set to run 4 minutes fast per day. See p. 8.

solar flare A short-lived bright patch on the sun's surface, which causes extra ionization in gases such as the earth's upper atmosphere due to ultraviolet light from the flare.

spectrogram Photograph of a spectrum.

spectrograph An instrument used to photograph spectra.

spectrum The various colors of light from a source spread out in the sequence from red to violet (long wavelength to short wavelength), as in a rainbow. Invisible wavelengths extend from the red to infrared to radio waves, and from blue-violet to ultraviolet and X rays. The spectrum of the sun is often called a Fraunhofer spectrum. Like the spectra of most stars, it lacks certain colors, in gaps called Fraunhofer lines or absorption lines.

stratosphere A layer of the earth's atmosphere above the turbulent troposphere.

sunspot A region on the sun's surface about 1000° cooler than its surroundings. Spots usually occur in pairs, one with north-magnetic polarity, the other with south-magnetic polarity.

superior planet A planet farther from the sun than the earth is (Mars, Jupiter, Saturn, Uranus, Neptune, or Pluto).

telluric line A spectrum absorption line caused by gases in the earth's atmosphere. See **lines, spectrum.**

terminator The edge between the dark and sunlit portions of the moon (or of a planet).

thermocouple An electric device that generates electric current when heated and can be used to measure the energy arriving per second in a beam of light from the sun or from a planet or star.

troposphere The lower layers of the earth's atmosphere (below the stratosphere), where the temperature decreases with altitude and where there are winds and turbulence in the air.

turbulence Whirls or vortices in a fluid (or a liquid or gas).

ultraviolet "Color" of invisible light with wavelengths shorter than those of visible light (less than about 4000 A).

Universal Time The time of day (and the date) at Greenwich, England (longitude 0°); used by astronomers to avoid the confusion of different times used at different longitudes around the earth.

variable star A star that changes in brightness due to pulsations of its surface, or flares, or eclipse by a companion star.

wavelength The distance between the crests (or troughs) of regular waves. Visible light of various colors has wavelengths ranging from about $\frac{1}{70,000}$ inch to about twice that length. See **spectrum.**

Yagi antenna A set of parallel dipole antennas connected through their centers, which has higher sensitivity to radio waves coming from one direction. It is not as directional as a paraboloid ("dish") radiotelescope. See Figure 91.

zenith The direction or point in the sky directly overhead, accurately located by a plumb line (a thread with a weight) or the perpendicular to a quiet liquid surface. The zenith is different for each different location on the curved surface of the earth.

Suggestions for

Further Reading

GENERAL

Bell, L., *The Telescope*, New York, McGraw-Hill, 1922.
Collins, A. F., *The Greatest Eye in the World*, New York, D. Appleton Century, 1942.
Dimitroff, G. Z., and Baker, J. C., *Telescopes and Accessories*, Philadelphia, Blakiston, 1945.
Miczaika, G. R., and Sinton, W. M., *Tools of the Astronomer*, Cambridge, Massachusetts, Harvard University Press, 1961.
Pendray, G. E., *Men, Mirrors and Stars*, New York, Harper, 1946.

Chapter 1

Bouwers, A., *Achievements in Optics*, New York, Elsevier, 1950.
Hardy, A. C., and Perrin, F. H., *Principles of Optics*, New York, McGraw-Hill, 1932.
Jacobs, D. H., *Fundamentals of Optical Engineering*, New York, McGraw-Hill, 1943.
Jenkins, F. A., and White, H. E., *Fundamentals of Optics*, New York, McGraw-Hill, 1957.
Johnson, B. K., *Optics and Optical Instruments*, New York, Dover, 1960.
Southall, J. P. C., *Mirrors, Prisms and Lenses*, New York, Macmillan, 1933 (also in paperback, New York, Dover, 1964).

Chapter 2

King, H. C., *The History of the Telescope*, Cambridge, Massachusetts, Sky Publishing, 1955.

Chapters 3 and 4

Ingalls, A. G., ed., *Amateur Telescope Making* (3 vols.), New York, Scientific American, 1953. (Earlier editions of Vol. 2 were published under the title *Amateur Telescope Making—Advanced*.)

Matthewson, G., *Constructing an Astronomical Telescope*, London, Blackie and Son, 1958.

Texereau, J., *How to Make a Telescope*, New York, Interscience Publishers, 1957.

Thompson, A., *Making Your Own Telescope*, Cambridge, Massachusetts, Sky Publishing, 1947.

Twyman, F., *Optical Glassworking*, London, Hilger Watts, 1955 (available from Engis Equipment Company, Chicago, Illinois).

Chapters 5 and 6

Bečvář, A., *Skalnate Pleso Atlas of the Heavens*, Cambridge, Massachusetts, Sky Publishing (16 charts; also available in a field edition on heavier paper; an *Atlas Catalogue* has been compiled to accompany these charts).

Keene, G. T., *Stargazing with Telescope and Camera*, Philadelphia, Chilton, 1962.

Kopal, Z., *The Moon: Our Nearest Celestial Neighbor*, New York, Academic Press, 2nd ed., 1963.

Mayall, M., *Field Book of the Skies*, New York, Putnam, 1965.

Sedgwick, J. B., *Amateur Astronomer's Handbook*, London, Faber, 1960 (distributed by Macmillan, New York).

Sedgwick, J. B., *Observational Astronomy for Amateurs*, London, Faber and Faber, 1956 (distributed by Macmillan, New York).

Vehrenberg, H., *Photographic Star Atlas*, Cambridge, Massachusetts, Sky Publishing.

Atlas Borealis, Cambridge, Massachusetts, Sky Publishing.

Atlas Eclipticalis, Cambridge, Massachusetts, Sky Publishing.

Chapters 7 and 8

Fillmore, W. I., *Construction of a Maksutov Telescope*, Cambridge, Massachusetts, Sky Publishing, 1961.

Kuiper, G. P., and Middlehurst, B. M., eds., *Telescopes* (Vol. 1 of *Stars and Stellar Systems*), Chicago, University of Chicago Press, 1960.

Kutter, A., *The Schiefspiegler*, Cambridge, Massachusetts, Sky Publishing, 1958.

Wood, F. B., *The Present and Future of the Telescope of Moderate Size*, Philadelphia, University of Pennsylvania Press, 1958.

Maksutov Telescope Construction, Cambridge, Massachusetts, Sky Publishing, 1963.

Chapter 9

Woodbury, D. O., *The Glass Giant of Palomar*, New York, Dodd, Mead, 1939.

Wright, H., *Palomar, the World's Largest Telescope*, New York, Macmillan, 1953.

Index

Abbé, Ernest, 124
Abbé oculars, 124, 125-26, 227
Aberration, optical: 18, 24, 25-30, 31, 42, 238, 321; elimination of, 218; reduction of, 76 (see also various types)
Aberration, stellar, 271, 321
Abrasives: amounts, 59-62; application, 61-62; sizes, 59-62, 73
Absorption lines, 325
Achromatic lenses, 27, 43, 44, 125, 126, 200-201, 207, 245
Achromatism, 31
Adler Planetarium, 81-82, 275
Agassiz Station, 93
Alexander, J. K., 251, 252, 315
Altazimuth mounting, 93, 94, 95
Aluminizing, 68, 83-90, 223
Amateur Telescope Making: 76, 83; —*Advanced*, 214; Vol. 3, 230
American Association of Variable Star Observers (AAVSO): 150, 154, 160, 161, 162-64, 166, 167, 168, 169, 174; Solar Division, 203, 204, 205
American Ephemeris and Nautical Almanac, 8-9, 12, 139, 256
Ansconian Color Photographs, 199
Aperture: 56, 321; and limiting visual magnitudes, 150, 152; Cassegrainian-Maksutov, 226; for photography, 210-11; for spectroscope, 207; large, 256; of dark-adapted eye, 151; reduction to improve seeing, 128
Apochromatic lenses, 28
Ashbrook, Joseph, 128, 315
Asiago Observatory, 298
Asteroids, 140-41, 262, 286
Astigmatism, 29-30, 123, 148, 212, 217, 224-25, 236, 238, 239, 240
Aurorae, 198, 204, 246
Australia, astronomy in, 289-91
Australian Commonwealth Observatory, 256-57, 289-92
Axis: 321; declination, 13, 92, 93, 96, 112, 113, 115, 285, 321; optical, 91, 321; polar, 13, 92, 93, 96, 112, 113-14, 294, 321
Axle, *see* Axis

Bailey, Edwin F., 45, 315
Baker, J. G., 150, 151, 223, 241, 315
Balancing a telescope, 106-15, 191
Barnard, E. E., 54, 136, 138, 139, 211, 212, 275, 276
Barnesite, 59, 63, 64
Barton, William H., Jr., 116, 315
Bates, Ralph S., 49, 315
Batten, Alan H., 170, 315
Beebe, William, 5
Binoculars: and seeing, 129; to view Jupiter's satellites, 138; to view variable stars, 161, 166
Brachyt reflector, 232-36
Brahe, Tycho, 39, 40, 153, 313
Brown, Earle B., 18, 30, 33, 55, 83, 200, 316
Brown, Larry W., 251, 252, 316

Cameras: 185-88, 190-91, 210; Schmidt, 211-23; wide-angle, 211
Carborundum: grades used, 59, 60, 61; how applied, 60
Cassegrainian telescope: 23, 24, 33-35, 239-40, 241, 243, 285, 321; computations, 34-35; field of view, 166; focal ratio, 33; -Maksutov telescope, 223-32; mounting, 34-35; tube length, 33; -type telescopes, 237-43
Catadioptric telescope, 241
Cave, Thomas R., Jr., 132, 134, 316
Celestial: coordinates, 10-12, 322; equator, 91, 100, 323; meridian, 6, 325; poles, 11-12, 91, 326; sphere, 6, 321
Center of gravity of a telescope, 113, 114
Centering, optical, 79, 92
Cepheid variables: 154, 156-59; cluster-type, 156, 158; color changes, 157; light curves, 156-57; luminosity range, 156-57; magnitude changes, 161; period range, 158; pulsation, 158-59; relation of luminosity to period, 156, 157-58; spectral changes, 157
Cerium oxide, 59
Charts for variable-star observing, 161, 162, 163-67, 168

331